An Introduction to the Bl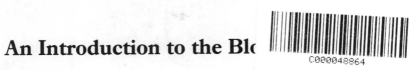

An Introduction to the First Climate Barrier

An Introduction to the Blood–Brain Barrier

Hugh Davson
Emeritus Professor,
Sherrington School of Physiology UMDS,
Guy's and St Thomas's Hospitals, London

Berislav Zloković
Associate Professor of Neurosurgery,
Physiology and Biophysics,
USC School of Medicine, Los Angeles

Ljubisa Rakić
Professor of Neurobiology and Biochemistry,
School of Medicine, Belgrade

and

Malcolm B. Segal
Reader in Physiology,
Sherrington School of Physiology UMDS,
Guy's and St Thomas's Hospitals, London

MACMILLAN

First published 1993 by
THE MACMILLAN PRESS LTD
Houndmills, Basingstoke, Hampshire RG21 2XS
and London
Companies and representatives
throughout the world

ISBN 0–333–53517–0

A catalogue record for this book is available
from the British Library.

Typeset by Wearset
Boldon, Tyne and Wear
Printed in Hong Kong

Contents

v

Preface

The possibility of producing a short introduction to the physiology of the blood–brain barrier was both discussed and agreed by the authors after a small symposium on the subject had been held at the Serbian Academy of Arts and Science in 1989. The present volume is the result; in it we have tried to present lucidly the physical factors governing transport from blood into the central nervous tissue and the cerebrospinal fluid, and then to describe some studies on specific aspects, notably the transport of amino acids, sugars and peptides. Finally, in view of the suspicion that some neurological diseases have as their basis a failure or impairment of the blood–brain barrier, we have included an account of some attempts to establish animal preparations that might serve as experimental models mimicking human pathology. If the reading of this book stimulates research on the pathology of some central nervous diseases, it will have achieved its main purpose; in addition, we trust that workers in the life sciences will find it a useful introduction to a field that has expanded explosively since the early prejudices against the concept of a blood–brain barrier were dispelled. We must conclude by thanking the Wellcome Trust, the British Council and the Federal Yugoslav Zavod for their financial help in promoting the co-operation between workers in Britain and Yugoslavia that has culminated in the writing of this book.

June, 1991

H.D.
B.Z.
L.R.
M.B.S.

Chapter 1

History and Basic Concepts

Classical Experiments

Intravital Staining

The concept of the blood–brain barrier derives from the classical studies of the pioneers in chemotherapy, such as Ehrlich, who administered dyestuffs parenterally in the hope that they would attack infective organisms. Thus Ehrlich observed that many dyes, after intravenous injection, stained the tissues of practically the whole body, while the brain was spared. Later, Lewandowsky (1900) showed that the Prussian blue reagents (iron salt and potassium ferrocyanide) did not pass from blood to brain, and he formulated clearly the concept of the blood–brain barrier (*Bluthirnschranke*). The more definitive demonstration of the barrier we owe to Goldmann, who showed (1909) that, after intravenous injection with trypan blue, the brain was unstained; the dye did not enter the cerebrospinal fluid (CSF), although the choroid plexuses and meninges were stained. In a second paper (Goldmann, 1913), he described experiments in which trypan blue was injected into the CSF; in this event, the brain tissue was strongly stained, so that Goldmann rightly concluded that there was, indeed, a barrier between blood, on the one hand, and brain tissue on the other. Any argument that the failure to stain the brain with trypan blue after intravenous injection was due to a peculiar staining feature of the nervous tissue was negated by this fundamental 'second experiment', the first experiment being the demonstration that nervous tissue was unstained after intravenous injection.

Penetration of Other Solutes

The blood–brain barrier, as initially revealed by studies on dyestuffs, was shown not to be peculiar to these organic molecules, and, in general, it proved that substances that usually failed to cross cell membranes also failed to cross the blood–brain barrier (Krogh, 1946). Now, it was early demonstrated that penetration into cells was governed by the lipid-solubility of the compound being studied measured by its oil–water partition coefficient,

$$B = \frac{\text{concentration in oil}}{\text{concentration in water}}$$

Figure 1.1, for example, from the classical study of Collander and Barlund (1933) on single plant cells, shows that ease of penetration through the cell membrane, measured by the molecule's permeability coefficient (p. 14), was directly related to

1

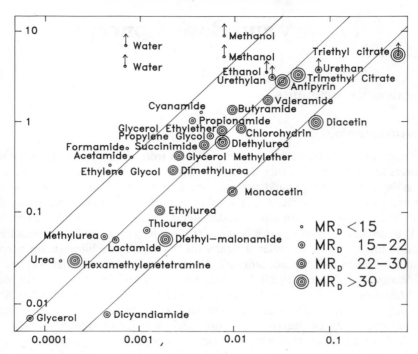

Figure 1.1 Permeability of *Chara* cells plotted against oil/water partition coefficient. Ordinates: permeability in cm/h × $M^{1/2}$. Abscissae: oil/water partition coefficient. From Collander, *Physiol. Plant.* (1949)

its partition coefficient, relatively lipid-insoluble substances, such as sucrose and glycerol, with partition coefficients in the region of 1×10^{-4}–1×10^{-5}, barely, if at all, penetrating cells; when the partition coefficient was in the region of 0.01, there was significant penetration, as with thiourea; with a partition coefficient of, say, 0.1, as with ethyl alcohol, penetration was very rapid. Early semiquantitative studies of passage of solutes into the brain from blood showed that the barrier was high for substances such as sucrose or mannitol but low for substances such as ethyl alcohol or propyl thiourea. Thus, as Krogh emphasized in 1946, the capillaries of the brain, or other lining membranes separating blood from the brain tissue, behaved like single cells, in marked contrast to the capillaries of most other tissues of the body, where it is found that passage from blood to the extracellular space is rapid and virtually independent of the partition coefficient.

Early Objections to the Concept

If we look back on the subject now over the period, say, 1920 to 1960, it becomes evident that Goldmann's second experiment was ignored, and it was repeatedly argued that the blood–brain barrier, as described by Goldmann's first experiment, was an artefact resulting from the failure of the dyestuff to be taken up by the tissue after leaving the blood vessels. The strongest argument adduced in support of this position was the appearance of the brain in electron-microscopical sections; previously the histology of the brain had been examined by two basic procedures that stained either the neurons (Golgi technique) or the glia. Pictures obtained by either technique left room for the assumption that the nervous tissue had a considerable extracellular space, comparable with that of other tissues. However, the osmium-stained preparations of the electron microscope revealed both glia and neurons, so tightly packed that it was argued that the extracellular space was negligible, so that if trypan blue and other acidic dyestuffs passed out of the capillaries, the staining would not be intense enough for observation in the light-microscope.

There is no need to recapitulate in detail the experimental studies that these claims stimulated. Since it was apparently insufficient to emphasize Goldmann's second experiment and its significance, more direct experimental proof of a barrier between blood, on the one hand, and the extracellular fluid of the central nervous system, on the other, was necessary. First, it was important to determine the actual size of the extracellular space; although the electron-microscopical studies suggested that this would be very small, compared with that in muscle and other connective tissues, nevertheless it must have an experimentally determinable magnitude.

The Extracellular Space of the Brain

Experimental Measurement

The basis for determination of the extracellular space of a tissue, such as muscle, has been the measurement of the concentrations of an 'extracellular marker' in the tissue and in the medium surrounding the cells when the system is in diffusional equilibrium with the marker. If the experiment is performed *in vivo*, the concentration in the extracellular fluid may be equated with that in the blood plasma, provided that there is ready equilibration between the two fluids. If the experiment is carried out *in vitro*, then the concentration in the bathing medium will be compared with that in the tissue. The requirement of the marker is that it should not penetrate cells, being confined to the extracellular space. In this case the extracellular space is given by:

$$\frac{\text{concentration in tissue (mmol/g-tissue)}}{\text{concentration in plasma–water or saline (mmol/g-H}_2\text{O)}} \times 100$$

With the *in vivo* experiment some of the marker will remain in the blood vessels, but allowance for this may be made by measuring the 'blood–space' by infusing labelled red cells.

Difficulties with Nervous Tissue

If there is a blood–brain barrier, however, it will be manifest most strongly with the extracellular markers, so that maintaining a steady level of, say, sucrose or mannitol, in the blood by intravenous infusion over periods of time would probably not lead to equilibration between the blood and extracellular fluid, the necessary requirement for estimating the space. The alternative procedure, then, would be to bathe a piece of brain in a saline medium containing the extracellular marker.

In vitro *Measurements*

With warm-blooded animals this technique is generally not very satisfactory, since the anoxia of the tissue usually causes the cells to swell at the expense of the extracellular fluid, giving an abnormally low value. However, the technique certainly permits a fair estimate of the probable minimum value. With skeletal muscle this varies and is of the order of 10–15%. Measurements on incubated mammalian brain carried out by Davson and Spaziani (1959) suggested an extracellular space that might be as high as 15–20%, and indicated that the very slow passage of sucrose, for example, from blood to brain could not be due to an absence of extracellular space. The cold-blooded brain of the frog gave less equivocal results and emphasized the magnitude of this space (Bradbury *et al.*, 1968).

Perfusion through the Cerebrospinal Fluid System

By employing the *in vitro* technique the experimenter is, in essence, circumventing the blood–brain barrier, profiting by the free diffusion of the extracellular marker from the outside medium into the extracellular fluid of the tissue. Clearly an *in vivo* method of circumventing the barrier in the intact animal is desirable, and it will be recalled that Goldmann (1913) in his 'second experiment' did precisely this by injecting trypan blue into the cerebrospinal fluid (CSF), from which it was able to diffuse into the adjacent central nervous parenchyma. It becomes important, therefore, to examine the relations between the CSF and the central nervous tissues, namely the brain and spinal cord.

The Cerebrospinal Fluid

Ventricles, Meninges and Subarachnoid Spaces

The fluid is contained within the ventricles of the brain, where it is called the internal cerebrospinal fluid, and it is also contained in the subarachnoid spaces surrounding the brain and spinal cord. These spaces are included between the external, *dural*, coat (that of the spinal cord is often called the *theca*) and the very thin *pia mater*. Thus, the three meninges, from without inwards, are the *dura mater*, the *arachnoid mater*, closely adherent to the dura mater, and the *pia mater*, which is closely adherent to the surfaces of the brain and spinal cord. The subarachnoid spaces are thus cavities separating the dura-arachnoid from the pia mater; this last, as we have stated, covers the surface of the brain and cord and lies on a layer of glial cells that separates the neurons from the pia, the two membranes being often referred to as the pia-glia. The general location of the internal or ventricular fluids is indicated in Figure 1.2, while Figure 1.3 illustrates the subarachnoid spaces. Within the subarachnoid space and lying on or in the pia are the large blood vessels that branch and plunge vertically into the substance of the nervous tissue. The internal and external cerebrospinal fluids are connected through the *foramen of Magendie* and two other smaller exits, the *foramina of Luschka*. It is now generally accepted that the great bulk of the cerebrospinal fluid is formed initially within the ventricles, being secreted by the choroid plexuses, as illustrated schematically by Figure 1.4.

The Choroid Plexuses

These are highly vascular pieces of connective tissue enclosed by the choroidal epithelium. Thus, the highly vascular cores produce a filtrate from blood plasma; from this filtrate the choroidal epithelium forms the cerebrospinal fluid, the

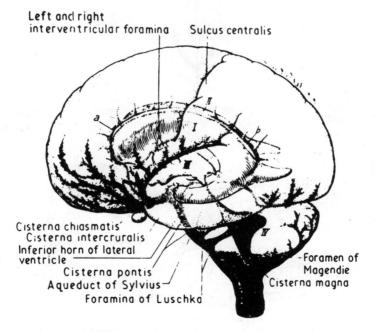

Figure 1.2 Illustrating the ventricles and cisterns of the human brain. From Clara, *Das Nervensystem des Menschen*, 2nd edn, J.A. Barth (1953)

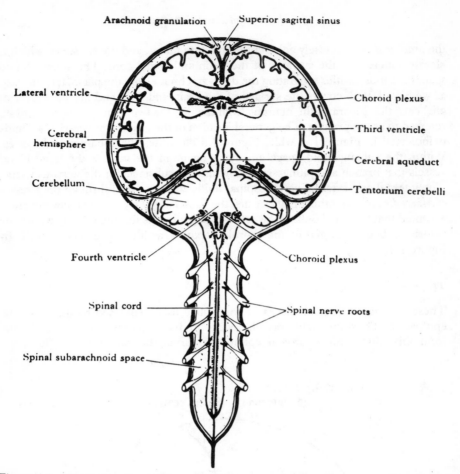

Arachnoid granulation

Superior sagittal sinus

Lateral ventricle

Choroid plexus

Cerebral hemisphere

Third ventricle

Cerebral aqueduct

Cerebellum

Tentorium cerebelli

Fourth ventricle

Choroid plexus

Spinal cord

Spinal nerve roots

Spinal subarachnoid space

Figure 1.3 Illustrating the subarachnoid spaces and circulation of the cerebrospinal fluid. From Millen and Woollam, *The Anatomy of the Cerebrospinal Fluid*, Oxford University Press (1962)

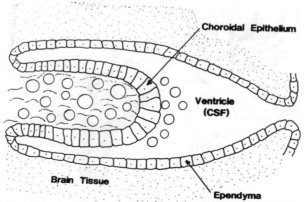

Choroidal Epithelium

Ventricle (CSF)

Brain Tissue

Ependyma

Figure 1.4 Choroid plexus as a vascular evagination into the ventricle. Note continuity of choroidal epithelium with ependyma

primary event being the active transport of Na^+ accompanied by the anions Cl^- and HCO_3^-.

Drainage

The CSF is formed continuously and must be drained away into the blood in order to maintain a reasonably uniform pressure—the *intracranial pressure* or *CSF pressure*. The site of this return to the blood is the large venous sinuses buried in the dura; at localized points the arachnoid membrane evaginates into the substance of the dura to form arachnoid villi, illustrated schematically in Figure 1.5. These arachnoid villi are covered with endothelium, which, however, offers no significant restraint to the permeation of water and large water-soluble molecules, including proteins. We need not go into the anatomy and physics of this drainage process further, and it is sufficient to emphasize that passage of substances out of the CSF into the blood by this bulk-flow process is unrestricted by comparison with the processes by which substances enter the CSF from the blood. This, as we shall see, has important consequences for the steady-state concentrations of the various solutes in the CSF.

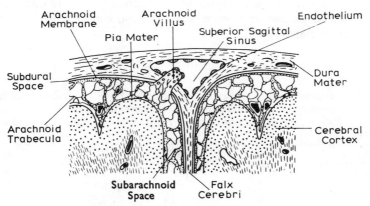

Figure 1.5 Illustrating the meninges and arachnoid villus projecting into the superior saggital sinus

Lymphatic Drainage

An additional locus of drainage is by way of the lymphatic system, probably along perivascular channels and finishing up in the large lymph ducts draining the head; passage along these channels offers little restriction to dissolved substance, so that Courtice and Simmonds (1951) found labelled plasma proteins and even erythrocytes in the cervical lymphatic ducts after introduction into the ventricles. These channels have been investigated in some detail by Bradbury and Cole (1980), Bradbury *et al.* (1981) and McComb and Hyman (1990).

Chemical Composition of the Cerebrospinal Fluid

The chemical composition of the fluid is shown in Table 1.1, where the concentrations of ions and non-electrolytes are compared with those in plasma, the ratio between these concentrations: Concn. in CSF/Concn. in plasma, being designated as R_{CSF}. Where ions, such as Na^+ and Cl^-, are concerned, it is of interest to compare the value of R_{CSF} with a similar ratio, R_{dial}, equal to the ratio: Concn. in plasma dialysate/Concn. in plasma. Thus, because of the Gibbs–Donnan distribution imposed by the impermeability of the capillary membrane to plasma protein ions, this ratio is not unity for Na^+ but equal to about 0.96, while the ratio for Cl^- is approximately the reciprocal of this, namely 1.04. Comparison of R_{CSF} with R_{dial} tells us whether the cerebrospinal fluid has been formed by a process of passive filtration or whether active processes have been involved. The differences between R_{CSF} and R_{dial} are small but highly significant and indicate the intervention of active processes in the elaboration of the CSF by the choroidal epithelium. In other words, the CSF is a *secretion* and not a mere passive filtrate from the blood plasma, as was at one time thought (Fremont-Smith *et al.*, 1931). Thus, the concentration of Na^+ is higher in CSF than in a plasma dialysate and the same is true for Cl^- and Mg^{2+}. By contrast, the concentration of K^+ is very much lower. Where non-electrolytes are concerned, it is interesting that the concentrations of glucose and amino acids are also considerably lower than in plasma or its dialysate.

Table 1.1 Concentrations of various solutes (meq/kg H_2O) in cerebrospinal fluid and plasma of the rabbit, and distribution ratios. R_{CSF} = concentration in CSF/concentration in plasma and R_{dial} = concentration in plasma dialysate/concentration in plasma. From Davson (1967)

Substance		Plasma	CSF	R_{CSF}	R_{dial}
Na		148.0	149.0	1.005	0.945
K		4.3	2.9	0.675	0.96
Mg^a		2.02	1.74	0.92	0.80
Ca^a		5.60	2.47	0.45	0.65
Cl		106.0	130.0	1.23	1.04
HCO_3		25.0	22.0	0.92	1.04
^{82}Br		1.0	0.71	0.71	0.96
^{131}I	high	13.0	2.6	0.20	0.85
	low	0.25	0.0025	0.01	0.85
$^{14}CNS^b$	high	8.25	4.50	0.545	0.73
	low	1.77	0.071	0.04	0.60
Glucose		8.3	5.35	0.64	0.97
Amino acids		2.84	0.89	0.31	—
Urea		8.35	6.5	0.78	1.00
Osmolality		298.5	305.2	1.02	0.995
pH		7.46	7.27	—	—

[a] From Bradbury (unpublished).
[b] From Pollay (1966).

The significance of some features of the concentrations of ions and non-electrolytes in CSF compared with those in plasma will emerge from the later discussions on the relations between blood, CSF and brain. For the moment, we may simply note that the CSF is a secretion from the blood, elaborated by the choroid plexuses. The fluid provides a cushion for the brain, of obvious importance as a protection from trauma, but in this book we are concerned with any role it may play in regulating the composition of the environment of the neurons and glial cells of the central nervous tissue. Because of this interest we shall have to delve, later, into the role of active transport processes in governing its composition.

Relations between CSF and Brain

The ventricles are lined with an epithelium called the ependyma and, as indicated schematically in Figure 1.4, the ependyma and choroidal epithelium are continuous with each other, having the same embryonic history. In fact, the choroid plexus may be viewed as a simple out-pouching of the pia mater into the ependymal lining of the ventricle, the pia mater becoming highly vascularized during the process and its covering ependyma acquiring the features of a secretory epithelium. The cells of the ependyma are differentiated from those of the adjacent choroidal epithelium in being less columnar, but the important difference, functionally, is the absence of tight junctions sealing the intercellular clefts. It is because of this absence that Goldmann's second experiment produced the result that it did, namely allowing the passage of trypan blue from the CSF into the adjacent nervous tissue.

The Stern–Gautier Hypothesis

Stern and Gautier (1921, 1922) were the first to make a systematic study of passage of a variety of substances from blood into the CSF; they established that bromide, thiocyanate, strychnine and some other substances passed from blood into the CSF, while many other substances were excluded. They then compared these results with those on the effects of intravenous injections of these substances and concluded that only those drugs that exerted an effect on the central nervous system also entered the CSF, and they concluded that the mode of passage from blood to brain was by passage into the CSF and thence into the brain. The theory was extended to suggest that the metabolic requirements of the brain would be met only through the intermediary of the CSF. As such, the theory was quite untenable, but the possibility that certain substances might have special access to the brain from the blood by way of the CSF has been resuscitated by Spector (see, for example, Spector, 1986), with respect to certain vitamins and nucleic acid precursors, but before acquiescing in the various propositions, it is best to examine to the full the possibility that the two barriers, blood–brain and blood–CSF, are matched to each other so that the function of controlling interchange between blood and brain tissue is achieved without mutual interference.

Modern Developments of the Second Experiment

Goldmann's experiment simply showed that trypan blue was able to stain the brain tissue if the blood–brain barrier was circumvented, but of course gave us no idea of the magnitude of the extracellular space in which it was distributed. The first quantitative assessment of this space, using the intracerebrospinal route for administration of the extracellular marker, was carried out by Davson, Kleeman and Levin in 1961; they administered sucrose through the spinal subarachnoid space, maintaining a steady concentration by the process of barbotage, namely flushing the system backwards and forwards with the solution. They estimated a spinal cord extracellular space of 12–14%.

Ventriculocisternal Perfusion

Rall *et al.* (1962) used a far better controlled system of introducing the extracellular marker, namely by perfusing the ventricles of the dog with an artificial CSF containing the marker; the fluid entered a lateral ventricle and was drained away from the cisterna magna (Figure 1.6). The brain was analysed after a lengthy period of perfusion, being first cut into pieces to give blocks of tissue at successive distances from the ependymal surface of the ventricle, as illustrated by Figure 1.7. By applying an appropriate equation defining the fall in concentration with distance from the ventricular surface, they computed an extracellular space of 12% for the caudate nucleus. In a later study, employing the same approach, Levin *et al.* (1970) obtained higher values listed in Table 1.2. The important point, from the aspect of studies on the blood–brain barrier, is that there is a considerable non-cellular volume of water in which highly water-soluble substances may distribute themselves, provided that they can pass out of the blood. Thus, the fact that, intravenous infusion of an extracellular marker, such as [34]S-labelled sulphate, for as long as 3 h leads to a concentration in the extracellular fluid of only 7% of that in the blood plasma indicates the presence of a steep barrier to escape from blood into this space (Figure 1.8).

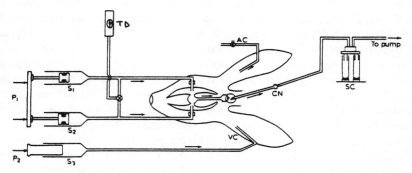

Figure 1.6 The technique of ventriculocisternal perfusion in the rabbit. P_1, infusion pump; P_2, intravenous infusion pump; S_1, S_2, S_3, 50 ml glass syringes. AC, arterial cannula; CN, cisternal needle; VC, venous cannula; SC, sample collector; TD, ventricular pressure transducer

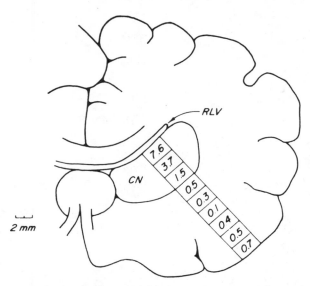

Figure 1.7 Showing inulin concentration as percentage of perfusate in tissue blocks from caudate nucleus outward. CN, caudate nucleus; RLV, right lateral ventricle. From Rall *et al.* (1962)

Table 1.2 Sucrose and inulin spaces in dog and monkey. From Levin *et al.* (1970)

	Cerebral cortex		Caudate nucleus	
Species	Sucrose space (%)·*mean*±s.e.	Inulin space (%)·*mean*±s.e.	Sucrose space (%)·*mean*±s.e.	Inulin space (%)·*mean*±s.e.
Dog	19.5±1.6 (*n* = 6)	18.8±1.6 (*n* = 6)	19.3±1.4 (*n* = 14)	19.2±1.4 (*n* = 9)
Monkey	19.6±2.0 (*n* = 4)	18.4±3.0 (*n* = 4)	17.5±0.8 (*n* = 5)	

It is worth noting from Figure 1.8 that at all times the concentration of sulphate in the CSF is *lower* than that in the brain extracellular space, indicating that, if one compartment of the CNS is to supply another, it is, in this case at any rate, the brain supplying the CSF.

Permeability of the Blood–Brain Barrier

Capillary Permeability

By 'barrier' in the present context we mean a restraint on the passage of certain solutes from blood to the tissue. In brain this restraint is very obvious when the situation in muscle or skin is compared; in this latter case the exchanges between blood and tissue are rapid, often so rapid that they are not easily given a

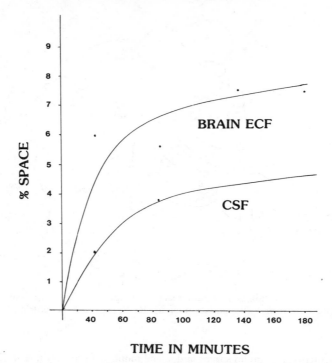

TIME IN MINUTES

Figure 1.8 The entry from the blood of [^{35}S]-sulphate into brain extracellular fluid and cerebrospinal fluid: brain space has been increased by 100/15 to allow for distribution in extracellular fluid only. Note that level in brain extracellular fluid is always above that in CSF (modified from Hollingsworth and Dawson (1973))

quantitative form. Nevertheless, when accurate studies are made with high resolution with respect to time (e.g. Pappenheimer, 1953), it can be shown that there are restraints on exchange between blood and these tissues, but, as indicated earlier, lipid-solubility does not play an important role, and the capillary membrane behaves like an artificial membrane with water-filled pores of some 60 μm diameter, i.e. diameters in the region of the diameter of plasma proteins such as albumin. These pores are located within the clefts between adjacent capillary endothelial cells; the clefts themselves are wide and may have diameters as large as 200 Å, but, if Curry and Michel (1980) are correct, they are filled with a meshwork of fibrillar material that acts as a molecular filter, restraining the passage of very large molecules such as albumin and globulin, but allowing virtually unobstructed diffusion of molecules such as glucose and amino acids.

Morphology of the Brain Capillary Barrier

We may anticipate our description of the quantitative establishment and measurement of the barrier between blood and extracellular space by stating at once that the barrier is the brain capillary endothelium itself. The brain capillary has a

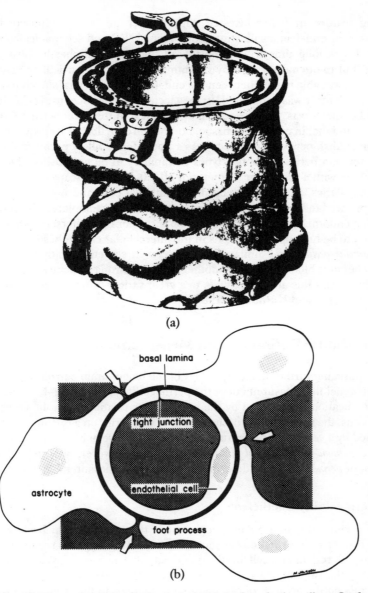

(a)

(b)

Figure 1.9 (a) Three-dimensional schematic drawing of cerebral capillary. On front side only the astrocyte processes are indicated. Above, in cross-section, the two layers covering the endothelial cells are indicated—namely the astrocyte processes (light) and the processes of other cells (shaded). From Wolff, *Z. Zelforsch.* (1963). (b) Diagram illustrating the close association of endothelial cells in brain capillaries with foot processes extending from astrocytes. The blood–brain barrier is produced by the continuous endothelium. The astrocytes encircle the microvessels, but are not sealed together and interstitial fluid has access (arrows) to the basement membrane and abluminal surface of the endothelial cell. From Goldstein (1988)

striking feature in being invested with a layer of closely apposed astrocytic processes, or end-feet, as illustrated by Figure 1.9(a) and schematically by Figure 1.9(b). For a long time it was considered that this glial sheath constituted the barrier, but the demonstration by Brightman (1965) that particulate matter, such as ferritin, was able to pass between the end-feet ruled the glial sheath out so far as acting as a barrier was concerned. In the electron microscope, using classical fixing methods, there was no obvious morphological difference between the brain capillary and that in connective tissue, but the introduction by Karnovsky (1967) of the horseradish peroxidase molecule as a tracer for capillary permeability enabled the distinction between the two types of capillary to be established. Horseradish peroxidase, with a molecular diameter of 50–60 Å, easily escapes from connective tissue capillaries, passing between the endothelial cells and not being held up at what appeared to be tight junctions but were, in fact, incomplete seals between the apposing endothelial cells. In the brain, on the other hand, horseradish peroxidase was seen to be held up by junctions in the intercellular clefts; these junctions were true *zonulae occludentes*, similar to those seen in secreting epithelia, so that the central nervous blood capillary endothelium has a strong structural affinity with an epithelium; and this affinity extends to a great variety of transport features, as we shall see (Reese and Karnovsky, 1967).

Permeability: Definition and Measurement

Before pursuing further the morphology of the blood–brain barrier, let us consider in some detail the measurement of the permeability of the blood–brain barrier and the complications introduced by the brain's close relations with the cerebrospinal fluid. Thus, the serious study of the blood–brain barrier on a quantitative basis was preceded by a variety of studies on the exchanges between blood and cerebrospinal fluid, the *blood–cerebrospinal fluid barrier*. First, however, we must define the concept of *permeability*, and describe its quantitative measurement and definition.

The Permeability Coefficient

By the permeability of a membrane we mean the ease with which molecules can pass across it; with a simple cell, such as the spherical egg of a sea-urchin, or the disc-shaped red blood cell of the mammal, this permeability is measured by estimating the amount of a given solute entering the cell in unit time. This amount, x, depends on the area, A, of cell membrane exposed to the medium in which the penetrating solute is dissolved, and on the difference in concentration across the membrane at any time, t, during the passage of the solute.

Expressed mathematically, the *permeability coefficient*, P, is given by the *permeability equation*:

$$dx/dt = PA(C_{out} - C_{in}) \tag{1.1}$$

the experimental situation being indicated by Figure 1.10, x being the amount of

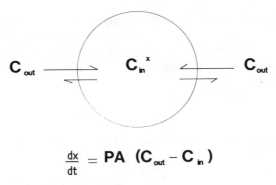

$$\frac{dx}{dt} = PA \ (C_{out} - C_{in})$$

Figure 1.10 Penetration of solute into cell

solute in the cell at any time, t. Usually it is the *concentration* of the solute in the cell that is measured, given by $C = x/V$, where V is the volume of water in the cell. Thus, $dC/dt = 1/V \, dx/dt$, and substitution in Equation (1.1) gives:

$$dC/dt = PA/V(C_{out} - C_{in}) \tag{1.2}$$

Usually it is possible to keep the outside concentration, C_{out}, constant, in which case Equation (1.2) can be integrated simply to give:

$$P = \frac{V}{A(t_2 - t_1)} \ln \frac{C_{out} - C_{in(t_1)}}{C_{out} - C_{in(t_2)}} \tag{1.3}$$

where $C_{in(t_1)}$ and $C_{in(t_2)}$ are the measured concentrations at times t_1 and t_2. If the experiment is conducted so that the concentration in the cell is initially zero, and the concentrations at measured times, t, are determined, the equation simplifies to:

$$P = \frac{V}{At} \ln \frac{C_{out}}{C_{out} - C_{in}} \tag{1.4}$$

The dimensions of the permeability coefficient are given by:

$$\frac{\text{volume (cm}^3)}{\text{area (cm}^2) \times \text{time (s)}} = \text{cm s}^{-1}$$

Basic Assumptions

The permeability equation involves several assumptions, one of which is that the delay in equilibration of the concentrations on either side of the membrane is due to transit through the membrane, diffusion in the cell water and outside medium being relatively rapid, so that local changes in concentration are rapidly evened out. In other words, that the inside and outside media are *well mixed*, so that the gradient of concentration between outside and inside occurs across the membrane. Another assumption is that passage from outside to inside the cell is restrained to the same extent as passage in the reverse direction. Where the equilibration between outside and inside depends on simple passive diffusion, due to the random motions of molecules, this may be expected and is demanded by the second law of thermodynamics. Thus, we may envisage a cell in which there are separate permeability coefficients, P_{in} and P_{out}, governing passage into and out of the cell, respectively.

The permeability equation becomes:

$$dx/dt = P_{in}AC_{out} - P_{out}AC_{in} \qquad (1.5)$$

at equilibrium, i.e. at infinite time, when $dx/dt = 0$, we have

$$\frac{C_{in}}{C_{out}} = \frac{P_{in}}{P_{out}} \qquad (1.6)$$

Thus, at equilibrium the concentration inside the cell could be higher than that in the medium if P_{in} were greater than P_{out}; in other words, the solute will have to move up a concentration gradient before equilibrium is reached, a process requiring energy. In the reverse case, with P_{in} less than P_{out}, the equilibrium position would be one with the concentration inside less than that outside, the solute being prevented from diffusing down its concentration gradient, a situation also requiring the input of energy. In the one case we may say that the cell has *accumulated* the solute, and in the other that it has tended to *exclude* or *excrete* it. In both cases the cell is working against the passive diffusive forces that tend to equalize differences in concentration, or *chemical potential*. Such processes are described as *active transport*, and are common in biological systems, including the blood–brain barrier, so that usually the basic equation used to describe transport from one medium to another is Equation (1.5), with separate permeability coefficients for influx and efflux, P_{in} and P_{out}.

Ionic Permeability

Where ions are concerned, the situation is not so simple, since the value of the permeability coefficient in any one direction will be influenced by the potential difference across the cell membrane. Thus, the resting, or membrane, potential of muscle or nerve, is such that the inside of the fibre is negatively charged in relation to the outside (Figure 1.11). Hence, positive ions, such as K^+, will be accelerated into the fibre, to give a value of P_{in} greater than P_{out}; the reverse applies to negative ions, such as Cl^-. Thus, in defining the driving force causing the penetration of an ion into or out of a cell, we must indicate, not only the difference in concentration, but also the difference of potential across the membrane. These two factors together constitute the *electrochemical potential* of the ion. If the electrochemical potential is the same on both sides of the membrane, the system is said to be at equilibrium, the differences of concentration being matched by appropriate differences of potential, and this seems to be the situation with regard to K^+ and Cl^-. If the potential and relative concentrations do not match, we say that the system is not at equilibrium, and if we are considering a steady-state condition, then we must postulate the expenditure of energy in establishing and maintaining

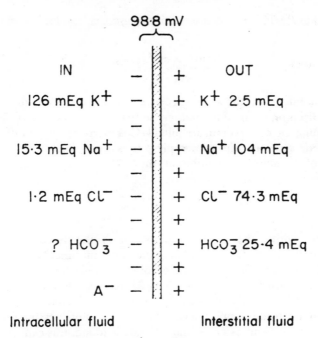

Figure 1.11 The distribution of ions and potential across nerve or muscle cell membranes. The membrane is permeable to K^+, Cl^- and HCO_3^- but effectively impermeable to Na^- and the organic anions, A^-. The relative concentrations of the permeable ions are theoretically governed by the Nernst equation relating these to the membrane potential

the condition. To quote an example, we shall see that the concentrations of Cl^- inside and outside the choroid plexus epithelial cell are widely different, that within the cell being very much less than that outside; there is a difference of potential across the epithelial cell that tends to accelerate Cl^- out of it, making P_{out} greater than P_{in}, but, according to Saito and Wright (1987), the difference of potential is, of itself, inadequate to account for the concentration difference, so that in this steady state condition the Cl^- ion is not at electrochemical equilibrium, a state requiring the continuous supply of metabolic energy.

The Transfer Coefficient

In many experimental systems it is not easy to measure the effective area of membrane exposed to the solute, so that a coefficient that indicates the relative permeabilities of the membrane to different solutes becomes desirable. Thus, when making comparisons within the same system, where the area-to-volume relationship remains the same, it is sufficient to use the term PA/V of Equation (1.2), so that the equation becomes:

$$dC/dt = K(C_{out} - C_{in}) \qquad (1.7)$$

with K equal to PA/V. K is called the *transfer coefficient*, and has the dimension t^{-1}, i.e.

$$\frac{cm/s \times cm^2}{cm^3} = s^{-1}$$

When measurements on the same species are made, it is likely that A/V will not vary greatly from one animal to another, so that the transfer coefficient is widely used in defining the blood–brain and blood–CSF barriers. When different species are compared, say rats and guinea-pigs, it is quite likely that, although the dimensions of the animals are different, the A/V ratios are sufficiently similar to justify comparison of transfer coefficients.

Clearance

Expressed in words, the transfer coefficient is the fraction by which the concentration difference ($C_{out} - C_{in}$) is reduced in unit time; thus, a value of 0.01 means that in unit time the concentration difference has been reduced by 1/100, or 1%. If, as is possible under some conditions, back-flux is ignored, the unit becomes a fraction of the outside concentration 'cleared' in unit time and transferred to the inside compartment. Thus, with a solute passing from plasma to tissue, if a value of the transfer constant of 0.01 is found, this can be described as the transfer of 0.01 ml of the plasma to one gram of tissue, to give a figure with dimensions $ml\,g^{-1}\,min^{-1}$, i.e. $0.01\ ml\,g^{-1}\,ml^{-1}$ or $10\ \mu l\,g^{-1}\,min^{-1}$.

The *PS* Product

In many studies of the blood–brain barrier, in which penetration of solute from blood into the brain tissue is measured, the coefficient defining the barrier is often described as the *PS* product, i.e. the product of the permeability coefficient, as correctly defined by Equation (1.1) with dimension cm/s, and the area of membrane exposed to the brain, or, more correctly, to the brain water with which the solute equilibrates, with dimension cm^2. The dimensions of permeability $\times$ surface area should be $cm/s \times cm^2$, i.e. cm^3/s. Usually, however, S, the surface area, is defined as the *area per unit weight of brain*, i.e. with dimensions cm^2/g, or since the specific gravity of brain is about unity, $cm^2/cm^3 = cm^{-1}$. In this case the *PS* product has dimension: $cm/s \times cm^{-1}$, or s^{-1}, i.e. it has the dimension of the *transfer coefficient*, K, defined earlier as PA/V, where A is the total area of membrane exposed to the penetrating solute. To avoid misunderstanding, therefore, the symbol S should be used to represent area per unit amount of tissue, while A represents the total area of membrane.

Volume : Area Ratio

If it is required to convert the transfer coefficient to a permeability coefficient, then we must multiply K by the ratio between volume and area (V/A); thus, if we have a transfer coefficient of, say, $0.001 \, \text{s}^{-1}$ for transport from blood into brain and we know that the area of blood capillaries of the brain is $100 \, \text{cm}^2$ per cm^3 of brain water with which the plasma is equilibrating, then the permeability coefficient becomes:

$$\frac{0.001 \times 1}{100} = 1.10^{-5} \, \text{cm/s}$$

We may note, in parentheses, that we must be careful to define the water of the brain with which the plasma is equilibrating; thus, with ^{24}Na it is, essentially, the extracellular water, which is about 20% of the total brain water. In this case the V/A fraction becomes 0.2/200 and the permeability coefficient is correspondingly reduced to $2 \times 10^{-6} \, \text{cm/s}$.

Half-life

Of practical interest in the study of kinetics of permeability processes is the time taken to reach a fixed degree of equilibration when a concentration gradient has been established; thus, the *half-life* is the time required to reach 50% equilibration, and is given by substitution into the simple permeability equation:

$$dC/dt = K(C_{\text{out}} - C_{\text{in}}) \tag{1.7}$$

where

$$K = i/t \ln (1 - C_{\text{in}}/C_{\text{out}})$$

Thus, at half-equilibration the term in the parentheses is equal to 0.5, and the time, $t_{1/2}$, is given by $K = 1/t_{1/2} \ln 0.5$—i.e.

$$t_{1/2} = \ln 0.5/K = 0.7/K$$

Thus, for sodium the transfer coefficient for equilibration between blood and CSF is about $0.007 \, \text{min}^{-1}$, whence $t_{1/2}$ is equal to $0.7/0.007 = 100$ min approximately.

Membrane Permeability as a Special Case of Diffusion

The permeability process that we have described here is a special case of diffusion of solutes in aqueous solution, a process that occurs as a result of the random motions of the solute molecules. In the permeability case the diffusive process has been considered to be confined to a membrane; this does not mean that diffusion does not take place in the phases of the system separated by the membrane, but simply that the diffusive process across the membrane is so slow that processes occurring in the so-called bulk phases can be ignored by comparison. Let us imagine that we have placed two solutions of concentrations C_1 and C_2 in contact with each other, as in Figure 1.12(A), C_1 being greater than C_2. At the junction between the solutions there will be more random movements of solute from left to right than in the opposite direction; we can say that the flux of solute from left to right is greater than the flux from right to left, and that there will, after a time

(A)

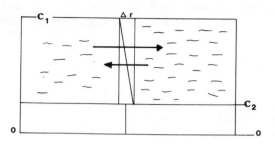

(B)

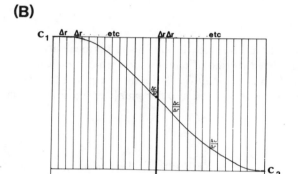

Figure 1.12 (A) The solutions of concentrations C_1 and C_2 have been put in contact; there is a steep gradient of concentration across the small element of solution, Δr. Concentrations are represented by the height of the line above the baseline. (B) After a certain period diffusion has proceeded, so that concentrations in the left-hand compartment fall and those in the right-hand compartment rise. An infinite number of concentration gradients have been set up, indicated schematically by sections Δr thick. The concentration profile throughout the solutions is arbitrary but can be calculated by appropriate solution of the Fick equation

interval, be a net flux in the direction C_1 to C_2, the tendency of the net flux being to equalize the concentrations in the two compartments.

Fick Equation

The equation governing this diffusive process across the area of contact is the Fick equation, which can take the form

$$\mathrm{d}x/\mathrm{d}t = DA\mathrm{d}C/\mathrm{d}r \tag{1.8}$$

The differential dx/dt expresses, as before, the rate of transport, i.e. the amount of solute in moles crossing the boundary in time dt; the differential dC/dr is the concentration gradient at the point considered, i.e. at the boundary in Figure 1.12(A). We must appreciate that, after a few seconds, the situation will have differed from that in Figure 1.12(A), since the concentrations will no longer be uniform on each side of the barrier; consequently, there will be a large number of separate boundaries separating solutions of slightly different concentration because, once diffusion has started across the original surface of contact, gradients will be established, causing diffusion from one point to the next, as illustrated schematically in Figure 1.12(B). Without going into detail, we may accept that the calculation of D from measurements of change in solute concentration on the left- and right-hand sides of Figure 1.12 will be difficult, but by no means impossible, and the solutions to the Fick equation for various situations, e.g. when a spherical cell is suspended in an aqueous medium containing a solute of initial concentration C, have been given in appropriate textbooks. Thus, Figure 1.13 gives the theoretical solutions that enable one to calculate the course of equilibration with time, the degree of equilibration being plotted against the factor Dt/r^2, where D is the diffusion coefficient, t is the time elapsed since the systems were placed in contact, e.g. a sphere, a cylinder or a flat sheet of tissue or, say, a sheet of jelly consisting of predominantly water, and r is the radius or half-thickness of the system. If, experimentally, the degree of equilibration between the tissue and medium has been measured, by chemical or isotopic analysis, then, from a knowledge of t and r, the diffusion coefficient in the tissue can be deduced. If the solute is confined to the extracellular space, then a 'tortuosity factor' reduces the diffusion coefficient, since the molecules must pass round the cells. This may reduce the effective coefficient by a factor of as much as 2.

Rate of Equilibration
With a knowledge of this diffusion coefficient in an aqueous medium, we may predict, from the dimensions of the system, just how rapidly a tissue will come into equilibrium with its environment. For example, when a brain slice is placed in an aqueous medium containing a labelled solute, it is important to know how rapidly the extracellular fluid of this tissue will come into equilibrium with the medium. There is no membrane barrier between the two compartments, namely bathing medium and tissue, so that the Fick diffusion equation must be applied. As an example, we may compute the time required for a small solute, such as urea, with a diffusion coefficient of 1.4×10^{-5} cm^2/s to come to 50% equilibrium with its outside medium. From Figure 1.13, we see that the value of Dt/r^2 for 50% equilibrium is about 0.04 for a sphere, 0.08 for a cylinder and 0.19 for a thin sheet. If we take the case of a thin sheet, e.g. a tissue slice, then if r is 1 mm, $t_{1/2}$ becomes 266 s, i.e. of the order of 4 min. If r is 10 μm, on the other hand, $t_{1/2}$ is only 0.0266 s. This calculation emphasizes the importance of the spatial dimension for rapid equilibration to occur by simple diffusion. As we shall see, failure to appreciate this factor has led to erroneous conclusions regarding transport of sugars into the cells of brain slices (p. 157).

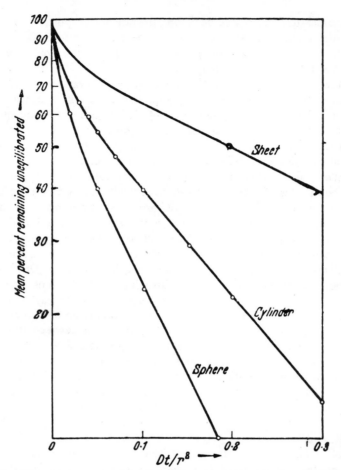

Figure 1.13 The time course of equilibration of some simple geometrical shapes by diffusion. The mean value of the fraction which has still to equilibrate is given against the parameter Dt/r^2. D = diffusion constant, r = radius or half thickness. From Harris, *Transport and Accumulation in Biological Systems.* Butterworth, London (1956)

Membrane Permeability

To return to the system in which two compartments are separated by a membrane that restrains free diffusion from one side to the other, we can see that we have assumed that gradients of concentration in the bulk of the two solutions separated by the membrane have been abolished, because of the long time taken to cross the membrane compared with the time for free diffusion to allow equalization of concentration differences. Thus, we are able to treat the solutions C_1 and C_2 as uniform spatially, changing with time, of course, until they become equal on each side of the membrane but otherwise uniform. In this situation, the Fick equation applies but can be very much simplified. Thus, if the membrane is thin, the concentration gradient, dC/dr, which is confined to the membrane, may be represented approximately by:

$$\frac{C_{out} - C_{in}}{\text{membrane thickness } (\tau)}$$

as in Figure 1.14 and we have:

$$dx/dt = DA(C_{out} - C_{in}) \qquad (1.9)$$

If we compare Equation (1.9) with the simple permeability equation (1.1), we see that P, the permeability coefficient, is equivalent to the diffusion coefficient of the solute in the membrane, D, divided by the membrane thickness.

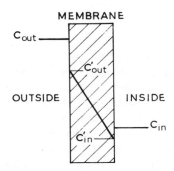

Figure 1.14   The gradient across the cell membrane

Michaelis–Menten Kinetics

The permeability coefficient defines the rate at which a difference of concentration across a membrane is equalized. It is, as can be seen by inspection of the permeability equation, independent of the actual concentrations. In many situations of biological interest it is found that the measured permeability coefficient is not independent of concentrations across the membrane, becoming smaller at higher concentrations. Sometimes there is an asymmetry, as in the case of the erythrocyte, one side of the membrane being differently influenced compared with the other side. This dependence on concentration suggests that there is some limitation on the availability of space on the membrane for the solute molecules to cross, i.e. that, as the concentration on one side rises, there is an 'overcrowding', so that the fraction of the total molecules crossing in unit time changes. In simple diffusion across a membrane, however, the measured independence of the permeability coefficient of concentration indicates that 'there is plenty of room' for the molecules, so that at any time the same fraction of the concentration will cross in unit time whether the concentration be 1 molar or 1 millimolar. The finding that the fraction decreases with rising concentration, i.e. the permeability coefficient decreases with rising concentration, demands that useful access to the membrane is in some way restricted.

Carrier-mediated Transport

This restriction has brought into use the concept of *carrier-mediated transport*, it being assumed that, in order to cross the membrane efficiently, the solute molecule must attach itself to some carrier in the membrane, the number of carriers, or attachment sites, being limited and liable eventually to *saturation*. On this basis, the fraction of the concentration that can be carried at any given moment will depend on the number of sites occupied, or rather the number unoccupied, and eventually a point will be reached when the amount of solute crossing the membrane in unit time is independent of the concentration of the solute; in this case the carrier is said to be saturated, and carrier-mediated kinetics are often called 'saturation kinetics'.

Competition

The classical studies on carrier-mediated transport involved the measurement of transport of sugars across the red blood cell membrane (Widdas, 1954; LeFevre, 1962); the transport of a single hexose, such as D-glucose, exhibited saturation kinetics; moreover, different hexoses showed different apparent affinities for the carrier, as evidenced by the rapidity with which they crossed the membrane. The sugars would compete with each other, so that addition of D-mannose to a solution of D-glucose would reduce the transport of D-glucose. This competition showed strong stereospecificity, so that L-glucose exerted little inhibitory effect on the penetration of D-glucose.

Facilitated Transport

The dependence of transport on the apparent presence of carriers in the membrane has given rise to the general concept of facilitated transport, a form of transport across the lipid plasma membrane that enables highly lipid-insoluble molecules to pass through it. The original model of such a process was based on the attachment of the 'privileged' solute to a specific grouping on a carrier molecule that could shuttle it backwards and forwards across the lipid cell membrane. When the thinness of the cell membrane was appreciated, however, the concept of a shuttling carrier had to be abandoned, and instead the notion was adopted of a carrier protein, embedded in the cell membrane, that could facilitate transport of specific molecules that had affinity for certain groups of atoms at its surface, from one side to the other. Mere attachment to the carrier molecule would not be sufficient to permit transport, and a conformational change in the carrier protein was postulated, a change that would enable the attached solute molecule to detach itself at the opposite side of the membrane.

The Enzyme Analogue

An enzyme-catalysed reaction presupposes, in the first place, a reversible attachment of a substrate molecule to an enzyme, so that there is a strong analogy between facilitated transport and enzyme-catalysed reactions. In this case the treatment developed by Michaelis and Menten (1913) should be applicable to the transport process. The Michaelis–Menten equation for a chemical reaction is

$$v = \frac{V_{\max} [S]}{K_m [S]} \tag{1.10}$$

where v is the rate of reaction in units of, say, $\mu mol\ g^{-1}\ min^{-1}$, and where $V_{\max}$ is the maximum value of v, which occurs when the concentration of the substrate, S, is very low; K_m is the equilibrium constant for the reaction between solute and enzyme:

$$K_m = \frac{[E]\ [S]}{[ES]} \tag{1.11}$$

Where [E] is the total concentration of enzyme, [S] is the concentration of substrate and [ES] that of the substrate–enzyme complex. K_m is, in fact, equal to the concentration of the substrate when the enzyme is half-saturated and is usually considered as an inverse measure of the *affinity* of the substrate for the enzyme (see, however, Neame and Richards, 1972).

Lineweaver–Burk Plot

To determine $V_{\max}$ and K_m it is usual to make a Lineweaver–Burk plot as in Figure 1.15(a), i.e. if we plot $1/v$ against $1/[S]$, the intercept on the ordinate is $1/V_{\max}$ and on the abscissa $-1/K_m$, since rearrangement of Equation (1.9) gives

$$1/v = \frac{K_m}{V_{\max} [S]} + \frac{1}{V_{\max}} \tag{1.12}$$

The slope of the line is $K_m/V_{\max}$.

Hofstee Plot

The Lineweaver–Burk plot is one of several methods of deducing the kinetic parameters K_m and $V_{\max}$ from the measured effects of concentration of solute on rate of transport. In the Hofstee plot (1959) the rate of transport, v, is plotted against the ratio $v/[S]$, as in Figure 1.15(b). Thus, the basic Michaelis–Menten formulation is transformed algebraically to

$$v = V_{\max} - \frac{v}{[S]} \times K_m \tag{1.13}$$

$V_{\max}$ is the rate of transport when the concentration of solute is infinite, i.e. when $v/[S]$ is zero, and is thus given by the intercept on the ordinate. When $V_{\max}$ has been found, K_m is obtained by finding the point on the ordinate where $v = \frac{1}{2}V_{\max}$, the corresponding point on the abscissa being $\frac{1}{2}V_{\max}/K_m$. In the case illustrated by Figure 1.15(b) $V_{\max}/2$ is approximately 0.34, and $\frac{1}{2}V_{\max}/K_m$ is approximately 1.1, when $K_m = c.\ 0.34/1.1 = 0.3$ mM.

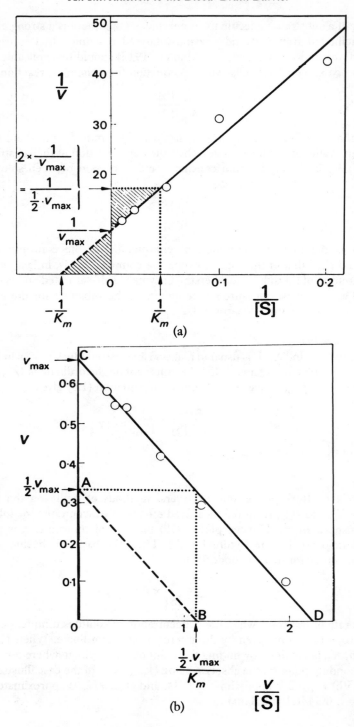

(a)

(b)

Facilitated Kinetics

Widdas (1952) and Rosenberg and Wilbrandt (1955) applied Michaelis–Menten reaction kinetics to the analogous problem of facilitated, or carrier-mediated, transport. In general, the passage of a solute across a membrane was considered to represent two carrier-mediated steps—into the cell and out of it. Thus, the flux, J, expressed as, say, micromoles per gram of cells per minute—$\mu\text{mol g}^{-1}\text{ min}^{-1}$— would be given by

$$J = \frac{V_{\max}}{C_1 + K_m} \cdot C_1 - \frac{V_{\max}}{C_2 + K_m} \cdot C_2 \qquad (1.14)$$

where C_1 and C_2 are the concentrations of solute on the inside and outside of the cells.

Under conditions where back-flux from the cell was negligible, i.e. at the early stages of equilibration or when a cell lost solute into a large volume of solution, the *unidirectional flux*, J_u, became:

$$J_u = \frac{V_{\max}}{C_1 + K_m} \cdot C_1 \qquad (1.15)$$

which would be the same as for an enzyme-catalysed chemical reaction. Thus, the efflux of solute from a cell into a large volume of solution, J_u, could be measured with different concentrations of the solute, C_1, and a Lineweaver–Burk plot would enable the calculation of an affinity, given by the reciprocal of K_m, and a maximum rate of transport, $V_{\max}$.

Under conditions where fluxes in both directions had to be considered, the mathematical treatment was more complex.

The Diffusional Component

If transport across the membrane depended entirely on attachment to, and release from, some hypothetical carrier, the curve of influx plotted against concentration of the solute should flatten off completely when the carrier had been saturated, as in Figure 1.16(A). In practice, this type of curve is not often found, because the solute can also penetrate, albeit slowly, without utilizing the carrier, so that there is no level of concentration beyond which rate of penetration does not increase. Thus, the more usual curve obtained by plotting rate of penetration against concentration is that shown in Figure 1.16(B); the rate of penetration increases

---

Figure 1.15 (a) Double reciprocal plot of the uptake of γ-aminobutyrate by brain slices. Shaded areas are similar triangles, showing that the plotted straight line cuts the abscissa at a value equal to $-(1/K_m)$. v = rate of uptake of γ-aminobutyrate, $\mu\text{mol min}^{-1}\text{ g}^{-1}$ tissue; [S] = concentration of γ-aminobutyrate in suspending medium, mM; $v_{\max} = 0.115$ $\mu\text{mol min}^{-1}\text{ g}^{-1}$ tissue; $K_m = 22$ μM. Incubation 10 min, 25 °C. (b) Plot of v against $v/[S]$ for the saturable component of the uptake of benzylamine by Ehrlich ascites carcinoma cells. From Neame and Richards (1972)

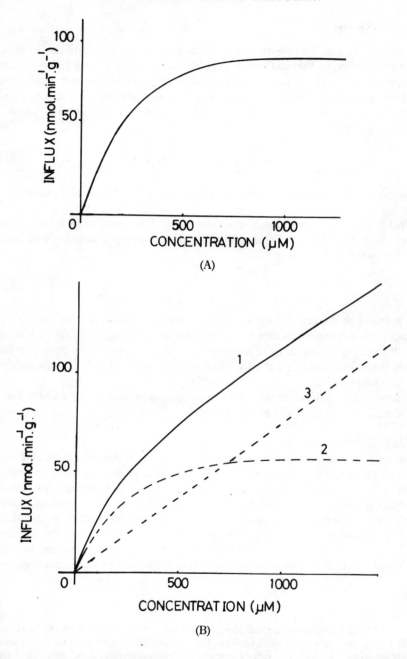

Figure 1.16   (A) Typical curve for penetration of solute from one compartment to another governed completely by a saturable process. (B) There is a non-diffusional component that leads to a linear rise in concentration with time. The curve (1) may be resolved into the saturable (2) and non-saturable (3) components. From Neame and Richards (1972)

indefinitely with concentration (curve 1), but the rate of increase decreases at a certain point, when it becomes linear; it is at this point that the carrier has become saturated, and further increases in flux are due to non-carrier-mediated transport. Transport under these conditions is described by the modified equation:

$$v = \frac{V_{max}\,[S]}{K_m + [S]} + K_d\,[S] \qquad (1.16)$$

where K_d is the 'diffusional constant' defining uptake by the non-carrier-mediated process. Practically, the linear portion of curve 1 is considered to represent the non-carrier-mediated, or diffusional, component, and curve 1 is considered to be made up of a linear and a non-linear component; subtraction of the linear component gives the true Michaelis–Menten relation (curve 2).

Use of Labelled Solutes

The pioneering work on facilitated transport was carried out using chemical, or less direct, methods for analysis of the concentrations of the sugars whose transport properties were being studied; and this imposed limits to the lower concentrations that could be employed. With the availability of isotopically labelled solutes, such as [^{14}C]-glucose, it was possible to study the effects of concentration down to very low, and effectively zero, concentration of the solute. Thus, under 'carrier-free' conditions, the concentration of solute was virtually zero, and a simplified equation describing transport could be applied, namely:

$$v = \frac{V_{max}}{K_m} \, (C_{out} - C_{in}) \qquad (1.16a)$$

if, for example, labelled glucose were penetrating a suspension of cells or a tissue. v was defined as the quantity (e.g. μmoles) of solute entering unit mass, or volume of tissue in unit time, so its dimensions could be represented as μmol ml^{-1} min^{-1}, and it could be represented symbolically as $1/V\,dx/dt$, when comparing it with the simple permeability equations for a two-compartment system described earlier.

Thus, we have

$$1/V\,dx/dt = \frac{V_{max}}{K_m} \, (C_{out} - C_{in}) \qquad (1.17)$$

Since C_{in}, the concentration of the penetrating solute in the tissue at any time, t, is given by x/V, $1/V\,dx/dt$ becomes dC/dt:

$$dC/dt = \frac{V_{max}}{K_m} \, (C_{out} - C_{in}) \qquad (1.18)$$

Comparing this with our simple two-compartment permeability equation

$$dC/dt = \frac{PA}{V} \, (C_{out} - C_{in}) \qquad (1.2)$$

we see that, under these carrier-free conditions, we may equate the ratio V_{max}/K_m

with the ratio PA/V, which we have defined as the transfer coefficient, K, with dimension time^{-1}.

Thus, the measurement of the values of V_{max} and K_m enables us to compute just how fast equilibration may take place between two compartments, e.g. blood plasma and brain water, when the concentration of the facilitated solute is virtually zero, i.e. when all the carriers are available for transport with negligible competition among solute molecules.

Inhibition

Competitive Inhibition

By competitive inhibition we mean the reduction in rate of transport of our 'substrate molecule' by addition to the medium of another 'inhibitor molecule' to the medium, the feature of the inhibition being that it can be at least partially reversed by adding more of the 'substrate molecule' to the medium. Inhibitor and substrate are thus competing for carrier sites on the membrane, and the effectiveness of the inhibitor is governed by its ability to compete with the substrate, i.e. by its affinity. Kinetically speaking, it is an arbitrary matter as to which molecule we define as the substrate and which the inhibitor if both are genuinely being transported by the same carrier molecule. In general, the behaviour of a competitive inhibitor can be characterized by a change in the apparent value of K_m, which may be designated as K_a; thus, Sen and Widdas (1962) showed that the value of K_m for transport of glucose across the erythrocyte membrane was increased by adding the aglucone of phlorizin, phloretin, to the medium.

V_{max} is the maximum rate of transport when the concentration of solute is infinitely high, so that the presence of a competing substrate, the competitive inhibitor, would not be expected to alter this parameter, the inhibitor being effectively 'squeezed off' the carrier by the very high concentration of the substrate. In fact, the absence of effect on V_{max} associated with an apparent change in K_m is often used as a working definition of competitive inhibition.

Kinetic Analysis

Kinetic analysis of the effects of a competitive inhibitor, based purely on the assumption of availability of carriers for a substrate and competition for places on the carrier sites, led to a relation between K_m, the equilibrium constant for the substrate, and K_i, the equilibrium constant for the inhibitor when acting alone. Thus, the equation describing transport in the presence of an inhibitor is

$$v = \frac{V_{max}\,[S]}{[S] + K_m}\left(1 + \frac{[i]}{K_i}\right) \tag{1.19}$$

This equation is identical with the straightforward Michaelis–Menten equation

$$v = \frac{V_{max}\,[S]}{[S] + K_m} \tag{1.10}$$

with K_m replaced with an 'apparent K_m' equivalent to $K_m(1 + [i]/K_i)$, or K_a. K_m is therefore increased by a factor $[i]/K_i$, where K_i is equivalent to K_m, in the sense that it represents the concentration at which the carrier is 50% saturated by it. Thus, if, in separate types of experiment, the K_m for, say, galactose, were estimated from a simple study of the effects of galactose concentration on its rate of penetration into a cell, and then a value of K_i were deduced from the effects of galactose on transport of glucose, the values of K_m and K_i for galactose should be the same.

Determination of K_i

The inhibitory power of a substrate is determined in the first place by measuring the decrease in rate of penetration of a solute, v, by increasing concentrations of the inhibitor, $[i]$. Neame and Richards (1972) have discussed the methods, which have the same pitfalls as those involved in the accurate determination of K_m for uncomplicated transport of the substrate. Essentially we must deduce K_i from an apparent dissociation constant, K_a, measured in the presence of the inhibitor, and the true K_m measured without an inhibitor, related to each other by the equation

$$K_a = K_m\left(1 + \frac{[i]}{K_i}\right) \qquad (1.20)$$

Figure 1.17 illustrates a double-reciprocal, or Lineweaver–Burk, plot of rate of transport, v, against concentration of solute in the absence and presence of the inhibitor; the lines intersect at a common V_{max}, as the inhibition is competitive.

In the special case when the concentration of the solute molecule is kept well below the K_m for its transport, we may plot the velocity of transport, $1/v$, against the concentration of inhibitor; this gives a straight line for which K_i is deduced from the intercept on the abscissa as in Figure 1.18.

Physiological Interest

This competitive inhibition can be of considerable physiological interest. Thus, amino acids cross the blood–brain barrier by facilitated transport, and it appears that many of those in the circulating blood, such as tryptophan and leucine, employ the same carrier, and therefore compete with each other for transport from blood to brain. As we shall see in Chapter 2, an abnormal level of one amino acid, such as phenylalanine, may seriously impair the ability of another amino acid, tryptophan, to gain access to the brain, thereby causing abnormal brain development.

Non-competitive Inhibition

An inhibitor is said to be non-competitive if its effects cannot be reversed by adding excess of the substrate; the reason for this could be that the inhibitor had such a high affinity for the carrier molecule that its reaction was irreversible. Thus, for some time it was considered that cytochalasin B, a highly specific inhibitor of glucose transport in many systems, was a non-competitive inhibitor, but more careful studies showed that its effects could be reversed, at least partially, by addition of glucose to the medium. Reagents that react with SH-groups exert a

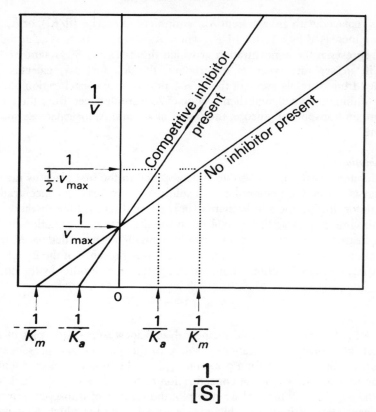

Figure 1.17 Double reciprocal plot showing the effect of a fixed concentration of competitive inhibitor on the rate of transfer (v) of substrate at various concentrations ([S]) (cf. Figures 1.20 and 1.23). The value for $1/v_{max}$ is unchanged by the presence of the inhibitor, but that for $1/K_m$ appears reduced (i.e. K_m appears increased) to $1/K_a$, where

$$K_a = K_m \left(1 + \frac{[i]}{K_i} \right)$$

From Neame and Richards (1972)

chemical change in the carrier molecule that cannot be reversed by the substrate, and are described as non-competitive inhibitors, e.g. $HgCl_2$, N-ethyl-maleimide, and so on. We may assume that, in many cases of non-competitive inhibition, the agent reacts with some part of the carrier molecule, which need not necessarily be the grouping that specifically adsorbs the solute being transported, but, by its reaction, alters the characteristics of the carrier molecule so as to prevent it from fulfilling its role as a transporter.

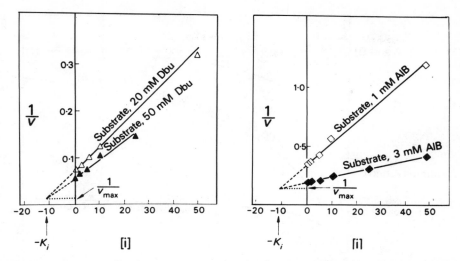

Figure 1.18 Determination of K_i from a plot of $1/v$ against [i]. The amino acid phenylalanine inhibited competitively the transfer of α,γ-diaminobutyrate (Dbu) (*left*) and of α-aminoisobutyrate (AIB) (*right*) into Ehrlich ascites carcinoma cells. In each case, K_i for phenylalanine was found to be about 11 mM, which is consistent with a single common carrier for phenylalanine, Dbu and AIB. v = mmoles of substrate/kg cell water/min; [i] = concentration of phenylalanine in suspending medium, mM. In each case v_{max} refers to corresponding substrate. Incubation at 37 °C: α,γ-diaminobutyrate, 2 min; α-aminoisobutyrate, 1 min. From Neame and Richards (1972), redrawn from data published by Christensen and Liang (1966)

Active Transport

When the transport of a solute across a membrane relies on a supply of energy, i.e. when it is active, then the kinetics of transport usually have the features of carrier-mediated transport, the difference between this form and the facilitated transport we have just been describing, being the reliance on a source of energy. A metabolic inhibitor will inhibit the transport, and this type of inhibition comes under the category of non-competitive inhibition, K_m being usually unaltered because the inhibition does not necessarily involve interaction with the sites on the carrier to which the transported solute attaches itself.

Kinetics

Kinetically the presence of non-competitive inhibition is revealed by a decrease in V_{max} often without a change in K_m. Figure 1.19 illustrates hypothetical curves of rate of transport versus concentration of a substrate in the absence of inhibitors

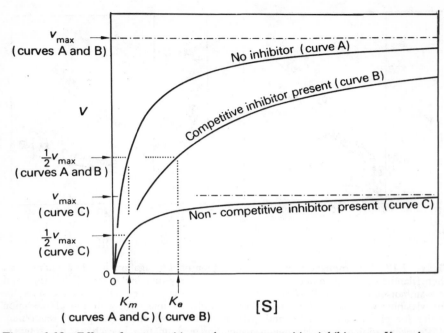

Figure 1.19 Effect of a competitive and a non-competitive inhibitor on K_m and v_{max}. Curve A: the transfer of substrate in the absence of inhibitor. Curve B: the transfer of substrate in the presence of a competitive inhibitor; K_m appears altered to a value equal to K_a, where

$$K_a = K_m \left(1 + \frac{[i]}{K_i} \right)$$

but v_{max} is unaltered. Curve C: the transfer of substrate in the presence of a non-competitive inhibitor; the value of v_{max} is reduced, but that of K_m is unchanged. $v =$ rate of transfer; [S] = concentration of substrate. From Neame and Richards (1972)

(curve A) and in the presence of a competitive inhibitor (curve B) and a non-competitive inhibitor (curve C). K_m, defined as the concentration for half-maximal rate, $V_{max}/2$, is the same for the uninhibited state and for that when the non-competitive inhibitor is present. V_{max} is reduced by the non-competitive inhibitor.

The Nature of the Carrier

Because of the extreme thinness of the plasma membrane of cells, the concept of a mobile carrier, capable of shuttling from one side to the other, is impossible to maintain, although kinetic analyses, based on this hypothesis, yielded plausible equations to describe facilitated transport. We may assume, then, that the carrier is a protein embedded in the lipid bilayer with a head-and-tail arrangement so that reactive groups face both cytoplasmic and extracellular surfaces of the lipid bilayer. The part of the protein embedded in the lipid bilayer would have to be hydrophobic to enable it to remain in this hydrophobic environment; on the other hand, it is presumably coiled so as to constitute a hydrophilic pore that attracts hydrophilic molecules, such as sugars, into it and facilitates their transport from one side of the membrane to the other. Such a pore could consist of alpha-helical regions of the polypeptide chain, the atomic groupings favouring attraction to the hydrophilic solute being determined by the order of amino acids linked in this helix.

A protein molecule of this sort could, then, constitute a 'selective pore' available to molecules that would make easily reversible links with the atomic groupings in it. Thus, the preferred molecules would make a series of jumps along the carrier protein, and their passage would be facilitated only because a route through the lipid bilayer, constituting the major part of the cell membrane, was forbidden by their lipid-insolubility.

Active Transport

When the facilitated transport involves a movement of the solute against a gradient of electrochemical potential, then, of course, more is demanded of the carrier protein than that it should provide a channel through which the actively transported solute travelled. Association with the carrier molecule, involving Michaelis–Menten kinetics, must also be linked with the liberation of energy, and, as we shall see later, the association with the transporter protein is accompanied by a change in its conformation, a change that is associated not only with the release of energy but also with a change in the effective exposure of the transporter molecule to one or other side of the membrane. Thus, simultaneous exposure of the solute–carrier complex to both sides of the membrane must be prevented, so that models of the process of active transport involve a 'gating system' such that, when the transported molecule links to the carrier, a gate is automatically shut that excludes it from returning from the same side at which it entered. Such gating systems are well established in the process of active transport, but the extent to which they occur in the passive processes of facilitated transport discussed here remains to be seen.

Identification and Isolation

The identification and isolation steps rely primarily on being able to label the transporter protein with an appropriate 'probe' that has a strong affinity for the specific carrier site, so strong an affinity, indeed, that it remains attached to the protein during successive isolation and purification pocedures. So far as the sugar transporter is concerned, the mould product, cytochalasin B, which is a potent competitive inhibitor of glucose transport in many facilitated systems, including the erythrocyte (Taverna and Langdon, 1973), has been employed. Its efficacy as a label, or 'probe', can be greatly increased, moreover, by irradiation of the substrate–protein complex with powerful visible light, a process that converts the weaker hydrogen-bond links to covalent links, so that the probe remains attached to the purified protein even during SDS–PAGE analysis of its molecular weight. The isolated transport protein can often be tested for its transporting ability by artificially incorporating it into vesicles called *liposomes*, consisting of small lipid-coated droplets dispersed from a mixture of natural or artificial lipids in an aqueous medium. The liposomes in which the transporter is incorporated can be suspended in a medium containing the labelled solute, e.g. $[^{14}C]$-glucose; and uptake can be measured by filtering off the suspension after a given time and analysing it for radioactivity. Thus Carter-Su *et al.* (1980) used vesicles reconstituted from adipocyte membranes in which they had incorporated the purified glucose transporter isolated through its reactivity with concavalin A. They showed that uptake of $[^{14}C]$-D-glucose was inhibited by adding non-labelled D-glucose to the medium but not L-glucose.

The Anion Transporter

The first transport molecule to be isolated was that which facilitates the extremely rapid exchange of anions across the red cell membrane, by Rothstein and Ramjeesingh (1980). Disulphonic stilbene (DIDS) was tightly bound and acted as the probe. Thus, at low temperatures it acted as a competitive inhibitor of transport; on raising the temperature, a covalent link was formed so that DIDS could now be used in the purification process. The transporter protein was a glycoprotein of 90 kilodaltons (kD) called, from its position in the electropherogram, *band-3 protein*. By splitting the protein from the outside and the inside of the membrane, the regions projecting out of the lipid bilayer were identified, as was the region remaining in the bilayer, and presumably constituting the channel that facilitated anion transport. This splitting is indicated schematically in Figure 1.20, and leads to three segments: a soluble cytoplasmic portion of 40 kD containing the N-terminus of the protein (N_t–P_2); a transmembrane segment of 17 kD (P_1–P_2) and a C-terminal portion of 35 kD (P_1–C_t) which is also transmembrane and has carbohydrate moieties on its outside aspect. It is the 17 kD segment that reacts with DIDS, etc. Further cleavage studies indicated that the 17 kD and 35 kD

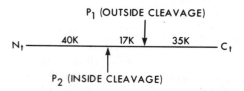

Figure 1.20   Chymotryptic cleavages of band 3. The outside cleavage (P_1) is in intact cells and the inside cleavage (P_2) in inside-out vesicles. The 17 000 dalton (17 K) and 35 000 dalton (35 K) segments are intrinsic and appear to be transmembrane. The 40 000 dalton (40 K) N-terminal segment is soluble after cleavage. After Steck *et al.* From Rothstein and Ramjeesingh (1980)

segments, which are intrinsic to the membrane, can be resolved into two functional peptides, one of 15 kD containing the DIDS-binding site and derived from the 17 kD segment, and another of 9 kD derived from the 35 kD segment. It was concluded that the 15 kD segment looped back on itself in the membrane so that it traversed it three times, as in Figure 1.21; the 9 kD segment probably also loops through the membrane.

Model

Rothstein and Ramjeesingh (1980) have suggested a model of the transport process illustrated by Figure 1.22, where the band 3 protein is represented as a pair of cylinders embedded in the lipid bilayer. The hydrophilic groups of the

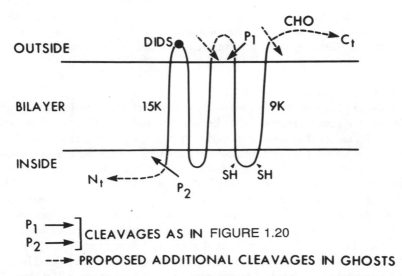

Figure 1.21 A proposed structure for the arrangement of the intrinsic chymotryptic segments of band 3 in the bilayer. The 15 000-dalton (15 K) and 9000-dalton (9 K) segments are indicated by solid lines. From Rothstein and Ramjeesingh (1980)

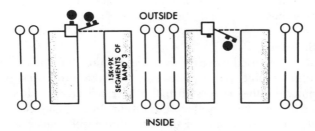

Figure 1.22 A functional model for the role of band 3 in anion transport. From Rothstein and Ramjeesingh (1980)

protein peptide chains face inwards to form a water-filled pore, while hydrophobic groups of the same chain face towards the lipids in which they are embedded. The features of anion transport across the erythrocyte membrane demand something more than a simple water-filled pore; thus, transport is selective for certain anions; moreover, a *'gating mechanism'* must be invoked, as indicated by the dotted line, since the rapid movement of an anion in one direction is contingent on movement of another anion in the opposite direction, so that it is essentially a *facilitated exchange* that takes place.

The manner in which a gate may be shut on a molecule is not difficult to envisage in terms of molecular biology; the solute molecule attaches itself to the portion of the transporter that is facing, say, the outside of the cell; as a result of this attachment a change in the distribution of electricial charge along the transporter could occur, leading to what is called a 'conformational change', the flexibility of the C—C bonds in a polypeptide chain permitting considerable alteration in configuration of the polypeptide chain that might well expose groupings that formerly faced the outside of the cell to the inside, or cytoplasmic, surface.

The D-Glucose Transporter [Note 1]

By the use of photoaffinity labelling of erythrocyte cell membranes with cytochalasin B, the D-glucose transporter has been shown to be associated with a *band 4.5* polypeptide, rather than band 3 as earlier thought; it appears as a broad band in SDS–PAGE isolation procedures, covering the molecular weight range 45–60 kD, with a maximum at 54 kD (Carter-Su *et al.*, 1982; Chen *et al.*, 1986). The broadness of the band indicates some heterogeneity of the transporter, and this is due to post-translational changes that have taken place through glycosylation and possibly phosphorylation. Thus, removal of the carbohydrate residues converted the broad band to a narrow peak, indicating a molecular weight of some 46 kD. Adipocytes, i.e. the cells of fatty tissue that are able to synthesize fats by uptake of D-glucose from the blood, exhibit facilitated transport of D-glucose. The photoaffinity cytochalasin B-labelled transporter isolated from these cells migrated into band 4.5, like the erythrocyte transporter. Liver cells, or hepatocytes, take up glucose rapidly and from them, too, a transporter protein of 45–50 kD has been isolated. Finally, skeletal muscle cells, which show facilitated transport of glucose, likewise contain in their cell membranes a transporter protein with similar characteristics to those of the erythrocyte. [Note 2]

Amino Acid Sequence

Mueckler *et al.* (1985) used a hepatoma cell as a source for cloning a cDNA for a 492 amino acid residue polypeptide that had the properties of a glucose transporter molecule; they suggested that a liver cell might well synthesize this important protein concerned in glucose transport by so many cells of the body. The membrane-spanning region of the transporter will contain amino acids of strong lipophilicity, a necessary condition for the polypeptide chain to remain embedded in the hydrophobic medium constituted by the lipid bilayer. By employing a technique developed by Kyte and Doolittle (1982) they identified the transmembrane sequence and presented the model of the D-glucose transporter illustrated in Figure 1.23. From their amino acid composition, the membrane-spanning segments 3, 5, 7, 8 and 11 were considered to form amphipathic alpha-helices, i.e. with helices betraying both lipophilicity and hydrophilicity; these would contain several serine, threonine, glutamine and asparagine residues. On this basis, OH— and NH_2— side-chains might line the transmembrane channel and play a key role in binding hexoses and thus facilitating their passage through the membrane.

Amino Acid Carrier Types

The situation with these metabolites is more complex than with sugars, since there are several types of carrier corresponding to the different chemical characteristics of the amino acids. This is true of most, if not all, of the transport systems of the tissues as well as in individual cells; and we are indebted to Christensen (see, for example, his 1979 review), for a formal classification of the carrier systems, based mainly on his studies of transport into the Ehrlich ascites tumour cell. In general, transport could be described in terms of three main systems—one for *acidic*, such as glutamic and aspartic acids, one for *basic*, such as lysine and arginine, and one

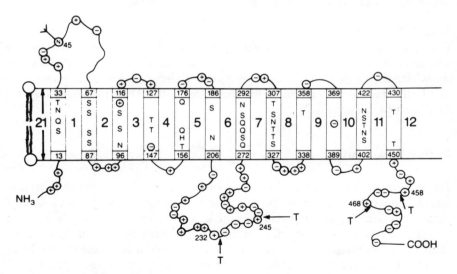

Figure 1.23 Proposed model for the orientation of the glucose carrier in the membrane. The 12 putative membrane-spanning domains are numbered and shown as rectangles. The relative positions of acidic and basic amino acids are indicated by circled '−' and '+' signs, respectively. Unchanged polar residues are indicated by their single letter abbreviation. The predicted position of the N-linked oligosaccharide at Asn-45 is shown. The arrows point to the position of known tryptic cleavage sites in the native, membrane-bound erythrocyte glucose transporter. From Mueckler *et al.* (1985)

for *neutral* amino acids, such as leucine and alanine. Competition would occur between members of the same group but little, if any, between members of different groups. The neutral amino acids were subdivided into two main subgroups, described as the *A*, or *alanine*, group and *L*, or *leucine*, group. The members of the L group are often described as large neutral amino acids. Neutral amino acids within these subgroups compete strongly between themselves but only weakly with members of the other subgroup.

Neutral Amino Acids

Transport of a given neutral amino acid seems to involve both A and L systems to some extent, i.e. the carriers are not exclusively specific for any one neutral amino acid. It was necessary to find an artificial amino acid that might characterize one or other of the subgroups accurately. Christensen *et al.* (1965; 1969) showed that methyl-alpha-aminoisobutyric acid (MeAIBA) acted as a good model for the A system, so that MeAIBA did not compete with L-system amino acids. The bicyclic amino acid BCH (2-aminobicyclo 2,2,1-heptane-2-carboxylic acid) was a good model for the L system. The main features of the two systems are shown in Figure 1.24; the reactivity of the L system is proportional to the hydrocarbon mass of the side-chain, so that the large amino acids are mainly carried on this system. Uptake on the A system shows a dependence on the concentration of Na^+ in the medium, indicating that the transport is energized by an active transport of this ion.

A and ASC Systems

The uptake of alanine by Ehrlich ascites cells cannot be completely inhibited by saturation of the A and L systems, i.e. by high concentrations of MeAIBA and phenylalanine, so that Christensen postulated a sodium-dependent system that specifically transported alanine, serine and cysteine (the ASC system); its features are described in Figure 1.25.

Active Transport

The movements of solutes that we have so far discussed are what the thermo-dynamician would describe as downhill events, the solute passing from a state of higher free energy, or chemical potential, to one of lower; in the case of non-electrolytes, the concentration of the solute defines its state of free energy. Many processes taking place in biological systems are not so simple thermodyna-mically, so that we find situations in which solutes are moved against their gradients of concentration, i.e. uphill—a process that is called active transport. So far as sugars and amino acids are concerned, this uphill transport is manifest during absorption from the small intestine or from the proximal tubule of the kidney; thus normally the urine is free of glucose because, during the passage of the glomerular filtrate along the tubule, glucose is transported into the extratubu-lar space and thence into the blood vessels against a gradient of concentration.

THE L SYSTEM

Formally defined for: The Ehrlich cell
Substrates: Most neutral amino acids; reactivity in proportion
 to hydrocarbon mass of side chain. Excluded: AIB, N-
 Me amino acids. Not excluded: Histidine, tryptophan.
Vmax: Characteristically variable
Dependency on Na$^+$: None
pH sensitivity: Minimal
Exchanging properties: Very strong, so that net operation
 shown only with special care
Other apparent occurrences: Ubiquitous, including mature
 mammalian erythrocyte. Similar systems may lack
 exchanging property.

THE A SYSTEM

Formally defined for: The Ehrlich cell
Substrates:
 range: All neutral amino acids
 characterizing: AIB and MeAIB (glycine, proline,
 sarcosine, serine, methionine, norleucine)
 least reactive: Valine; other branched-chain, apolar
 amino acids
Vmax: Rather constant for all but a few substrates.
Dependency on Na$^+$: First-order; causes one Na$^+$ to migrate
 per amino acid molecule
pH sensitivity: Scarcely detectable at pH 5
Exchanging properties: Weak; weakly reversible
Other apparent occurrences: Hamster intestine; kidney, boney
 tissue; brain.
 Conspicuously absent in erythrocytes.

Figure 1.24 The L and A systems for transport of neutral amino acids. From Christensen (1969)

THE ASC SYSTEM

Formally defined for: The Ehrlich cell
Substrates: Characteristic, 3- and 4-carbon aliphatic and
 hydroxyaliphatic amino acids; proline, cysteine.
 No inhibition detected by MeAIB, MeAla (discrimination
 from A system)
Vmax: Characteristically variable; several amino acids inhibit
 without migrating detectably by it.
Dependency on Na$^+$: First order.
pH sensitivity: Intermediate. Characteristically less than for A
 system.
Stereospecificity: Exceptional
Exchanging properties: Weak
Other occurrences: In rabbit reticulocyte, pigeon erythrocyte,
 but with strong exchanging action, and with several
 sodium ions migrating from each amino acid molecule.
 Ubiquitous?

Figure 1.25 The ASC system. From Christensen (1969)

Similarly, the glucose in the duodenum is rapidly absorbed into the blood plasma of the intestinal vessels, once again against a concentration gradient. These active transport processes share some of the features of the facilitated transport discussed above, especially the 'carrier-mediation' revealed by the competition between different sugars or amino acids among themselves for absorption; the carrier mediation suggests that the movement against a gradient involves the attachment to a transporter molecule; because, in some way, the association of the solute molecule with the transporter is linked to the release of energy, the solute can be transported across the membrane even though it is passing uphill. In the case of amino acids and sugars there is a definite linkage of the transport with transport of the Na^+ ion, so that absorption of glucose or amino acid can be greatly reduced by removing Na^+ from the medium. Thus a dependence of transport of a non-electrolyte, such as glucose, on the presence of Na^+ provides a clue to the presence of an active transport of the glucose, so that it does not rely only on passive downhill diffusion. Experimentally, then, in studies of transport in the brain, a dependence of the transport on the presence of Na^+ would suggest that we are dealing with active transport.

Active Transport of Na^+

It is beyond the scope of this little book to discuss in any detail the theories and facts of active transport of ions, processes that are vital to the life and function of all living cells. In view of the probable role of active transport of Na^+ in the secretion of the cerebrospinal fluid, and the extracellular fluid of brain and cord, however, we may briefly consider some aspects of this process.

Stored Blood

When blood is stored in the cold, the erythrocytes tend to lose their K^+ and take up Na^+ from the plasma. If the process goes on for long enough, the concentration of Na^+ within the cells rises sufficiently to cause osmotic flow of water, which eventually leads to haemolysis. However, if, before this, the cells are warmed up, the Na^+ is pumped out while the lost K^+ is re-accumulated. In its normal state at 37 °C the cell membrane is able to maintain a high internal concentration of K^+ and a low one of Na^+ in the face of gradients of concentration that, if passive diffusion were allowed to occur, would be dissipated. At a low temperature the metabolic energy necessary for maintaining these concentration gradients is lost, and the system runs down. Re-establishment of the metabolic machinery allows the Na^+ to be extruded; and the mechanism is generally described as that of a *sodium pump*, the ion being driven against a gradient of concentration. In the steady state at normal temperature the pump is able to remove Na^+ ions as fast as they enter, while K^+ is accumulated in its place, the two processes being linked so that a Na^+–K^+-linked pump is envisaged. In specialized cells such as the neuron or muscle fibre this active process is important for maintaining gradients of K^+ and Na^+ that are ultimately responsible for the conduction of action potentials. In non-conducting cells, on the other hand, we find the same process of active pumping of Na^+ out of the cell; thus, the cell membranes are permeable to Na^+, and Na^+ tends to diffuse into the cell unless it is pumped out. To a greater or lesser extent, the internal ion that replaces Na^+ is K^+, so that a high content of K^+ is a general feature of tissues. In some cells, notably the erythrocyte of the cat, there is no accumulation of K^+, so that the concentrations of Na^+ are about the same inside the cell and in the surrounding plasma. Yet there is still an active pump, and the reason for the necessity of a pump is that a cell containing proteins and permeable to the Na^+, K^+, Cl^-, HCO_3^- ions of the medium, will inevitably swell up by an osmotic intake of water caused primarily by inward diffusion of Na^+ and accompanying anions.

Colloid Osmotic Swelling

The situation may be represented simply by Figure 1.26, with only Na^+ and Cl^- as the permeable ions; the protein molecules within the cell may be treated as polyvalent electrolytes, and their presence causes the establishment of a Gibbs–Donnan type of equilibrium such that the total concentration of ions within the cell is always greater than the total concentration outside. Thus, unless the higher concentration of Na^+ and Cl^- ions is counteracted by an active process, the mere passive influence of the Gibbs–Donnan distribution of ions will lead to ultimate swelling and often rupture of the cell. Viewed in this light, the Na^+ pump is necessary for the integrity of any cell as soon as it has acquired the capacity to synthesize high-molecular-weight substances that cannot escape across the cell membrane.

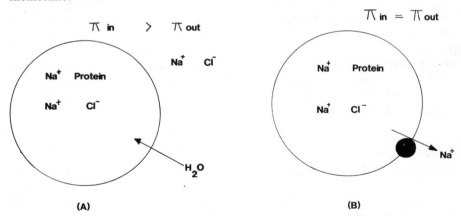

(A)   **(B)**

Figure 1.26 (A) The Gibbs–Donnan distribution of ions will cause the total osmolality of the inside of the cell to be greater than the non-protein-containing medium outside the cell. Water must enter the cell and this is followed by ions, the two processes occurring indefinitely unless the cell membrane can resist the colloid osmotic pressure driving the fluid into the cell. (B) The sodium pump actively removes this ion from the cell maintaining equality of osmolarity across the cell membrane. Failure of the Na pump will destroy this equality.

Variants on the Pump Theme

The sodium pump must, on this view, have developed earliest in the evolution of the cellular organism; as cells became specialized, variants on the pump were developed, such as the linking to movements of K^+ and Ca^{2+}, while the need to accumulate metabolites, such as sugars, in competition with others organisms, might lead first to the development of a facilitated carrier system and later to the linkage of the carrier system to the Na^+ pump, the gradient of concentration of Na^+ across the cell membrane, established by the pump, being used as a source of energy that drives the non-electrolyte into the cell.

Na^+,K^+-ATPase

One very interesting class of inhibitors of active transport of sodium is constituted by the cardiac glycosides, typified by ouabain (Schatzmann, 1953). These inhibit the action of an enzyme intimately connected with active transport of Na^+ and K^+, namely adenosine triphosphatase (ATPase), which catalyses the dephosphorylation of ATP to form ADP, a process that makes energy available for uphill events. There is more than one ATPase in the cell, and this one is characterized by the fact that it is optimally active if both Na^+ and K^+ are present in the medium, and it is therefore called Na^+,K^+-ATPase.

Asymmetry of ATPase

The cell membrane exhibits an asymmetry in its behaviour to Na^+ and K^+ ions; thus, from its outside it transports K^+ from a low to a high concentration of this ion, while from its inside it transports Na^+ from a low concentration to a high concentration outside. This asymmetry in action is reflected in differing effects of Na^+ and K^+ on the Na^+,K^+-ATPase according as these ions are on the inside or outside of the cell. Thus, Whittam (1962), by introducing varying concentrations of Na^+ into the red cell, showed that the splitting of ATP in the cell was accelerated by increasing concentration of this ion but was unaffected by changing the concentration of K^+. By contrast, omission of K^+ from the outside medium caused a fall in hydrolysis of ATP, while replacement of Na^+ by choline had no effect.

ATPase as the Transporter

The enzyme Na^+,K^+-ATPase is more than a catalyst concerned with the hydrolysis of ATP, and its reversal, because it is an intrinsic membrane protein, actually spanning the lipid bilayer as with band-3 protein. It functions, then, as the postulated carrier undergoing conformational changes when the actively transported ions are attached to or detached from it. These conformational changes result in changes of affinity of the ions for the transporter molecule, namely ATPase, leading to release of the ion when exposed to one side of the membrane. Associated with the conformational changes in the ATPase molecule that permit these movements of ions against gradients of concentration, there is a hydrolysis of ATP that provides the energy for these uphill ionic movements.

Early Model

One of the earliest proposed schemes for the active Na^+–K^+ exchange process is that illustrated by Figure 1.27; the carrier Y, takes on Na^+ internally, transporting it to the outside interface, where it releases the Na^+ and where the carrier now becomes altered so as to attract K^+, which thus gets carried back to be released at the other interface. The altered carrier, X, is converted to Y and it is this change in the carrier, which has since come to be recognized as a conformational change in the shape of the ATPase molecule, that involves the supply of energy, i.e. the hydrolysis of ATP.

More Recent Model

The model of Figure 1.27 begs the question as to what the carrier molecule is, how it is transported, and the chemical change that is supposed to occur that alters its affinity for the actively transported solute. With the recognition that the enzyme ATPase not only catalyses the energy-giving hydrolysis of ATP but is also to be regarded as the transporter molecule, the two forms of the carrier depicted in the early model of Figure 1.24 may be translated into two forms of ATPase which, as we have seen, is an intrinsic membrane protein spanning the lipid bilayer. In constructing the model it is borne in mind that Na^+ ions from a cytoplasmic medium with low internal concentration of these ions and high concentrations of K^+ are exchanged for K^+ ions in the extracellular medium with high concentration of Na^+ and low of K^+. The system must be able to undergo a change in affinity from a high-K^+ plus low-Na^+ affinity to one of high affinity for Na^+ and low affinity for K^+ on the cytoplasmic side of the cell and vice versa on the extracellular side. Furthermore, the cation-attracting sites on the transporter molecule must be able to change their exposure from one facing the cytoplasmic side, to one facing the extracellular side, the so-called *gating reaction*. The shift in affinity, and the gating reaction, must be governed by a reaction with the substrate that delivers energy for the transport, i.e. ATP. [Note 3]

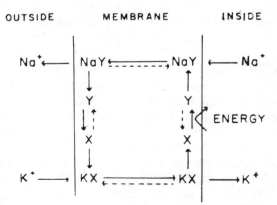

Figure 1.27 Carrier-based transport mechanism. After Hoffman, *Biophysics of Physiological and Pharmacological Actions.* Amer. Ass. Adv. Sci. (1961)

Conformational Changes

The fundamental experiments on ATPase in this transport situation have revealed that the ATPase can undergo conformational changes from one state that is associated with an affinity for K^+—the K^+-affinity or E_2 state—to a state with high affinity for Na^+—the Na^+-affinity or E_1 state—facilitated by an effect of ATP; and from a Na^+ (E_1) to a K^+ (E_2) state due to phosphorylation by ATP (E_2P). These forms of ATPase have been defined in some detail by Glynn and Richards (1982); essentially the E_1 form is that of the unphosphorylated enzyme, stable in sodium media, while the E_2 form is that which is stable in potassium media. In addition, E_1 has high affinity for ATP and ADP and can be phosphorylated by ATP. E_2 has lower affinity for ATP and ADP and can be phosphorylated by orthophosphate but not by ATP.

Occlusion of Cations

According to this concept, the cations being transported may, at a given point, be segregated within the membrane and subsequently released at the opposite side to that from which they entered. According to Glynn and Richards (1982), this process, called *occlusion*, may be indicated by the chain of reactions illustrated below:

$$E_1 + nNa_i^+ + ATP \rightleftharpoons E_1 \cdot ATPNa_n \rightleftharpoons E_1P(Na_n) + ADP$$
$$\Updownarrow$$
$$E_2PNa_n \rightleftharpoons E_2P + nNa_0^+$$

the parentheses indicating occlusion, i.e. an inability to exchange with Na^+ ions in intra- or extracellular medium. This occlusion was physically demonstrated by Glynn *et al.* (1984), three Na^+ ions being occluded per molecule of E_1P.

Model

The model of the Na^+–K^+ exchange put forward by Skou (1989) on the basis of modifications of earlier models is illustrated by Figure 1.28. Here E_1 and E_2 are the two basic forms of ATPase, while E', E'', etc., are phosphorylated modifications of these forms. Parentheses indicate occlusion of Na^+ or K^+ within the membrane.

In general, ATP increases the rate of deocclusion of K^+ from $E_2'(K_2)$ and, in the presence of Na^+, shifts the distribution towards $E_1 \cdot ATP \cdot Na_3$; this is followed by a phosphorylation from ATP with an occlusion of Na^+. These reactions describe the transfer of K^+ from the membrane phase to the cytoplasmic medium, followed by the exchange of the inwardly translocated K^+ for outgoing Na^+, and by transfer of Na^+ to the membrane phase, i.e. by occlusion of this ion. The phosphorylation leads not only to an occlusion of Na^+, but, through a step with deocclusion of Na^+, to the formation of the ADP-insensitive, K^+-sensitive phosphoenzyme, E_2–P. This phosphoenzyme has a high affinity for K^+ and is dephosphorylated by K^+ at the extracellular side of the membrane. Binding of E_2P to K^+ leads to a dephosphorylation leading to an occlusion of K^+, i.e. to its

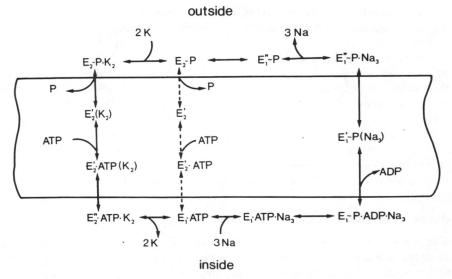

Figure 1.28 Na$^+$–K$^+$ exchange by Na$^+$–K$^+$-ATPase. Reaction with the cations is consecutive and the scheme is based on the Albers–Post scheme, the modifications of this scheme by Karlish *et al.* and on the scheme by Nørby *et al.* for formation of phosphoen-zymes and with some further modifications. Symbols E, E$'_1$, E$''_1$, E$_2$, E$'_2$ and E$''_2$ refer to different enzyme conformations. Parentheses indicate cations that are occluded, i.e. in the membrane phase inside gates, which are closed cytoplasmic and extracellular media (Skou, 1989)

transfer from the extracellular medium to the membrane for subsequent release into the cytoplasm. Thus, the subsequent deocclusion of K$^+$ at the cytoplasmic side of the membrane by a low-affinity effect of ATP completes the cycle.

The Conformational Change
The structure of the Na,K-ATPase molecule has been elucidated; essentially it consists of two polypeptide chains, alpha- and beta-, in the ratio of 1:1, with molecular weights in the regions of 100 and 40 kD, respectively. The carbohydrate part has a molecular weight of about 15 kD. Radiation inactivation of the enzyme suggests a molecular weight of 300 kD, indicating a dimeric organization of the two polypeptide chains. X-Ray analysis of the crystallized preparation indicated a structure consisting of two symmetrical rod-like structures probably consisting of an alpha-beta-protomer, i.e. a dimer composed of one of each alpha- and beta-protomers. The height of the transporter, perpendicular to the surface of the membrane, was 100 Å, i.e. it stretched through the lipid bilayer, and there was a cleft between the rods of about 20 Å in that half of the molecule facing the cytoplasmic surface of the membrane with a part of the connection inside the lipid bilayer. The molecule apparently protrudes some 40 Å on the cytoplasmic side and 20 Å on the extracellular side. The intramembranous part of each protomer is about 25% of the mass of the alpha- and beta-subunit; practically all of the rest of

the beta-subunit is on the extracellular side, whereas the cytoplasmic part of the alpha-subunit is about three times larger than the extracellular part.

The change from the E_1 to the E_2 condition of the ATPase, which is accompanied by changes in the affinities for the Na^+ and K^+ ions, is assumed to involve, also, a change in the exposure of the affinity site from the extracellular to the cytoplasmic medium, and vice versa. Such a change in physical exposure is assumed to involve a physical change in the shape of the ATPase molecule, and a variety of studies, such as those employing circular dichroism, have amply confirmed the difference in structure according as the enzyme was exposed to sodium- or potassium-rich solutions. The changes in the arrangement of the alpha-subunit that are presumed to take place on passing from the E_1 to the E_2 form of the ATPase molecule are illustrated in Figure 1.29.

Active Transport of Sugars and Amino Acids

The study of the processes whereby ions are able to move against gradients of electrochemical potential, i.e. studies of active transport of ions, has occupied the minds of physiologists from early times, since it has been realized that the very integrity of the cell depends on the sodium pump, while the maintenance of the differences of concentration of potassium between inside and outside of conducting cells, such as neurons or muscle fibres, relies on the same basic mechanism.

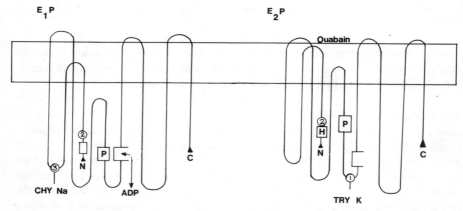

Figure 1.29   Model for arrangement of the α-subunit in E_1 and E_2 forms of Na,K-ATPase. The encircled numbers mark the sites of primary tryptic cleavage in KCl (1) and (2) or NaCl (3) and chymotryptic cleavage in NaCl (3). In the E_1P conformation, bonds 2 and 3 are exposed in cleavage, while bond 1 is protected. Transition to E_2P is accompanied by protonation of an ionizable group close to the NH terminus. In the E_2P conformation, bond 3 is protected, while bond 1 is exposed to trypsin and the position of bond 2 is such that it is cleaved secondary to cleavage of bond 1 within the same α-subunit. It is proposed that transition from E_1P to E_2P is accompanied by movement of a part of the segment containing the aspartyl phosphate from a relatively hydrophilic to a more hydrophobic environment. The segment between bonds 2 and 3 is proposed to engage in cation binding and formation of the pathway across the membrane. From Jorgensen (1985)

The necessity for an uphill mechanism of transport of sugars and amino acids was recognized as soon as the mechanism of absorption of glucose from the small intestine, or the reabsorption of sugars and amino acids from the kidney tubule, were investigated. Thus, glucose, introduced into an isolated loop of duodenum, is rapidly absorbed into the blood; and measurements of the concentrations in plasma and duodenal fluid during the process indicated that, in spite of the concentration in the duodenal fluid falling far below that in the blood plasma, the absorption proceeded until the concentration in the duodenal fluid was virtually zero. The process did not involve metabolism of the glucose molecule, since it occurred with its non-metabolizable analogue, 3-O-methylglucose (Campbell and Davson, 1948). In a similar way, in the proximal tubule of the kidney, glucose and amino acids pass across the tubular epithelium into the blood plasma against gradients of concentration, so that by the time the fluid has passed along the tubule its concentrations of glucose and amino acids are, usually, zero. Thus, these non-electrolytes have been transported against gradients of concentration, a process requiring the injection of energy.

Dynamics

Studies on the dynamics of this uphill transport of sugars and amino acids established several points (Crane, 1977). Thus, the transport exhibited carrier-mediated features, so that there was competition between substrates of similar chemical structure, e.g. between glucose and mannose, or between glycine and alanine; as a corollary to this, the process showed self-inhibition, in the sense that the fractional change in concentration was reduced when the actual concentration of the substrate was increased. The feature that differentiated the process from that of facilitated diffusion was, first, the fact that transport occurred against a gradient of concentration or electrochemical potential, and, second, that, because of its dependence on a metabolic supply of energy, it was inhibited by metabolic inhibitors such as dinitrophenol or cyanide. The most interesting discovery was the dependence of the uphill transport of these non-electrolytes on the presence of Na^+ in the medium. This was early demonstrated by Riklis and Quastel (1958), who showed that, by completely replacing Na^+ by K^+ in the intestinal fluid, absorption of glucose was prevented. Again, Kromphardt *et al.* (1963) showed that the influx of glycine into ascites tumour cells could be blocked by removal of Na^+ from the external medium. The dependence of intestinal absorption of glucose on the concentration of Na^+ is illustrated by Figure 1.30, which shows the changing slopes of the Lineweaver–Burk plots of sugar absorption at different concentrations of Na^+, indicating increasing affinity of glucose for the system as the concentration was raised from zero to 145 mM.

The Gradient Hypothesis

The active transport of Na^+ from a cell is an energy-demanding process, and the result of the extrusion of this ion from a cell is that the cell has been supplied with

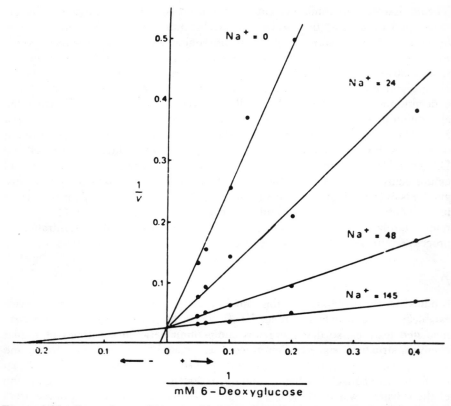

Figure 1.30   Dependence of the rate of 6-deoxyglucose transport on the concentrations of sugar and sodium. From Crane, Forstner and Eicholtz, *Biochim. Biophys. Acta* (1965)

a source of energy that it can employ for one or more specific functions. For example, in the neuron, the extrusion of Na^+ leads to accumulation of K^+ that is the basis of the ionic gradients leading to the resting and action potentials. The basis of Crane's *gradient hypothesis* (1977) is that in transporting epithelia we may assume that the same energy-requiring process of Na^+ transport may be linked to the transport of a non-electrolyte, such as glucose, which requires energy for it to occur. Thus, the failure of active transport of glucose from the intestine or renal tubule due to lack of Na^+ is due to a break in the link between this process and that of Na^+ transport. In some way the dissipation of the energy of the electrochemical potential of Na^+ could be associated with the supply of energy for uphill transport of a non-electrolyte. The dependence of the two processes, namely active transport of Na^+ and transport of non-electrolyte against a gradient of chemical potential, has been demonstrated most strikingly by the inhibition of the transport of the non-electrolyte by the inhibitor of ATPase, e.g. ouabain.

Thus, Rosenberg *et al.* (1965) showed that the absorption of the non-metabolizable cycloleucine from the intestine was completely inhibited by ouabain; and, in general, the effects of Na^+ deficiency and ouabain were similar.

Liposomes

By making artificial cells, or liposomes, out of the membranes of epithelial cells, the concentration of Na^+ within the cell can be varied at will, and in this way Kessler and Semenza (1983) showed that the transport of glucose into liposomes, made of brush-border membranes of intestinal epithelium, was inhibited by a rise in concentration of Na^+. In addition, the potential across the artificial cell's membrane could be altered at will, and it was shown that the transport of glucose into the cell was favoured by internal negativity, i.e. the effect of extrusion of Na^+ by the sodium pump.

Bi-Bi Reaction

The kinetic studies of Kessler and Semenza, in which the influence of glucose on the transport of Na^+, and the influence of Na^+ on the transport of glucose were measured suggested a process that enzymologists call a bi-bi reaction, indicating that the two substrates, Na^+ and glucose, were attached separately to a carrier protein, or symporter, and in order, and were released in the same order at the opposite side of the membrane, i.e. in the 'first-on first-off' sequence (Hopfer and Groseclose, 1980). Thus, the first step was, presumably, attachment of a Na^+ ion to the symporter; this would increase the affinity of the symporter for glucose, which would then attach to a specific glucose site. At the opposite side of the membrane the Na^+ would be released, thereby lowering the affinity for glucose, which would then be released.

Phlorizin

This glucoside, by competing for the glucose-binding site on the symporter, inhibits active transport of glucose by the intestinal brush-border epithelium. Of great interest was the finding that the binding of phlorizin was affected by Na^+ in the same way as transport of glucose. Thus, Aronson (1978) measured absorption of [^{3}H]-phlorizin by isolated renal microvillus vesicles, and showed that uptake was reduced by as much as 90% in the absence of Na^+; by establishing diffusion potentials across the vesicles, he showed that internal negativity favoured phlorizin binding, just as it favours glucose uptake. Thus, both internal negativity and external Na^+ favour the binding of sugar to the transporter molecule; and it was suggested that the transporter, in its sugar-free condition, was negatively charged and so driven to face the outside medium, where it would be ready to take on a sugar molecule.

Model

A model basically similar to many others suggested to describe the cotransport of Na^+ and sugar, and suggested by Kessler and Semenza (1983), is illustrated in

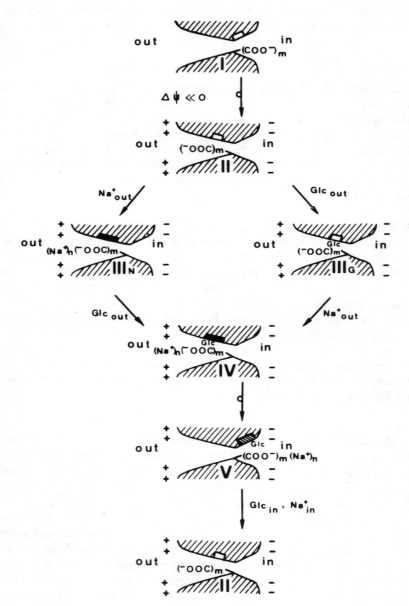

Figure 1.31 A likely mode of operation of the small-intestinal Na^+, D-glucose co-transporter(s), as a 'gated channel (or pore)'; the positioning of the 'gate' is modulated by $\Delta\psi$ and by its binding Na^+ (a 'shovelling mechanism'). From Semenza *et al.* (1984)

Figure 1.31, and is based on their deductions from kinetic studies indicating that the binding of glucose and Na^+ was a bi-bi reaction (Hopfer and Groseclose, 1980). The model also assumes that the sugar-binding site may expose itself to either side of the membrane as a result of a conformational change, the conformational change acting essentially as a gating mechanism that exposes the bound sugar to the outside medium or the inside of a channel. The gated channel is asymmetrical with respect to the plane of the membrane; in particular, when the potential difference is zero, and at low substrate concentrations, all binding sites have spontaneously inwardly directed orientation. Thus, in Form I of Figure 1.31, Na^+ and glucose inside the membrane have access to the transporter and tend to trap the glucose inside the cell; this is the basis of the inhibition by Na^+ and glucose when they are inside the cell. In the presence of a potential, the 'gate' and the glucose-binding site move towards the outside (Form II). Sodium in the outside medium can now bind to the gate (Form IIIN), thus increasing the affinity of the glucose binding site. Alternatively, the sugar may bind first to its outwardly exposed site (Form II), leading to Form IIIG. From IIIG or IIIN the 'fully occupied' form, Form IV, is generated in which the gate charge is neutralized by Na^+. This makes the gate snap back (Form V) in the 'spontaneous' inwardly directed position. In Form V the substrates are now exposed to the inside of the cell where Na^+ and glucose are liberated. Reappearance of the native negative charge on the gate, through loss of Na^+, makes it again respond to the negative inside potential, snapping back to the outside (Form II). The combined effects of uptake and loss of Na^+, and the changes of potential, are thus to make the sugar-binding site more or less active, and in some way to modify the conformation of the transporter molecule so as to change the effective exposure of the binding site to inside or outside of the cell. [Note 4]

The Glucose Symporter Molecule

Fluorescein isothiocyanate (FITC) inhibits Na^+-dependent glucose uptake by intestinal brush-border membrane vesicles, and the Na^+-dependent phlorizin binding completely and irreversibly, and thus may be employed as a label for the Na^+-dependent glucose transporter. Using this as a label, Peerce and Wright isolated by SDS chromatography a 75 kD protein that presumably is the carrier protein. The same authors found that addition of Na^+ to a preparation of membrane vesicles quenched the fluorescence of the compound, indicating a change in the local environment of the probe consistent with a change in protein configuration. By labelling the glucose-binding site with FITC and the Na^+-binding site with another fluorescent compound, namely N-acetylimidazole, Peerce and Wright (1986) estimated the distance between the two binding groups by the technique of fluorescent energy-transfer. Their estimate was 35 Å, so that any conformational change in the transporter induced by binding on one site must be quite large if the other site is to be modified. The Na^+-binding site, occupation of which by Na^+ increases the affinity of the transporter for glucose, would appear to contain tyrosyl residues, since specific reagents that block these groups, such as

N-acetylimidazole or tetranitromethane, inhibit glucose transport and phlorizin binding, an inhibition that may be prevented by Na^+ (Peerce and Wright, 1985).

Conformational Change

Peerce and Wright (1984a, b) studied the conformational change in the Na^+–glucose symporter by measuring the quenching in fluorescence when the symporter was labelled with FITC and treated with Na^+; thus, the $K_{0.5}$ for this Na^+-specific quenching was 25 mM, similar to the apparent K_m for Na^+ activation of glucose transport. Thus, they concluded that Na^+ first bound to the symporter; this induced a conformational change, revealed by fluorescence quenching, that increased affinity of the symporter for glucose.

Amino Acid Sequence

Wright and his colleagues (Hediger *et al.*, 1987a, b) injected a preparation of rabbit's intestinal pol(A)$^+$RNA into oocytes of *Xenopus laevis* and showed that, after incubation for some time, they were capable of transporting methylglucose from the medium in a Na^+-dependent fashion, a process that was inhibited by phlorizin. Subsequent cloning enabled the preparation of a DNA and formation of an RNA enabling the synthesis of the presumed cotransporter, which was then sequenced. The model is illustrated by Figure 1.32 with its accompanying hydropathy plot [Note 5], indicating the presence of some eleven membrane-spanning, i.e. highly lipophilic, segments. The feature of the hydrophilic domain was the presence of two highly polar regions, near the C terminus, one linking membrane-spans 10 and 11 containing 40 charged residues in three concentrated clusters. The second, on the opposite side of the membrane between spans 7 and 8 had 17 acid and basic residues. Two short hydrophilic segments, one on each side of the membrane, contained potential N-linked glycosylation sites. The authors considered that the two highly charged hydrophilic segments were involved in sugar binding. Interestingly, there was no amino acid homology with the glucose transporter from the erythrocyte or with the *E. coli* H^+–sugar cotransporter, indicating that the Na^+–sugar cotransporter was a novel protein different from those involved in channels and pumps.

The Renal Symporter

The transporter involved in the renal brush-border Na^+–glucose transport may be larger than the 75 kD unit identified by Peerce and Wright. Nieh *et al.* (1987) concluded that there was a hydrophobic region on the transporter localized close to the glucose-binding site which led to high-affinity binding to phlorizin and to high-affinity inhibition of Na-dependent D-glucose transport by phlorizin and also by glucosides with long but not short aliphatic chains. They synthesized two derivatives of *n*-decylglucoside which bound covalently to the transporter, inhibiting Na–glucose transport irreversibly. With these labels they were able to identify four polypeptides as belonging to the transporter, with molecular weights of 75 kD

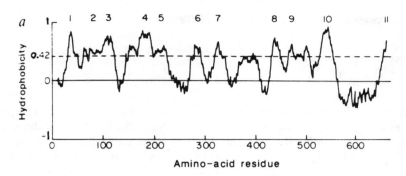

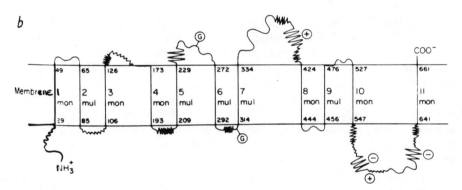

Figure 1.32 (*a*) Hydrophobicity plot of the Na$^+$/glucose cotransporter amino acid sequence. The method of Eisenberg *et al.* was used with a 21 amino-acid window, and the numbers 1 to 11 refer to postulated membrane-spanning segments. (*b*) Proposed model for the orientation of the Na/glucose cotransporter in the membrane. The transmembrane helices were detected and analysed according to the method of Eisenberg *et al.* Depending on the hydrophobic moment, the segments are labelled either monomer (mon) or multimer (mul). The structure of the non-transmembrane regions was examined according to secondary structure predictions of Garner *et al.* G indicates N–X–T/S sequences which represent potential N-linked glycosylation sites. The secondary structure elements are indicated as follows: $\curvearrowright$, B-turn; $\rightsquigarrow$, β-sheet; $\mathcal{WWM}$, α-helix; and $\rightsquigarrow$, random. Clusters of negative and positive charges are represented as $\ominus$ and $\oplus$. From Hediger *et al.* (1987b)

and 82 kD, and also 64 kD and 47 kD. According to Lin *et al.* (1984), who used the technique of radiation inactivation to assess the molecular weight of the transporter, the molecule is very large, with a weight of 345 kD, whereas the functional unit necessary for Na-dependent phlorizin binding had a molecular weight of 230 kD. They suggested that the phlorizin-binding unit consisted of two 75 kD plus two 82 kD subunits, giving a total molecular weight of 232 kD, while two additional subunits of 64 and 47 kD would be necessary to make the complete transporter of total molecular weight about 343 kD.

Application to the Blood–Brain Barrier

Two-compartment Analysis

Early quantitative studies on the blood–brain barrier involved, usually, a continuous infusion of a given solute into the blood, such that a steady concentration was maintained in the plasma over periods of time that might last for several hours. At the end of a given period the animal was killed and decapitated and the brain was removed for analysis. By repeating the experiment using different periods of time after establishing the intravenous infusion, a curve could be plotted of concentration in brain water against time. Some of these experiments (e.g. Davson, 1955) showed that the blood–brain system could be treated as a so-called *two-compartment system*, similar to that envisaged earlier for a cell bathed in a medium containing the penetrating solute; in this case the medium was the plasma, with concentration represented by C_{pl}, and the cell contents represented by the amount of the solute, X_{br}, in the brain water at any time, t. Thus, the simple permeability equation could be applied:

$$dX_{br}/dt = PA(C_{pl} - C_{br}) \tag{1.21}$$

If we knew that, at equilibrium, when $dX_{br}/dt = 0$, C_{br} was equal to C_{pl}, then we should be justified in using a single permeability coefficient, P, instead of P_{in} and P_{out}.

If we treat C_{br} as X_{br}/V, where V is the volume of brain water corresponding to the area A, we have

$$dC_{br}/dt = PA/V(C_{pl} - C_{br}) \tag{1.22}$$

If A and V are not known, we have to employ the transfer coefficient, K, equal to PA/V.

$$dC_{br}/dt = K(P_{pl} - C_{br}) \tag{1.23}$$

If the plasma concentration has been held constant, then Equation (1.23) is simply integrated to give

$$C_{br}/C_{pl} = (1 - e^{-Kt}) \tag{1.24}$$

or

$$\ln(1 - C_{br}/C_{pl}) = -Kt \tag{1.25}$$

Thus, if a number of measurements of C_{br} are made during the passage of a substance into the brain at different times, we may plot the function $\ln(1 - C_{br}/C_{pl})$ against time, and the slope will give K, the transfer coefficient.

Permeability Coefficient: Capillary Area

To deduce the permeability coefficient, we must know A, the area of capillary membrane exposed to the volume, V, of brain water, since $P = K \times V/A$. Estimates of capillary area per unit mass of brain vary; thus, Crone (1963) used a value of $240 \, cm^2/g$, whereas Pappenheimer considered that a value of $50 \, cm^2/g$ was more appropriate. Subsequent workers have chosen $100 \, cm^2/g$ (e.g. Takasato *et al.*, 1984). Here g represents unit weight of brain; as the equations apply to the brain water with which the given solute equilibrates, appropriate allowance must be made. Thus, if all the water is available, this amounts on average to about 77%, but varies according to the predominance of grey or white matter. If we take the value of 77%, then the *V/A* ratio is 0.77/100, where *V* has been equated with mass.

Penetration of ^{24}Na

As an example of a study based on this technique we may look at Figure 1.33, which shows the curve of C_{br}/C_{pl} against time for uptake of ^{24}Na by the rabbit brain when the isotope was infused intravenously to maintain a constant value of

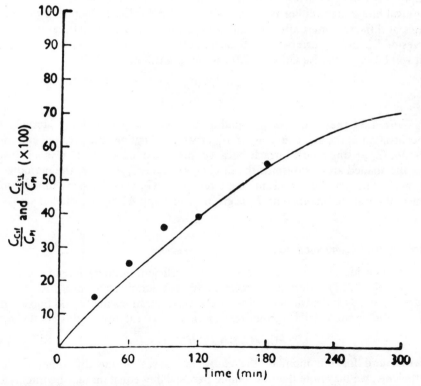

Figure 1.33 Penetration of ^{24}Na into the cerebrospinal fluid and brain tissue. Points represent the concentrations in the extracellular fluid of the nervous tissue, while the smooth curve represents the concentrations in the cerebrospinal fluid. From Davson, *J. Physiol.* (1955)

C_{pl}. Since Na^+ is predominantly extracellular, the value of C_{br} has been taken as the concentration in the extracellular water, or more correctly, the 'sodium space' deduced from steady-state measurements. The slope of the logarithmic plot gave a transfer coefficient of 0.0041 min^{-1} or $6.8 \times 10^{-5} s^{-1}$. If we take a value of 100 cm^2/g for capillary area and a sodium space of, say, 20%, the effective value of V/A becomes 2×10^{-3} cm and P becomes about 1.3×10^{-7} cm/s. The more accurate multicompartmental analysis of Davson and Welch (1971) gave a value of 8.6×10^{-8} cm/s.

Variable Plasma Concentration

A great deal of calculation can be avoided if the blood–brain barrier experiments are carried out with a constant plasma concentration; however, frequently the animal has been injected with a single bolus of the solute; in this case the course of change in C_{pl} must be measured at regular intervals. Usually, only a single brain sample is feasible, so that a value of the transfer coefficient can be obtained by a graphical integration, either using this single value for C_{br} or by taking the mean values at different times after the initial bolus, in separate animals, so that mean curves of C_{br} and C_{pl} can be plotted against time.

It will be seen that Equation (1.23) can be re-written:

$$K = \frac{\int_0^t dC_{br}}{\int_0^t (C_{pl} - C_{br}) dt} \quad (1.26)$$

In Figure 1.34 the results of a hypothetical experiment have been plotted, the concentration of the solute in plasma, C_{pl}, rising and falling, and the concentration in brain, C_{br}, rising nearly linearly because the time of exposure is relatively brief. Now the shaded area represents the integral of $(C_{pl} - C_{br}) dt$ over the period zero to time, t. The line AB represents the integral of dC_{br} over the same time period. Hence, the transfer coefficient, K, is given by dividing AB by the shaded area.

When P_{in} and P_{out} are not Equal

We have considered the possibility that the coefficient defining flux of the solute into the cell, P_{in}, is different from the coefficient defining outward flux, P_{out}, so that at the steady state, when $dS/dt = 0$, the concentrations inside and outside the cell, or other system, will be given by the ratio of permeability, or flux coefficients:

$$C_{in}/C_{out} = P_{in}/P_{out} = r \quad (1.6)$$

If we ignore for the moment the cause or causes of the difference in flux coefficients, we may note that the simple permeability equation may be integrated easily if C_{pl} is kept constant, since P_{in} can be represented by rP_{out} or P_{out} by $1/rP_{in}$. Thus, the equation

$$dX_{br}/dt = P_{in} A C_{pl} - P_{out} A C_{br} \quad (1.27)$$

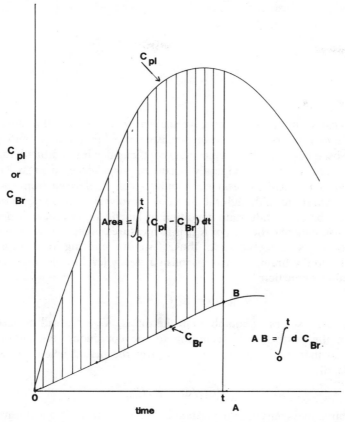

Figure 1.34 Estimating transfer coefficient, K, by a graphical integration. A single intraperitoneal injection of the solute has been given and at time t a sample of brain has been taken. K is equal to the value of AB divided by the shaded area, i.e.

$$K = \frac{\int_0^t dC_{Br}}{\int_0^t (C_{pl} - C_{Br})\, dt}$$

may be written:

$$dX_{br}/dt = rP_{out}A \times C_{pl} - P_{out}A \times C_{br} \qquad (1.28)$$

$$= P_{out}A(rC_{pl} - C_{br}) \qquad (1.29)$$

and

$$dC_{br}/dt = \frac{P_{out}A}{V}(rC_{pl} - C_{br}) \qquad (1.30)$$

and the integrated form of this at constant C_{pl} becomes:

$$\ln\left(1 - \frac{C_{in}}{rC_{out}}\right) = -\frac{P_{out}}{V}At = -K_{out}t \qquad (1.31)$$

Unidirectional Kinetics

In order to carry out the integration, we see that we must know the value of r, the steady-state distribution ratio between plasma and brain water. With passively entering substances with high permeability coefficients it is not difficult to measure steady-state ratios, or with naturally occurring substances, such as Na^+, K^+, glucose and amino acids, reasonable estimates can be derived from the normal resting concentrations, although the metabolic involvement of some solutes, such as glucose, robs the steady-state condition of kinetic significance. A device that permits an estimate of either K_{in} or K_{out} is to measure uptake or loss from the brain in the early stages of equilibration; thus, if we are studying influx of a labelled amino acid into the brain, we may establish a steady level in the blood and apply the permeability equation:

$$dC_{br}/dt = K_{in}C_{pl} - K_{out}C_{br} \qquad (1.32)$$

During the early stages of equilibration the influx, $K_{in} \times C_{pl}$ will of necessity be larger than the outflux and, according to the conditions, the latter may be neglected, so that the equation simplifies, over the period when this neglect is permissible, to

$$dC_{br}/dt = K_{in}C_{pl}$$

If C_{pl} is maintained constant, the relation between C_{br} with time is linear:

$$C_{br} = K_{in}C_{pl}t + \text{constant} \qquad (1.33)$$

whence K_{in} can be calculated. This technique was exploited with success by Baños *et al.* (1973) in their study of influx of amino acids. The criterion applied for applicability of the simple equation is that the curve of C_{br} against time remains linear over the period of measurement; significant outflux, which increases with time as C_{br} increases, is revealed as a failure of linearity.

Patlak Multicompartment Analysis

When the concentration in the plasma is not held constant, as in the experiments on amino acids described by Blasberg *et al.* (1983), the theoretical treatment of Patlak *et al.* (1983) shows how, in general, the blood–brain transfer constants can be evaluated from influx measurements. The theoretical treatment of Patlak *et al.* applies to a variety of possible situations, while the paper by Blasberg *et al.* demonstrates the application of their treatment to a special situation, namely the penetration of alpha-aminoisobutyric acid, the rapid uptake from the extracellular

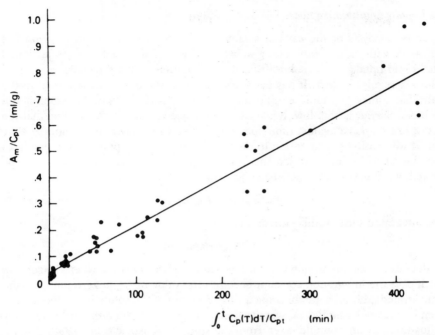

Figure 1.35 Graphical analysis of 49 experiments in the rat over a time course of 1–240 min. A plot of thalamic tissue [^{14}C]-AIB radioactivity/final plasma radioactivity (ordinate) versus the plasma arterial radioactivity integral/final plasma radioactivity (abscissa). The solid line represents the best linear fit by a least squares analysis of all the data points, excluding the 1 and 3 min experiments. The slope of the line in both graphs is equivalent to K_i and the ordinate intercept is equivalent to V_i. From Blasberg *et al.* (1983)

space into the cells, where it is accumulated, tending to reduce back-flux even during long periods after the bolus injection. Figure 1.35 illustrates the linear relation between brain uptake and the integrated mean concentration in the plasma. Transfer constants for different parts of the brain were in the region of 1×10^{-3} min^{-1}, being highest in tissue with predominantly grey matter.

Accumulation in Brain Cells

Some amino acids are accumulated by the brain cells, and this is a useful feature in the kinetic study of uptake, since, in effect, the amino acid passing out of the blood across the blood–brain barrier, may be rapidly removed from the extracellular space into a large 'pool', so that the concentration in the extracellular space builds up slowly and the time during which back-flux may be neglected is prolonged. This was the case with the study of Blasberg *et al.* (1983) illustrated above.

The Rapidly Equilibrating Space

A careful analysis of the earliest stages of penetration from blood to brain has indicated, with slowly penetrating substances especially, that there is an initial small rapid uptake of the solute from the blood, after which the course of uptake follows a regular course. It has been assumed that there is a small 'space' in the brain that comes into rapid equilibrium with the blood, i.e. between which it and the blood barrier is very low. Kinetically this space appears in the finding that the plot of brain uptake against time does not intersect the origin of the uptake–time plot. If we confine our attention to the studies of very slow penetration of solutes from blood to brain, in which the simple equation, ignoring backflux, may be applied, we may consider the basic equation

$$dC_{br}/dt = K_{in}C_{pl}$$

The integrated form of this equation is

$$C_{br} = K_{in}C_{pl}t + \text{constant}$$

To determine the integration constant, we consider the situation when $t = $ zero, in which case the integration constant becomes the value of C_{br} at zero time, i.e. the value immediately after establishing a concentration of the solute in the blood, and given by extrapolating the C_{br}-versus-time line back to zero on the ordinate. This is illustrated by an example taken from the study of Zlokovic *et al.* (1988) (Figure 1.36) showing the penetration of TRH across the blood–brain barrier of the perfused guinea-pig head. Penetration is very slow, so that after 20 min of exposure to TRH in the blood, the ratio C_{br}/C_{pl} is only about 0.03, compared with one of about ten times this value for thiourea, considered to be a slowly penetrating solute. At zero time the intercept on the ordinate is about 0.008, and this is converted into an *'initial volume of distribution'*, V_i, by estimating the volume of brain that, when having completely equilibrated with the blood plasma, would give the value of C_{br}/C_{pl} shown by the intercept on the ordinate.

Operational Quantity

The rapidly equilibrating space is an operational quantity not necessarily having a uniform meaning for different solutes, and is essentially an expression of the fact that the plot of uptake against time does not extrapolate to zero at zero time. It could represent uptake through the non-barrier regions, for example, and in this case we might expect it to be the same for a group of polar molecules, such as mannitol, inulin, etc. However, a careful comparison of the kinetics of uptake of L-glucose, raffinose and inulin revealed differences (Lucchesi and Gosselin, 1990) that would be hard to interpret.

Compartments

The above approach has involved treating the blood–brain system as made up of only two effective compartments, the blood plasma on the one hand and the

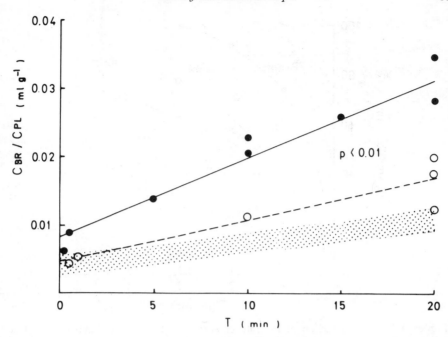

Figure 1.36 Kinetics of entry of [³H]-TRH into the parietal cortex of perfused guinea-pig brain in the absence (solid points and line) and presence of 2 mM bacitracin (open points and dashed line). ³H radioactivity, dpm g⁻¹ of brain/dpm ml⁻¹ plasma perfusate, is plotted against the perfusion time, *T*. Shadowed area represents [³H]-mannitol space obtained in a separate series of 15 experiments. Each point represents a single experiment. K_{in} values were determined as the slope of regression lines from the multiple-time series (ml min⁻¹ g⁻¹), and compared by analysis of variance (*p*). From Zloković *et al.* (1988)

available brain water on the other; this was justified with sodium because the available water is almost completely confined to the extracellular space. If we had employed K⁺, however, this would not have been true, so that two kinetic steps at least are involved, first from blood to extracellular space and second from extracellular space to cells, and experimentally the system is found, indeed, to be kinetically more complex. If we had employed a strongly lipid-soluble substance such as ethyl or propyl thiourea, we should have found a two-compartment treatment correct experimentally; this is because the extracellular and intracellular compartments can be treated as a single one, the barriers between blood and extracellular fluid, and between extracellular fluid and intracellular fluid, being small, so that the two steps are difficult to resolve in time.

Thioureas and Glucose

Thus, Figure 1.37 illustrates penetration of thiourea into the brain of the rabbit; the penetration follows a logarithmic curve corresponding to a two-compartment

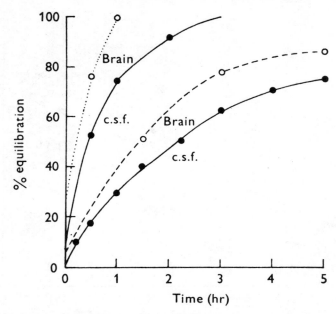

Figure 1.37 A comparison of the rate of entry of ethyl thiourea (upper curves) and thiourea (lower curves) from the blood into the brain (open circles) and into the cerebrospinal fluid (closed circles). From Davson *et al.* (1963)

system, although of course, there are three compartments—namely blood, brain extracellular fluid and brain intracellular fluid. With the more lipid-soluble ethyl thiourea, penetration was more rapid but obviously followed a simple two-compartmental kinetic course. A similar situation prevails with glucose, as we shall see (Chapter 2), but here it would appear that the step from extracellular to intracellular fluids is much more rapid than the step from plasma to extracellular fluid, so that it is this latter step that governs the kinetics (Lund-Andersen, 1979).

Cerebrospinal Fluid

We shall see that the presence of this fluid, flowing over the surfaces of the brain, represents the introduction of a new compartment that may influence the kinetics of transport from blood to brain tissue. This could have been the case with the examples of Na^+ and ethyl thiourea shown above, and the fact that the kinetics are two- instead of three-compartmental will require explanation, and will be discussed later. In a number of experimental situations the presence of the CSF can be ignored simply because of the limitations of time; this is true of the *single-pass techniques*, which we may now consider.

Single-pass Techniques

If a solute passes very rapidly across the capillaries of the brain, the permeability coefficient, relative to other substances, may be assessed by measuring the uptake by the brain during a single pass of blood through the capillaries, so that penetration into the brain is a measure of crossing the blood capillaries into the extracellular space, the subsequent passage into cells being virtually irrelevant owing to the short time of measurement.

Indicator Dilution Technique

Crone (1961, 1965) measured the amount of the solute that passed out of the blood during a single circuit through the head. The technique consisted of giving a steady infusion of the solute through the carotid artery, withdrawing at the same time blood from the superior sagittal sinus, i.e. blood leaving the brain directly. Analysis of the arterial and venous bloods gave a measure of the *extraction*, E, of the solute from the blood, provided that allowance was made for dilution of blood entering the brain through other arteries. These dilution effects were measured by including in the solution, infused intra-arterially, a 'non-diffusible reference substance', i.e. a substance of sufficiently high molecular weight, such as serum albumin bound to Evans Blue, that it is effectively confined to the vascular system. The concentration of solute in the venous effluent, C_{test}, varies according to the permeability of the blood–brain barrier, as illustrated by Figure 1.38. Thus, the curve showing the change in C_{ref}, the concentration of Evans Blue–albumin, indicates the curve for zero extraction, and from the differences between this curve and those for other substances, extractions can be calculated, the extraction, E, being given by the ratio $(C_{ref} - C_{test})/C_{ref}$. The permeability coefficient of the solute in question is given by the equation

$$P = \dot{Q}/A \ln (1 - E) \tag{1.34}$$

where $\dot{Q}$ is the rate of blood flow per gram of brain per sec and A is the area of capillaries in the same weight of brain [Note 8]. Using this technique, Crone (1965) deduced the permeability coefficients shown in Table 1.3. The high values

Table 1.3 Permeability constants, in cm/s, deduced from analysis of inflowing and outflowing blood of brain. After Crone (1965)

Substance	Permeability constant (cm/s $\times 10^5$)
Fructose	0.16
Glycerol	0.21
Thiourea	0.29
Propylene glycol	0.38
Urea	0.44
Antipyrine	3.3
Ethanol	>10

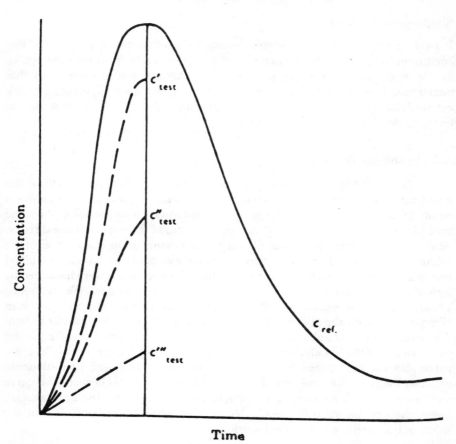

Figure 1.38   Time–concentration curves in the effluent blood from an organ obtained after the 'square wave' injection into the afferent vessel. C_{ref}, reference substance which does not leave the capillaries; C_{test}, various diffusible test substances. From Crone (1965)

for antipyrine and ethanol emphasize the importance of lipid-solubility.

Later studies from Yudilevich's laboratory (Yudilevich and De Rose, 1971; Yudilevich *et al.*, 1972) have demonstrated the value of the technique in establishing the carrier-mediated nature of transport of amino acids and sugars across the blood–brain barrier. A further refinement was made by Zlokovic and Segal (Preston *et al.*, 1989), who applied the single-pass technique to the perfused isolated choroid plexus, experiments that will be described in later chapters of this book.

The Brain Uptake Index (BUI)

The technique developed by Oldendorf (1971) also depends on measuring brain uptake after a supposititious single pass through the capillary circulation, but, instead of deducing brain uptake from the extraction from the circulating blood, Oldendorf measured the concentration of the substance under investigation in the brain some 15 s after administration of an intracarotid bolus injection, the animal being decapitated, and the brain removed and analysed. The amount taken up by any given animal's brain will vary according to a variety of circumstances, especially the rate of blood flow, so that a reference standard was included in the bolus, namely tritiated water, ^3HOH, the penetration of which, being very rapid and limited, apparently, by the rate of flow of blood through the brain, would act as a reference standard by which to compare penetration of more slowly penetrating compounds. In later studies labelled butanol was substituted for tritiated water, its penetration being much greater and truly blood-flow-limited.

Experimentally, then, the animal was given a bolus injection of a mixture of ^3HOH, acting as reference substance, and the ^{14}C-labelled test solute, and after 15 s it was decapitated and the brain was analysed for ^3H and ^{14}C. If we define the extraction of the solute, E, as the ratio of uptake by brain, Q_b, and the total quantity of solute available in the bolus, Q_t, we have

$$\text{extraction of test solute, } E_t = Q_{tb}/Q_{ti} \qquad (1.35)$$

$$\text{extraction of reference, } E_r = Q_{rb}/Q_{ri} \qquad (1.36)$$

The brain uptake index, BUI, is defined as the ratio between the extractions $\times 100$:

$$100 \, E_t/E_r = \frac{100 \, Q_{tb}/Q_{rb}}{Q_{ti}/Q_{ri}} \qquad (1.37)$$

Thus, with the test substance tritiated water, we have

$$\text{BUI} = \frac{^{14}C/^3H \text{ (brain)}}{^{14}C/^3H \text{ (injectate)}} \times 100 \qquad (1.38)$$

Value of the BUI

Measurement of the BUI for a variety of solutes permits an ordering of their rates of penetration from blood into brain; thus, Figure 1.39 illustrates the different values for amino acids, and the contrast between amino acids that can be synthesized by the brain—the non-essential amino acids—and those that the brain must obtain from the blood circulation—the essential amino acids—is striking. Later analysis of the BUI has permitted the deduction of transfer coefficients (PS) for various solutes and Figure 1.40 demonstrates the obvious relationship between PS (the transfer coefficient) and octanol:water partition coefficient. In general, however, great care has to be taken when interpreting values of BUI; thus, barbiturate anaesthesia increases the BUI, but it reduces cerebral blood flow from 1.61 ml min^{-1} g^{-1} to 0.59 ml min^{-1} g^{-1}. Miller *et al.* (1985) have shown that, in fact, the influx of solutes into the brain, deduced from studies of the BUI but

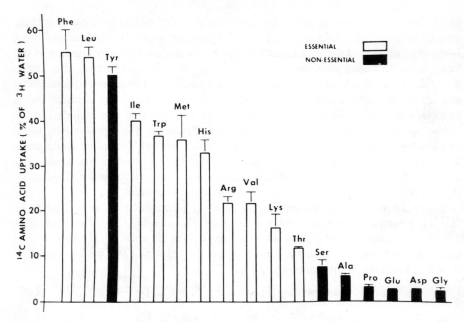

Figure 1.39 Relative uptakes of amino acids by rat brain when a single bolus of the labelled amino acid is injected into a carotid artery together with ^3H_2O. In the rat, tyrosine is probably an essential amino acid. From Oldendorf (1971)

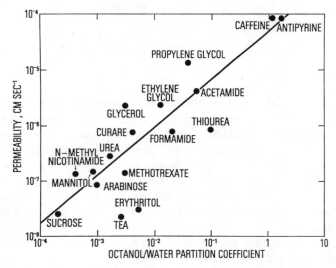

Figure 1.40 Cerebrovascular permeability as a function of octanol–water partition coefficient. From Rapoport *et al.* (1979)

allowing for alterations in blood flow, is actually decreased by anaesthesia; thus, with a more sluggish flow of blood, the extraction of a solute during a single pass through a capillary will be increased, and this will be out of all proportion to any change in extraction of a rapidly penetrating solute such as butanol. In this way the BUI may lead to erroneous conclusions. As we shall see, however, in the hands of Pardridge, it has proved a valuable tool in the analysis of Michaelis–Menten kinetics of the blood–brain barrier.

Michaelis–Menten Kinetics

Crone (1965), employing his single-pass extraction technique, showed that the transport of hexoses into the brain had carrier-mediated features, the extraction decreasing as the concentration of the sugar in the blood was raised, indicating a self-inhibition. Since the rate of glucose utilization by the brain seems to be governed by the rate at which the cells can be supplied, this depression of extraction with increasing plasma concentration is of obvious value, a high plasma level having a lower extraction, and so not overloading the brain cells with this metabolite. A low blood sugar, on the other hand, would be associated with a relatively high extraction and so mitigate the effects of the hypoglycaemia so far as brain cells were concerned. Oldendorf (1971), using his BUI technique, likewise demonstrated relatively high rates of penetration of D-glucose, D-mannose and D-galactose but low BUIs for L-glucose or D-fructose. The BUI for D-glucose was depressed by raising the concentrations of various sugars in the injectate. In a more elaborate study, Pardridge and Oldendorf (1975a, b) deduced values of K_m, which, as we have seen, indicate the concentration of the solute at which the carrier is half-saturated, and acts as an inverse measure of the affinity of the carrier for the hexose. They found a value of 9 mM for D-glucose, which compares with a normal plasma concentration of about 7 mM; thus, the concentration in the plasma is in the range where effects of changes in concentration may influence the degree of saturation of the carrier and thus aid in homoeostasis—a hyperglycaemia, for example, would lead to saturation of the carrier and put a brake on uptake across the blood–brain barrier.

The Brain Capillary Transporter Protein

Dick *et al.* (1984) used the photoaffinity labelling technique for identifying and subsequent isolation of a glucose-transporting molecule in cerebral isolated microvessels from the rat and pig. With the usual SDS–PAGE technique they identified a protein of molecular weight about 53 kD, and showed that antigenically it was similar to the glucose transporter isolated from human erythrocytes. In a similar way Kasanicki *et al.* (1987), using bovine brain microvessels, separated a protein of 55 kD exhibiting a broad band in the SDS–PAGE electrophoresis pattern; removal of sugar by endoglycosidase F sharpened the band to give an apparent molecular weight of 46 kD. Other tests confirmed the strong analogy with the human erythrocyte glucose transporter.

Localization

Gerhart *et al.* (1989) prepared a polyclonal antibody to a synthetic 13 amino acid peptide corresponding to the carboxy terminus of the glucose transporter of human hepatoma cells and rat brain (Mueckler *et al.*, 1985; Birnbaum *et al.*, 1986). With this antibody they were able to localize the transporter throughout the central nervous system; microvessels were, as we should expect, the principal location of the transporter, these being symmetrically distributed on luminal and abluminal sides of the endothelium. Interestingly, microvessels of the subarachnoid vessels and intima pia were also richly supplied, indicating the involvement of transport from the leptomeninges in the nutrition of the brain substance.

Amino Acids

In general, the studies of Pardridge, employing the BUI technique, have illustrated in a remarkably lucid fashion the factors governing transport of amino acids from blood to brain; special features of this transport will be described in Chapter 2 and here we need only note that the K_ms deduced for transport across the blood–brain barrier by the BUI and other techniques are in the neighbourhood of the plasma concentrations of the amino acids, so that the possibilities of mutual inhibition between members of the same class, e.g. large neutral amino acids, are strong, and, in fact, one of the earliest clinical applications of Michaelis–Menten theory consisted in the demonstration that the clinical signs of phenyketonuria are due to defective transport of tryptophan across the blood–brain barrier because of the abnormal competition arising from high blood levels of phenylalanine in this condition. In general, Pardridge was able to deduce apparent K_ms for the different amino acids in the blood, based on the known competition with the other amino acids in the plasma; and on this basis he was able to compute a series of theoretical influx rates that agreed reasonably well with the published experimental values (Pardridge, 1977).

Monocarboxylic Acids

The studies of Oldendorf (1971, 1971/2, 1973) have shown that transport of monocarboxylic acids is carrier-mediated; thus, the BUI for L-lactic acid was some 15% compared with its stereoisomer D-lactic acid, which had a BUI of 3%. Penetration of both acids was depressed by raising the concentration (self-inhibition). Gjedde and Crone (1975) noted that transport of ketone bodies such as hydroxybutyrate was increased during starvation, suggesting that carriers were being produced as a result of this stimulus. Analysis of the transport process indicated increases in both K_m and V_{max}. In experimental hepatic failure (portocaval shunted rats) Cremer *et al.* (1975) showed that the BUIs for butyrate and pyruvate were decreased as a result of a decrease in V_{max} without change in K_m.

Regional Variations

In the unanaesthetized rat Miller and Oldendorf (1986) found a constant value of K_m when different brain regions were studied; the mean value was 1.37 mM. V_{max}, however, did vary, being highest in the cerebral cortex at 0.08 ± 0.08 μmol min^{-1} g^{-1} and 0.22–0.27 in the caudate–putamen, thalamus–hypothalamus.

Isolated Brain Microvessels

By appropriate techniques of homogenization of brain tissue and subsequent sedimentation procedures, suspensions of isolated brain capillaries, free from glial cells and neurons, may be prepared, and some of the features of blood–brain transport have been deduced from measurements of uptake of solutes by suspensions of these microvessels (Brendel *et al.*, 1974; Hjelle *et al.*, 1978; Goldstein and Betz, 1983; Joó, 1985). Studies using this preparation are essentially studies of uptake by endothelial cells and need not reflect the complete transport process from luminal to abluminal sides of the capillary, or vice versa. As the ends of these tubular fragments of capillary are patent, we must assume that the solutes in the suspension medium have access to both sides of the capillary membrane, although the measurement of an uptake in the first few seconds of exposure may well indicate permeability of the abluminal side of the capillary.

Barrier Asymmetry

The technique has permitted the evaluation of Michaelis–Menten parameters for solutes that exhibit saturation kinetics in the intact animal (Goldstein *et al.*, 1984). Of interest is an apparent asymmetry of the capillary membrane with respect to transport of amino acids. Thus, the A type of carrier system, typified by the transport of methyl AIBA, is Na$^+$-dependent and involves, probably, active transport. Studies on the passage from blood to brain of amino acids have indicated, when employing the Oldendorf technique, that the A system is not present so far as the blood–brain barrier is concerned; by contrast, the L system for large neutral amino acids is a prominent feature of the barrier (Pardridge and Oldendorf, 1975b). On the other hand, when transport from brain extracellular fluid to blood is studied, using ventriculocisternal perfusion, there is a very definite carrier-mediated transport of A-type amino acids, so that, as Betz and Goldstein (1978) have emphasized, the brain capillary exhibits an asymmetry with respect to its luminal and abluminal surfaces. Isolated capillaries were shown to accumulate α-methyl AIBA in concentrations greater than that in the medium, a process that was sodium-dependent and inhibited by ouabain. In this connection, we must note that the isolation of brain capillaries often involves a stage in which the tissue is treated with collagenase; in this event the study of Cardelli-Cangiano *et al.* (1987) indicates that the activity of the amino acid A system is virtually abolished, while that of the L system is enhanced. Thus, conflicting results in the literature may reflect different preparative techniques.

Cultured Endothelial Cells

Theoretically, at any rate, an improvement in the isolated capillary preparation would be a monolayer of cultured endothelial cells grown on an inert permeable membrane, so that by using this to separate two fluid-filled chambers, transport across the endothelial cells could be measured. Audus and Borchardt (1986) described such a preparation, the cultured cells being grown on translucent polycarbonate filters; the endothelial cells were held together by tight junctions. Thus, short segments of ox brain microvessels attached to the substrate and spread and grew to form a complete monolayer some 10 days after seeding. The culture was placed in a horizontal 'Side-bi-Side' diffusion chamber and a solute such as [³H]-leucine was injected into one compartment and samples were taken from the other. Figure 1.41 shows transport at 37 °C and at 0–4 °C; the very strong

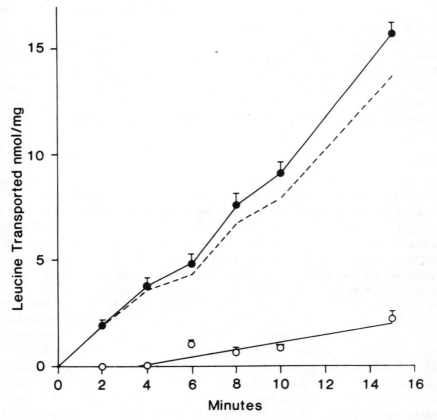

Figure 1.41 Time dependence of [³H]-leucine transport across brain microvessel endothelial cell monolayers grown on collagen-coated regenerated cellulose membranes at 0–4 °C (○) and 37 °C (●). The dashed line is the difference between 37 °C and 0–4 °C data. The final leucine concentration in the donor chamber, at time 0, was 105 μM. Data are mean ± s.e.m. (bars) values from at least three different monolayers. From Audus and Borchardt (1986)

influence of temperature on transport suggests the involvement of active transport requiring metabolic energy. The concentration dependence revealed Michaelis–Menten kinetics with a K_m of 0.18 mM and a V_{max} of 6.3 nmol mg^{-1} min^{-1}. Cycloheximide increased apparent transport in unit time, indicating that some of the amino acid passing across the blood–brain barrier is probably deflected into protein synthesis by the endothelial cell. [Note 6]

The Glial Layer

The isolated capillary differs from the capillary *in situ* in the brain in being stripped of its astroglial investment, and, although, as we shall see, this glial investment does not act as a barrier to diffusion of molecules that are restrained by the blood–brain barrier, it may be, as Davson and Oldendorf (1967) suggested, that the close transposition of the astrocytic end-feet exerts an influence on the permeability characteristics of the capillary endothelium. Evidence in favour of this concept has come from studies of endothelial cells in tissue culture, since it is possible to grow them in the absence or presence of astroglial cells, in this case a culture of so-called C6 cells derived originally from a rat astrocytoma. Beck *et al.* (1984) showed that endothelial cell layers cultured on smooth muscle, i.e. in the absence of glia, did not have the asymmetry regarding transport of A-type amino acids, whereas, if they were cultured in the presence of C6 cells, the asymmetry was present.

Phosphatase Distribution
Brain capillary endothelial cells, like those of many epithelia, show asymmetry in respect to the location of Na$^+$–K$^+$-ATPase, concerned in active transport, and the non-specific phosphatase; the ATPase is concentrated at the basolateral sides of the cell and the non-specific phosphatase at the apical border. Beck *et al.* (1986) showed that endothelial cells cultured with C6 cells had this asymmetrical distribution, which was lost if the cells were cultured in their absence.

Inductive Power of Astroglia
This power of the astroglia to determine the barrier characteristics of the central nervous capillary has been strikingly confirmed by a study of the developing chick embryo by Bertossi *et al.* (1989). Thus, at the 14th day i.d., isolated astrocytic end-feet, covering some 12.5% of the vessel surface, are associated with a significantly high frequency to regions of the endothelium where tight junctions between adjacent endothelial cells are forming. The astrocytic layer is about complete just before hatching, when the adult features of the blood–brain barrier are developed (Roncali *et al.*, 1986).

Again, the enzyme gamma-glutamyl transpeptidase, which catalyses the reaction

glutathione + amino acid $\rightarrow$ γ-glutamyl-amino acid + cysteinylglycine

has been considered to be involved in the active transport of amino acids across cell membranes (Orlowski, 1963). Orlowski *et al.* (1974) demonstrated high transpeptidase activity in endothelial cells of brain capillaries. DeBault and Cancilla (1980) showed that the high activity in isolated brain endothelial cells was lost during tissue culture; they showed that, if endothelial cells (ME-2 cells) were co-cultured with C6 cells, the enzyme was induced in the cultured endothelium. Finally, we may mention that Tao-Cheng *et al.* (1987) found that brain endothelium, cultured *in vitro*, exhibited more normal tight junctions if co-cultured with C6 cells, and these were increased in number. In the co-cultured system typically thin sections showed several layers of endothelial and astrocytic processes, sometimes with a basal lamina intercalated between the processes from the two cell types.

In vitro *and* in vivo *Models Compared*

Using their capillary depletion technique, Pardridge *et al.* (1990) have compared the permeabilities of the intact blood–brain barrier of the rat with those of a layer of *in vitro* cultured endothelial cells. Values for the *in vitro* model were some 150 times those for the *in vivo* model, indicating the great 'leakiness' of the *in vitro* preparation, and its questionable value as an indicator of normal capillary endothelial function. Astrocyte preconditioning of cultures caused an approximately 30% increase in resistance to the transport of sucrose.

Transplanted Tissues

Stewart and Wiley (1981) showed that the character of a capillary depended on the tissue in which it developed. They transplanted embryonic brain into embryonic gut before vascularization; the transplanted brain tissue was vascularized by blood vessels of gut origin, which nevertheless had the anatomical and biochemical properties of brain capillaries; on the other hand, when embryonic gut was transplanted to brain before vascularization, the transplanted gut, although vascularized by capillaries of brain origin, possessed capillaries without the blood–brain barrier features of brain capillaries. Thus, the vascular system acquires the character of the tissue that it invades, i.e. its host's. Presumably specific factors govern the development of the brain capillary, and these are presumably secreted by the astrocytes related to the developing capillary. The secreted factors are probably to be found among the several blood–brain barrier-specific proteins that are being isolated.

Transplanted Peripheral Sympathetic Ganglion

The superior cervical ganglion lacks a blood–nerve barrier (Jacobs, 1977) and Rosenstein and Brightman (1986) transplanted ganglia from mature rat donors into the IVth ventricles of other rats. They found that infusion of the recipient rat with horseradish peroxidase led to rapid escape into the implanted ganglionic tissue and soon the adjacent parenchyma of the recipient brain became stained, presumably through diffusion of the confluent extracellular spaces of graft and recipient tissue. Thus, in this case the donor tissue has retained its own blood–brain characteristics, by contrast with the situation described by Stewart and Wiley (1981).

Practical Applications
The behaviour of transplants in the central nervous system is of more than academic interest, since the possibility of remedying neuronal deficits by transplants has been suggested and put into practice. Perlow *et al.* (1979) implanted fetal mesencephalic tissue containing dopaminergic neurons of the substantia nigra in the lateral ventricles of rats in whom a Parkinsonian syndrome had been induced by destruction of the dopaminergic innervation of the corpus striatum with injections of 6-hydroxydopamine. The improvement of the condition led to an attempt on two cases of human Parkinsonism by Madrazzo *et al.* (1987), who made autotransplants of adrenal medulla in the head of the caudate nucleus in the hope that the explanted tissue would produce dopamine, the nigrostriatal transmitter that is deficient in the disease. The improvement in the condition was striking. The adrenal medulla has no blood–brain barrier (Jacobs, 1977), so, unless it acquired the barrier characteristics of its host tissue, as one might expect from Stewart and Wiley's experiments, it could liberate dopamine into the extracellular space of the corpus striatum. However, according to Ahlskog *et al.* (1989), patients undergoing the transplant exhibited normal blood–brain barriers, as determined by albumin and IgG concentrations in the CSF. The subject is a vexed one, and has been discussed by Broadwell (1988).

Model
Goldstein (1988) in his review of endothelial cell–astrocyte reactions has suggested the model illustrated by Figure 1.42. Thus, receptors for growth factors important in regulation of proliferation and differentiation are found when both types of cell are cultured. Platelet-derived growth factor (PDGF) can be synthesized by endothelial cells and has a mitogenic effect on glial cells. Endothelial cell growth factors (ECGF) are synthesized by neurons or astrocytes and stimulate endothelial cells to proliferate and glial cells to differentiate. Transforming growth factor β (TGFβ) blocks the mitogenic effect of other growth factors and may cause endothelial cells to differentiate. Finally, basement membrane (bm), formed by the endothelial cells and astrocytes, may influence the behaviour of both types of cell. This model indicates how some of these signals might co-operate during differentiation to establish the special character of the blood–brain barrier.

The Perfused *in situ* Brain

Limitations of Single-pass Techniques

The Oldendorf BUI technique represented a significant advance in the method of studying the blood–brain barrier quantitatively; its main limitation is the short time

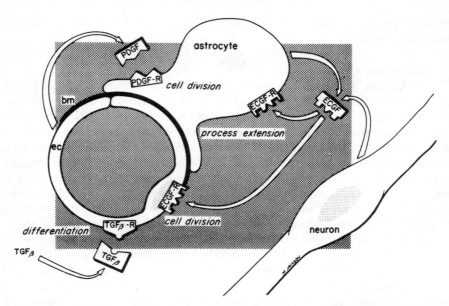

Figure 1.42 A diagram illustrating possible interactions between brain endothelial cells (ec) and astrocytes. Receptors for growth factors important in regulation of proliferation and differentiation are found when these cells are maintained in culture. Platelet-derived growth factor (PDGF) can be synthesized by endothelial cells and has a mitogenic effect upon glial cells. Endothelial cell growth factors (ECGF) are synthesized by neurons or astrocytes and stimulate endothelial cells to proliferate and glial cells to differentiate. Transforming growth factor β (TGFβ) blocks the mitogenic effect of other growth factors and may cause endothelial cells to differentiate. Finally, basement membrane (bm) formed by the endothelial cells and astrocytes may influence the behaviour of both cell types. From Goldstein (1988)

in which the investigated solutes remain in the circulation, so that if measurable uptake has not occurred during a single pass through the capillaries, the BUI becomes zero. Thus, the technique is of little or no value in measuring the permeability of the blood–brain barrier to relatively slowly penetrating solutes, such as ^{24}Na and other ions, and a great variety of peptides and amines that are of great biological interest so far as the relation between blood concentration and brain uptake are concerned. A return to the earlier technique of intravenous infusion over longer periods of time is sometimes feasible, provided that the solute is not significantly metabolized while in the circulation; thus, ^{3}H-labelled cycloleucine and AIBA have been investigated with success, the uptake of the label being indicative of uptake of the intact molecule. With amino acids that are readily metabolized, the infusion technique is relatively useless if labelled amino acids are employed. The modern developments of chromatography (HPLC) that permit the assay of very small quantities of the unlabelled amino acid or peptide have now permitted the use of infusion techniques. Of greater value, however, has been the development of techniques for perfusion of the animal's brain with an artificial blood containing the labelled solute; in this case access to the liver and other metabolizing regions is avoided, so that the uptake of the label can be used as a measure of the uptake of the amino acid and peptide.

Perfused Rat Brain

Takasato *et al.* (1984) described an *in situ* brain perfusion technique, the perfusion fluid being pumped retrogradely through the right common carotid artery (Figure 1.43), the rate being adjusted to minimize any contribution to the flow through the right brain by the animal's own blood. This contribution, which amounted to some 5% of the flow through the perfused brain, could be measured by incorporating a rapidly penetrating marker into the systemic circulation. Transfer coefficients were computed, and Figure 1.44 shows the computed permeability coefficients of a number of solutes as a function of their octanol–water partition coefficients. The computed permeability or transfer coefficients were comparable with those measured in intact animals; thus, for thiourea the transfer coefficient was 2.11×10^{-4} s^{-1} or 0.012 min^{-1}, equivalent to a half-life of some 58 min, comparable with a value of about 90 min in the rabbit using intravascular infusion (Davson *et al.*, 1963).

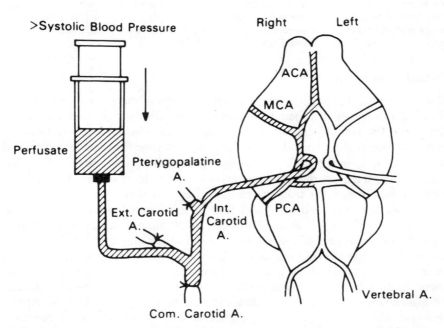

Figure 1.43 Diagram of technique for perfusing right cerebral hemisphere. A, artery. From Takasato *et al.* (1984)

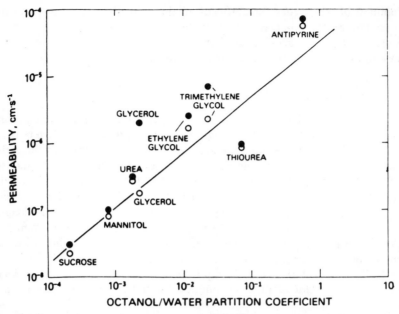

Figure 1.44 Relation of cerebrovascular permeability in the parietal cortex to octanol–water partition coefficient for 8 non-electrolytes. Open circles, permeability values for *in situ* brain perfusion technique; closed circles, values from intravenous injection technique (30). Each point represents a mean ± s.e. for $n = 3–5$ animals. Line is the least squares fit to *in situ* perfusion data and is given as $\log_{10}P = -4.53$ (±0.23, s.e.) + 0.814 (±0.098, s.e.) $\log_{10}$ partition coefficient. From Takastao *et al.* (1984)

Perfused Guinea-pig Brain

Zlokovic *et al.* (1986) profited by the unique anatomy of the guinea-pig's cerebral circulation to ensure that their fluid, perfused through the right common carotid artery with the contralateral artery tied, was uncontaminated by blood from the animal's own circulating blood. Thus, the communication between the carotid and vertebral systems in the adult guinea-pig is poor (Figure 1.45) and the forebrain relies largely on the external carotid artery, a circumstance that has not been found with any mammals other than the cavoids (Bugge, 1974). The internal carotid artery does not exist, and the blood flow in the internal ophthalmic artery is reversed under physiological conditions due to five anastomotic branches derived from the proximal part of the external carotid artery and the stapedial arterial system. The circle of Willis is complete but the posterior communicating arteries are narrow compared with the anterior communicating arteries and the ophthalmic artery. In the experiments it was found that the retrograde pressure, measured in the ipsilateral carotid artery, was always at least four times less than the arterial blood pressure, reflecting a naturally high resistance between the two circulations. During perfusion this was potentiated by keeping the perfusion pressure 2.5–4 kPa above the mean contralateral carotid pressure, which was usually within the

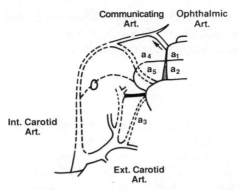

Figure 1.45 The cephalic arterial pattern in *Cavia porcellus*; a_1–a_5 are arterial anastomoses. Arrow denotes a reversed flow in the internal ophthalmic artery. From Zloković *et al.* (1987b)

range 10–12 kPa. The perfusion fluid contained 20% of sheep red cells, so that the perfused forebrain was adequately supplied with O_2, as revealed by applying a battery of biochemical tests. Thus, the perfusion could be carried on for as long as 30 min without deterioration of the brain, so that the study of a large number of slowly penetrating substances of physiological interest has become possible, as will be described in Chapter 3. Figure 1.46 illustrates the experimental set-up and

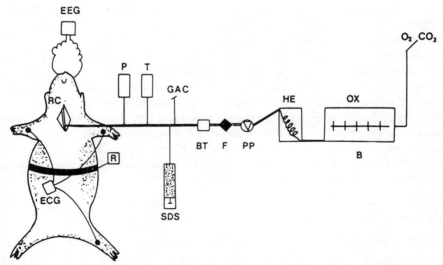

Figure 1.46 Schematic representation of the extracorporeal perfusion circuit employed for the vascular perfusion of the guinea-pig forebrain. RC, position of the cannula in the right common carotid artery of the guinea-pig; BP, arterial blood pressure measured from the contralateral carotid artery; P, pressure transducer for measurement of the perfusion pressure; T, thermistor; SDS, slow-drive syringe; GAC, gas analysis control; BT, bubble trap; PP, peristaltic pump; HE, heat exchanger; OX, oxygenator; B, blood reservoir. From Zloković *et al.* (1986)

Figure 1.35 (p. 61) shows brain uptake of ^{3}H-labelled thyroid releasing hormone (TRH). Uptake remained linear during the full 20 min of perfusion, indicating lack of significant back-flux, so that the simple influx kinetics could be applied (p. 60).

Regional Transport

It is often of interest to determine whether the blood–brain barrier is uniform throughout the brain or whether there are variations in uptake in different regions. Gross dissection of the brain after the barrier experiment and analysis of the pieces provides some indication, but the technique of quantitative autoradiography of different sections of the frozen brain provides a much more accurate localization of differences in rate of uptake (see, for example, Hawkins *et al.*, 1982, for amino acids and Hawkins *et al.*, 1983, for glucose). By appropriate computerization, three-dimensional pictures of regional transport may be built up (Hibbard and Hawkins, 1984).

The Cerebrospinal Fluid and the Blood–CSF Barrier

We have seen that the cerebrospinal fluid (CSF) lies in close relation with the central nervous tissue of brain and spinal cord, and it becomes of vital interest to know how solutes in the blood are transported into the CSF, or vice versa. A ready exchange of, say, sucrose between blood and CSF would provide a pathway for this solute to pass from blood to brain tissue, the sucrose accumulating in the CSF diffusing out of the CSF into the tissue across the ependymal lining of the ventricles and across the arachnoid and pia, as illustrated in Figure 1.47. Thus, as Goldmann's second experiment, and subsequent more quantitative studies, have shown, the ependyma is highly permeable to lipid-insoluble solutes. Because of its ready accessibility the exchanges between blood and CSF, described by the term 'blood–CSF barrier', were examined in detail before strict quantitative studies on the blood–brain barrier were carried out. Figure 1.48 illustrates an early quantitative study, the results emphasizing the importance of lipid-solubility in determining rate of passage from blood to CSF.

Kinetics

The two-compartment kinetic approach was, in fact, developed for the analysis of the blood–CSF barrier, so that transfer coefficients K_{in} and K_{out} were extracted from the kinetic results. Thus,

$$\frac{dC_{CSF}}{dt} = K_{in}C_{pl} - K_{out}C_{CSF} \tag{1.39}$$

As before, at infinite time, or the steady state, when $dC_{CSF}/dt = 0$,

$$C_{CSF}/C_{pl} = K_{in}/K_{out} = r \tag{1.40}$$

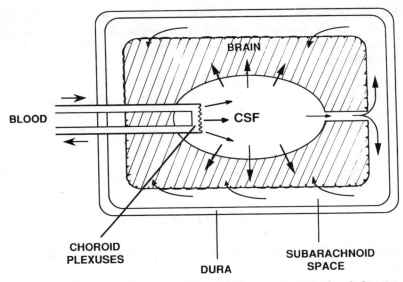

Figure 1.47 The pathway from blood into the cerebrospinal fluid and then into brain tissue either directly from the ventricles or from the subarachnoid space

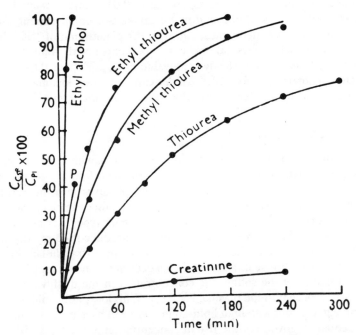

Figure 1.48 Penetration of different substances of increasing lipid-solubility into rabbit's cerebrospinal fluid. P = propyl thiourea. From Davson (1967)

So that, if r, the steady state distribution ratio of the solute between plasma and CSF (a ratio that can often be determined by simple chemical analysis if the solute we are considering is one naturally occurring in the blood, such as Na^+ or K^+) we may employ the equation:

$$dC_{CSF}/dt = rK_{out}C_{pl} - K_{out}C_{CSF} \qquad (1.41)$$

$$= K_{out}(rC_{pl} - C_{CSF}) \qquad (1.42)$$

If C_{pl} has been maintained constant, then the equation is simply integrated to give

$$C_{in}/C_{out} = r(1 - e^{-K_{out}t}) \qquad (1.43)$$

or

$$\ln\left(1 - \frac{C_{in}}{rC_{out}}\right) = -K_{out}t \qquad (1.44)$$

Thus, plotting $\ln[1 - (C_{in}/rC_{out})]$ against time should give a straight line with the slope equal to K_{out}.

As an example we may show Figure 1.49(a), in which the penetration of the moderately lipid-soluble methyl thiourea into the rabbit's CSF has been plotted against time; the curve suggests that the ratio of C_{CSF}/C_{pl} against time approaches unity, so that $K_{in} = K_{out}$. The plot of the logarithmic function against time (Figure 1.49b) is linear, whence the value of K_{out} or K_{in} of 0.0135 min^{-1} is obtained. With a number of solutes it has been found that a simple two-compartment analysis of the experimental measurements fails, e.g. with the penetration of ^{42}K, illustrated by Figure 1.50, which shows (a) the curve of uptake with time, and (b) the logarithmic plot based on the steady state value of C_{CSF}/C_{pl} of 0.675. We must now ask why it is that the blood–CSF barrier can be treated in some instances by simple two-compartment kinetics, and why, in other instances, this treatment fails.

The Mechanism of Penetration

We may assume, first, that with a solute such as thiourea, with kinetics conforming to two-compartmental analysis, the thiourea introduced into the plasma diffuses from the blood in the capillaries of the choroid plexuses into the extracellular space of these bodies. This should be a rapid process, since the blood capillaries of the choroid plexuses are not of the blood–brain barrier type; they are fenestrated and characteristic of blood capillaries that serve to produce fluid rapidly, as in the kidney glomerulus and the intestinal villus. From the extracellular fluid of the choroid plexus it will diffuse into the epithelial cells of this tissue and, according to the chemical nature of the solute, the concentration in the freshly secreted fluid will be a fraction of that in the plasma, e.g. rC_{pl}. With low permeability, r will be a small factor, e.g. 0.1, but with high lipid-solubility r will have its maximum value of unity. The equation governing the rise in concentration in the CSF will be:

$$dC_{CSF}/dt = K_F rC_{pl} - K_F C_{CSF} \qquad (1.45)$$

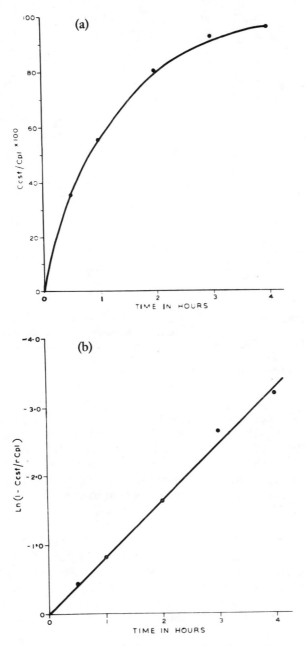

Figure 1.49 (a) Penetration of methyl thiourea into rabbit's cerebrospinal fluid. $C_{est}/C_{el} \times 100$ has been plotted against time after establishing steady concentration in the plasma. (b) Penetration of methyl thiourea into rabbit's cerebrospinal fluid. The logarithmic function has been plotted against time

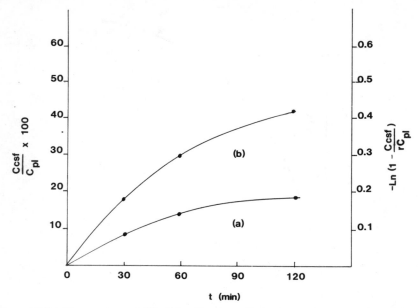

Figure 1.50 Penetration of K^+ from blood to CSF. (a) C_{CSF}/C_{pl} ($\times 100$) (left-hand ordinates) has been plotted against time, in minutes. (b) The logarithmic function (right-hand ordinates) taking account of the steady-state distribution ratio, $R_{CSF} = 0.675$, has been plotted. The logarithmic function fails to describe penetration, so that a multicompartment treatment is necessary. After Davson (1956)

where K_F is a flow-coefficient with dimensions of t^{-1}, and may be defined as the fraction of the total volume of CSF renewed in unit time. For example, the actual flow in the rabbit is some 10 μl/min, and the total volume of CSF in the rabbit is some 2.5 ml or 25 000 μl. Thus, the flow coefficient is $10/25\,000 = 4 \times 10^{-3}$ min^{-1}. The process is illustrated schematically in Figure 1.51. The equation is comparable with our simple two-compartment equation

$$dC_{CSF}/dt = K_{in}C_{pl} - K_{out}C_{CSF} \qquad (1.39)$$

where K_{in} is now rK_F. As r can vary from zero, when the substance is impermeable, to unity, when penetration into the epithelial cells is rapid, as with highly lipid-soluble substances, it is clear that K_{in} can never be larger than K_F, the constant defining rate of flow, or renewal, of the CSF.

Now K_F has been measured in many animals and is in the region of 0.004 min^{-1}, so that, on the basis of this simple treatment, the maximum value of K_{in} (or of K_{out}) is 0.004 min^{-1}.

It will be seen from Table 1.4, where values of K_{in} are shown for a number of non-electrolytes of increasing lipid-solubility, that K_{in} may be very much greater than this limiting value governed by rate of renewal of CSF. Clearly the model of Figure 1.51 is inadequate, because influx of the solute from the blood must be

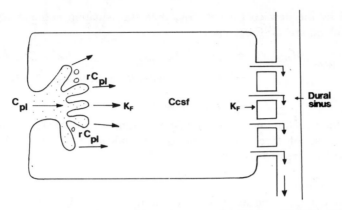

Figure 1.51 Simple scheme illustrating penetration of substance from blood in choroid plexus secretion, at rate K_F, associated with outflow through arachnoid villi

Table 1.4 Values of K_{in} or K_{out} (min^{-1}) for solutes of increasing lipid-solubility deduced from measurements of transport from blood to CSF of rabbit. From Davson (1967)

Thiourea	0.0057
Methyl thiourea	0.0135
Ethylthiourea	0.021
Propylthiourea	0.035
Ethyl alcohol	0.225

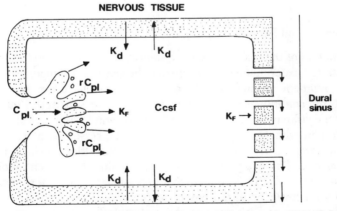

Figure 1.52 Similar to Figure 1.51, but an additional route of penetration is from the nervous tissue

greater than that supplied by the newly formed CSF. Figure 1.52 illustrates a modification of the model, according to which additional solute passes across the blood–brain barrier into the nervous tissue adjacent to the ventricles and subarachnoid spaces, and thence into the CSF. If the influx from this source is governed by the new coefficient, K_D, then the equation defining equilibration between blood and CSF becomes

$$dC_{CSF}/dt = K_F r C_{pl} + K_D C_{pl} - K_D C_{CSF} - K_F C_{CSF} \tag{1.46}$$

$$= (rK_F + K_D)C_{pl} - (K_D + K_F)C_{CSF} \tag{1.47}$$

$$= K_{in}C_{pl} - K_{out}C_{CSF} \tag{1.39}$$

Thus, the equation retains the simple two-compartment character although the system is one of three compartments, or, indeed, four, if the intracellular compartment is treated separately.

Steady State Ratios

We may note that, at the steady state, when $dC_{CSF}/dt = 0$, we have

$$\frac{C_{CSF}}{C_{pl}} = \frac{rK_F + K_D}{K_F + K_D} \tag{1.48}$$

Thus, so long as r is less than unity, the concentration in the CSF will be less than that in plasma, i.e. R_{CSF} will be less than unity. This is an important point, telling us that when there is a restraint on passage from blood across the choroid plexuses, such that the newly formed fluid contains a lower concentration of a solute than that in plasma, the steady state distribution ratio, R_{CSF}, will be less than unity. Moreover, the magnitude of the deviation from unity will be related to the permeability of the given solute across the blood–CSF barrier, so that when dealing with slowly penetrating substances, such as the plasma proteins, the value of R_{CSF} correlates with the molecular size of the protein (Felgenhauer, 1974).

Ventriculocisternal Perfusion

The contribution of the brain tissue to equilibration between blood and CSF may be demonstrated experimentally by perfusing the ventricles with an artificial CSF. At a given moment a concentration of ^{24}Na is established in the blood and maintained by continuous intravenous infusion (Davson and Pollay, 1963). Samples of the effluent fluid are analysed for ^{24}Na, and Figure 1.53 shows the rise in concentration with time. The concentration, expressed as a fraction of the plasma concentration, rises rapidly at first but then settles down to a slow and almost linear rise. There is good reason to believe that the concentration of ^{24}Na in the freshly secreted CSF is equal to that in plasma, i.e. that r in Equation (1.48) is unity; with a knowledge of the rate of secretion of CSF, then, it is possible to compute the amount of ^{24}Na entering the perfusion fluid in unit time, i.e. $K_F C_{pl}$. The amount leaving through the outflow cannula in unit time will be $(K_F + K_X)C_{CSF}$, where K_X is the rate of flow of the perfusion fluid. Thus, at the steady state, we may expect the value of the ratio

$$\frac{C_{outflow}}{C_{pl}} \text{ to be equal to } \frac{K_F}{K_F + K_X} \tag{1.49}$$

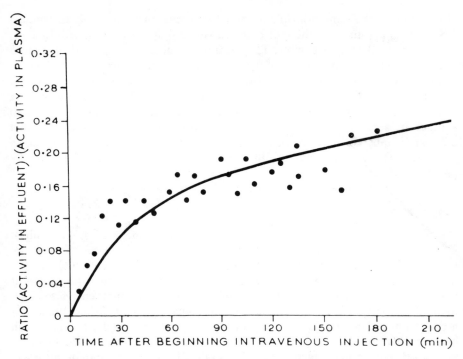

Figure 1.53 Penetration of ^{24}Na from blood into fluid perfusing the ventricular system of the rabbit. Points are experimental, while curve is theoretical. From Davson and Pollay (1963)

Substituting known values for the Ks, we obtain a maximum, or steady state, value of 0.133. It is clear from Figure 1.53 that the ratio has reached this value within about 30 min and continues to rise, indicating the addition of ^{24}Na from the adjacent brain tissue. By applying an appropriate three-compartment equation to the kinetics of ^{24}Na$^+$ uptake into the perfusion fluid, Davson and Pollay (1963) and Davson and Segal (1970) showed that the initial steep rise in the ratio was a measure of rate of secretion of CSF, while the slower rise was governed by diffusion from the brain tissue.

Rate of CSF Production

The rate of production of CSF may be measured by injecting an indicator into the ventricles and measuring the rate of disappearance; clearly, the indicator must be chosen so that it does not pass into the bloodstream in the choroid plexuses, nor yet through the brain capillaries after diffusion into the brain tissue. Davson and Spaziani (1960) studied a comparable system, the aqueous humour of the eye; they injected sucrose and found that it disappeared at a rate that indicated a flow of aqueous humour equal to some 1% of the total volume per minute. Heisey *et al.*

(1962) applied the same principle to the CSF system, perfusing with an artificial CSF containing inulin as the indicator that would only leave the system by flow, loss to the blood being negligible. They obtained a value of 164 µl/min or, a more interesting value, a renewal rate of 0.65% per minute. The same basic technique has been applied to a variety of species, the indicator solute of choice being blue dextran, a chemically inert substance of molecular weight 10^6 daltons, and one that can be estimated with accuracy colorimetrically. The rates vary from one species to another in accordance with the sizes of their brains, that for the rat being 2.2 µl/min and for man 520 µl/min, but when the rates are expressed as percentage renewal, they do not differ greatly, namely from 0.65%/min for the goat to 0.37%/min for man.

Clearance

When a non-diffusive indicator, such as blue dextran, is included in the artificial CSF, the decrease in concentration of this substance as it passes through the ventricles, is a measure of dilution by the nascent CSF only because blue dextran diffuses at a negligible rate into the adjacent nerve tissue during the course of perfusion. If a substance that diffuses readily into the tissue and thence into blood in the choroid plexuses and blood in the brain capillaries and finally into brain cells is present in addition to blue dextran, then the concentration of this substance will be lower than that of dextran (Figure 1.54), and we may calculate a 'clearance' of the solute concerned which may be of value in assessing the permeability characteristics of the blood–brain and blood–CSF barriers.

The clearance is defined as the volume of perfusion fluid, of average concentration $C_{in} + C_{out}/2$, cleared of the solute per minute. It is given by

$$\text{clearance} = \frac{F_{in}(C_{in} - R_D C_{out})}{(C_{in} + C_{out})/2} \tag{1.50}$$

where C_{in} and C_{out} are the concentrations in the inflowing and outflowing artificial CSF, F_{in} is the rate of perfusion and R_D is the steady state value of C_{in}/C_{out} for the blue dextran. If the uptake into brain tissue is measured at the end of the perfusion, it is possible to divide the clearance into two fractions, namely the amount lost to the brain and the amount lost to the blood (Davson *et al.*, 1982). As an example it was found that the total loss of aspartate was 69 units, composed of 5.6 units to the brain and 63.4 units to the blood. The relative contributions of the choroid plexuses and the vessels of the brain tissue, of course, could not be assessed.

Active Transport out of the CSF

In this connection the discovery that the choroid plexuses not only secrete a fluid but also actually have a 'kidney-type' mechanism of actively removing certain solutes from it against concentration gradients, may well emphasize the role of the CSF as a sink that removes unwanted solutes from the brain. Davson (1956) noted

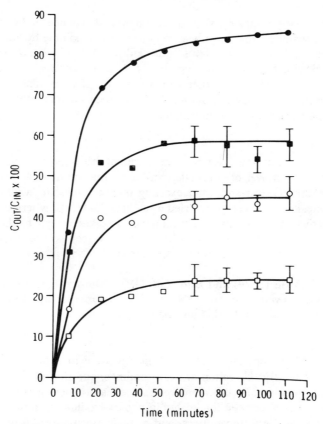

Figure 1.54 Ventriculocisternal perfusion of (■) [³H]-lysine, (○) [³H]-tryptophan, (□) [³H]-glycine and (●) Blue Dextran. Limits are s.e. Figures in parentheses, number of experiments. Limits for Blue Dextran less than ±1. Ordinates: $C_{out}/C_{in} \times 100$. Abscissae: Time in min. Points at midpoint at 15 min collection periods. From Davson *et al.* (1982)

that the kinetics of transport of the thiocyanate bromide and iodide ions across the blood–CSF barrier were quite anomalous, and he suggested that some metabolic event in the choroid plexuses was holding the level of these ions at very low levels in the CSF. Pappenheimer *et al.* (1961) studied clearance from the CSF of phenolsulphonephthaleine and Diodrast—two substances typically cleared by the kidney by a specific tubular secretory mechanism—when these solutes were included in an artificial CSF perfusing the goat's ventricular system, i.e. during ventriculocisternal perfusion. They found very high clearances and attributed these to an active transport from CSF to blood flowing in the choroid plexuses; and the uphill character of this transport was shown by Pollay and Davson (1963) when they maintained a higher concentration in the blood plasma than that in the perfusion fluid and showed that clearance continued. Para-aminohippurate and Diodrast are not naturally occurring substances, and their rapid clearance by the kidney is due to their utilizing a transport system that is concerned with removal of lipid-soluble materials that have been rendered water-soluble by being converted to glycosides, sulphates, etc. Thus, this 'kidney system', demonstrated in the choroid plexuses by the active uptake of p-aminohippurate, etc., may well represent a transport system that can assist the CSF to remove substances, produced in the brain, that have acquired the chemical character that enables them to use this particular transport mechanism.

Prostaglandins

Bito considered that the 'kidney system' might be important in the choroid plexuses in the removal of prostaglandins from the brain; thus, they would be liberated by the neurons and, after exerting their actions, they would have to be either chemically inactivated or carried away into the blood, where they would be rapidly inactivated by enzymes in the lungs. However, to get to the blood they would have to cross the blood–brain barrier (in reverse), so that a more effective way of removal might be by active transport from the CSF after diffusing into this fluid.

Bito and Davson (1974) and Bito et al. (1976) showed that prostaglandin $F_{2\alpha}$ was actively removed from the rabbit's CSF, a process that was inhibited by substances that inhibited the 'kidney system', e.g. probenecid.

Amine Metabolites

Serotonin (5-HT), dopamine and noradrenaline are central nervous transmitters, so that their fate after liberation at nerve endings, and that of their metabolites, have been of considerable clinical interest, since disturbances in the metabolism of these transmitters have been implicated in depressive illness. In the hope that the concentrations of these transmitters, and of their metabolites, in the CSF might prove of diagnostic value in assessing disturbances in the general handling by the central nervous system, a great deal of work has been devoted to measurements of these parameters. Except where the transmitter is primarily released in the spinal cord, the concentration in the lumbar fluid, usually the only fraction of the CSF available for study in human subjects, may well not reflect accurately changes that have occurred primarily in the brain; and a great deal of work has been carried out on experimental animals in which samples of ventricular, cisternal and lumbar fluid were compared.

Metabolic Pathways

Serotonin is converted by oxidative deamination to 5-hydroxyamino-acetic acid (5-HIAA). Dopamine is converted to 4-hydroxy-3-methyl-phenylacetic acid (homovanilic acid, HVA) by O-methyl and oxidative deamination. A minor metabolic pathway for noradrenaline is its conversion to vanillyl mandelic acid (VMA) and a major pathway to 3-methoxy-4-hydroxyphenyl-ethylene glycol (MOPEG or MHPG); about two-thirds of this in plasma is conjugated with sulphate (MHPG·SO_4). In the primate CSF, however, more than 80% is in the unconjugated form and in brain more than 90% (Elsworth et al., 1982).

Clearance of Metabolites

It is beyond the scope of this book to attempt a description of the various studies on clearance of transmitter metabolites from the central nervous system; the subject has been reviewed by Davson *et al.* (1987), and it must suffice to state that clearance mechanisms across the choroid plexuses certainly have been established for the sulphated conjugate of the noradrenaline metabolite, MHPG; the same is true of the serotonin metabolite, 5-HIAA (Ashcroft *et al.*, 1968), and the dopamine metabolite, HVA.

Blood–CSF Barrier to Polar Molecules

Highly water-soluble substances, such as sucrose or the sulphate ion, are often described as non-permeant to cells. This may be true of many individual cells, but where the blood–CSF and blood–brain barriers are concerned, there is a measurable transport from blood into the CSF and brain-tissue. The most probable mechanism of transport of, say, sucrose or mannitol, across these barriers is through 'leaky' intercellular junctions which behave as water-filled pores. If we confine attention to the blood–CSF barrier, we may note that penetration, when followed over a period of some hours, approaches a steady state with the concentration in the CSF only a fraction of that in the plasma. Figure 1.55 shows the uptake of sulphate from blood to CSF, and it is clear that a steady state value of C_{CSF}/C_{pl} equal to about 0.05 would be reached. The failure to reach an equilibrium state in which C_{CSF} is equal to C_{pl} follows from the fact that the system is a flowing one, new CSF entering the bulk of the CSF with a fraction of

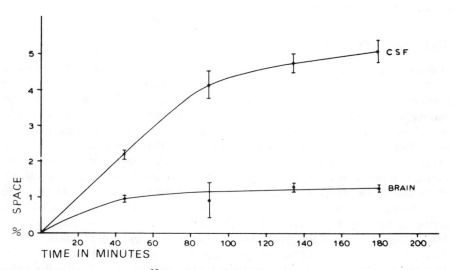

Figure 1.55 Penetration of $^{35}SO_4$ from blood into brain and CSF. Ordinate: Activity per g brain or CSF/Activity per g plasma–H_2O ($\times 100$). From Hollingsworth and Davson (1973)

the plasma concentration, namely rC_{pl}, and being drained away through channels that offer no impediment to CSF flow, namely the pores in the arachnoid villi. Thus, Equation (1.48) indicates that, so long as r is less than unity, K_{in} will be less than K_{out}, and at infinite time the steady-state value of C_{CSF}/C_{pl} will be less than unity. This is the situation with the sulphate ion, where the steady-state value is as low as about 0.05. Only when the contribution of the brain tissue, given by k_D, is sufficiently great will the steady-state ratio become equal to unity, as with the thioureas.

Locus of Penetration

The question arises as to the anatomical basis for the slow penetration of the barriers by these highly polar molecules, i.e. are there some interepithelial or interendothelial cell junctions that are not tight, or is there some pinocytotic vesicular transport process taking place? Lucchesi and Gosselin (1990) compared rates of penetration of polar molecules of increasing molecular weight, namely L-glucose, raffinose and inulin. They found that rates of penetration, measured by PS, were the same although, if free diffusion through large pores had been taking place, the value of PS should be inversely proportional to the square root of the molecular weight (Davson and Danielli, 1942). The authors concluded that penetration must be by way of vesicles; however, the same result would be obtained were penetration by way of bulk flow of fluid through large pores. Although the extracellular fluid of brain is stagnant compared with the CSF, there is no doubt, from Cserr's studies, that there is a definite, although slow, flow through the tissue to be ultimately drained through the CSF or lymphatic vessels associated with large blood vessels.

Sink Action of the CSF

When the penetration of very slowly penetrating substances into the brain tissue is studied, it is found that, as with the CSF, the steady-state approached after long periods of intravenous infusion is one in which the concentration in the extracellular space of the brain is much less than that in the CSF. This is clear from Figure 1.56, where it is seen that, as with the CSF, the concentration in brain water tends to a steady-state value very much less than that in the plasma. The brain extracellular fluid is, by contrast with the CSF, a stagnant fluid with a very slow turnover (Cserr *et al.*, 1981; Szentesvanyi *et al.*, 1984), so that an explanation of the low steady-state concentration applicable to the CSF cannot be extended to the situation in brain tissue. The actual explanation is given by the so-called 'sink action' of the CSF (Davson *et al.*, 1961); by this is meant the loss of solute from the brain tissue by virtue of the greater concentration in the extracellular fluid than in the CSF at any time during the approach to the steady state. The fact that diffusion from brain tissue to CSF is unrestricted means that the CSF will act as a sink to the brain tissue. The existence of a gradient from brain tissue to CSF is clear from Figure 1.56, and this is true of studies on simultaneous penetration of

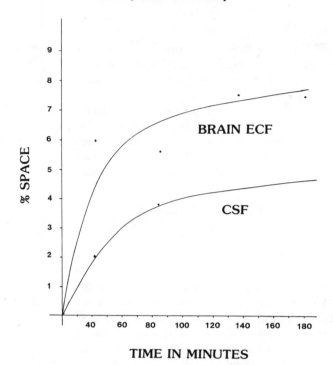

TIME IN MINUTES

Figure 1.56 The entry from the blood of $^{35}SO_4^{2-}$ into brain extracellular fluid and cerebrospinal fluid: brain space has been increased by 100/15 to allow for distribution in extracellular fluid only. Note that the level in brain extracellular fluid is still far below that in plasma and is above the level in CSF

sucrose (Oldendorf and Davson, 1967) and sulphate (Hollingsworth and Davson, 1973). Where rapidly penetrating substances are concerned, the sink action may not be manifest at the steady state because penetration of the blood–brain barrier and blood–CSF barrier is sufficiently rapid to level up any differences in concentration that occur during the approach to equilibrium. Nevertheless, there is a sink action, as Figure 1.35 (p. 61) shows, in which penetrations of the relatively lipid-soluble thiurea and ethylthiourea into CSF and brain tissue are plotted together. Here the brain concentration is not that in the extracellular fluid but that in the total brain water, so that the actual concentration in the extracellular fluid, which is important for exchanges with the CSF, must be considerably higher. The concentration in brain water is always higher than that in CSF, so that diffusion from brain to CSF must occur down the concentration gradient. It will be recalled that the kinetics of the blood–CSF barrier have invoked just such a diffusion from brain to CSF to account for the high rates of equilibration between blood and CSF that are found with lipid-soluble substances.

Physiological Significance

Physiologically, we may look at this sink action as a mechanism of clearing the brain of solutes that are formed by the cells and are 'unwanted'; thus, transmitters are synthesized by the neurons and released continuously. Special mechanisms exist within the tissue to dispose of them: e.g. with acetylcholine there is cholinesterase; with amines there is a special re-uptake mechanism in addition to enzymatic degradation with COMT and MAO. Nevertheless, an additional escape route may be of importance, and certainly the concentrations of such transmitters as dopamine and of the enzymatic degradation products such as homovanillic acid in the CSF reflect nervous activity in the brain or spinal cord.

The Blood–Brain and Blood–CSF Barriers

Similarity

It will be clear by now that the two barriers are very similar, and this similarity extends to the penetration of sugars and amino acids, these metabolites exhibiting Michaelis–Menten kinetica with respect to penetration into CSF. The physiological significance of this similarity is obvious; because of the easy communication between ventricles and subarachnoid spaces, on the one hand, and the brain tissue, on the other, if the brain is to be 'protected' by a barrier, this barrier must also control influx from blood to CSF.

.As we shall have occasion to emphasize later, this similarity between the barriers implies that the CSF and extracellular fluid of the brain and spinal cord are probably very similar in composition, so that the analysis of the CSF may provide important clues to the mode of control of a given solute in the extracellular fluid of the nervous tissue, as with ions such as Na^+, Cl^-, K^+, etc.

Multicompartmental Analysis

It will have become clear, by now, that a study of the blood–brain barrier must take account of the relations between the brain tissue and the CSF. Under given conditions the barriers have been treated separately, so that transfer coefficients for the blood–CSF and blood–brain barriers have been measured from experimental measurements of uptake against time, and as operational coefficients, telling us how the CSF or brain tissue will respond to transient changes in blood concentration, they are of obvious value. Nevertheless, because in many situations the relations between CSF and brain tissue have been ignored, accurate estimates of the permeability coefficients of solutes penetrating through one or other of the barriers have not been possible. The single-pass techniques largely avoid the necessity of considering the presence of the CSF when estimating permeability coefficients for the blood–brain barrier because of the short times involved. However, because of these short times, matters of seconds rather than minutes, these techniques exclude themselves from the study of a large number of physiologically important substances, such as peptides. Thus, kinetic analyses of transport from blood into brain, appropriate for long-term experiments lasting over periods of hours rather than seconds, are of great value but, because of their mathematical complexity, cannot be described in detail here, so a brief sketch is all that will be attempted.

Compartments

In a number of situations, the blood–brain barrier can be treated as a two-compartment system kinetically; nevertheless, as Patlak *et al.* (1983) have emphasized, the number of compartments is large, and their treatment in its general form applies to an indefinite number. However, basically, we can consider the blood plasma as one compartment, and then the extracellular fluid of the brain, the intracellular fluid of the brain cells and the CSF as three further compartments, making a four-compartment system the one that must be treated. The system can simplify to a two-compartment one when penetration from the blood into the various compartments is very rapid; thus, penetration into the brain of, say, ethylthiourea follows a two-compartment course because penetration into the CSF is rapid, and penetration into the cells of the brain is rapid, so that the limiting factor is, indeed, transport across the brain capillaries. With D-glucose, the studies of Lund-Andersen (1979) have shown that brain uptake follows a two-compartment process, and this is because uptake from extracellular space into the brain cells is so rapid that the limiting step in brain uptake is crossing the blood–brain barrier. Exchanges between extracellular fluid and CSF may well not complicate the situation because the penetration into the CSF is carrier-mediated, as with that of crossing the brain capillaries. The penetration of ^{24}Na into the brain was shown very early to be characterized by two-compartment kinetics (Davson, 1955); the reason for this was that the cells of the brain (so far as sodium was concerned) were a negligible compartment, reducing the number to three; next the rate of equilibration between blood and CSF, on the one hand, and blood and brain extracellular fluid, on the other, were about equal, so that exchanges between CSF and brain during the approach to equilibrium were negligible. Thus, the cerebral compartment was reduced to one. A more exact analysis by Welch (1969) and Davson and Welch (1971), using a mathematical treatment that involved all four compartments, showed that the error in treating the system as one of two compartments, so far as sodium was concerned, was negligible. With potassium, however, the studies of Davson (1955), Katzman and Leiderman (1953), Bradbury and Kleeman (1967) and Bradbury and Sarna (1977) have shown that a multicompartment treatment is necessary in which account is taken of uptake of ^{42}K by the large pool of potassium in the brain cells. Bradbury (1979) has summarized the estimates of a transfer coefficient from blood to brain based on the various treatments. The interesting feature is that the permeability of the blood–brain barrier to K^+ is probably some ten times that for Na^+ and Cl^- (Davson and Welch, 1971). Patlak *et al.* (1983) have provided a general mathematical treatment of a multicompartmental system in which, experimentally, the uptake of a solute by brain was measured at different times when the plasma concentration varied in a known manner; from this the unidirectional transfer coefficient could be deduced, i.e. when back-flux could be ignored. A specific application of the treatment to the uptake of alpha-aminoisobutyric acid (AIBA) was described by Blasberg *et al.* (1983).

Ventriculocisternal Perfusion

Patlak and Fenstermacher (1975) have shown that the permeability of the blood–brain barrier may be assessed by measurements of brain uptake when the solute of interest is dissolved in an artificial CSF that perfuses the ventricles. Thus, as Figure 1.57 illustrates, the solute diffuses into the extracellular space of the brain, but the rate at which its concentration will increase at different distances from the ventricle surface will depend on loss to the blood across the blood–brain barrier and loss to the brain cells. The successful mathematical analysis of the situation, so far as assessing the transfer coefficient for transport across the blood–brain barrier is concerned, demands that a steady state should be achieved. In this case the variation in concentration with distance from the ventricle follows the equation

$$C_x/C_0 = S\, e^{-\sqrt{(e^{-kp}/D_w)}x} \qquad\qquad (1.51)$$

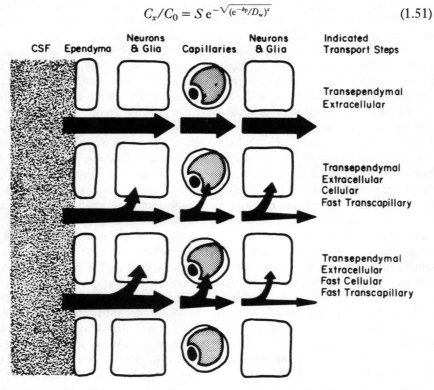

Figure 1.57 Several of the possible pathways within the brain tissue for a material introduced into the ventricular CSF. The arrows show the pathways, while their thickness indicates the relative importance of each pathway. From Fenstermacher *et al.* (1974)

Where C_x and C_0 are the concentrations in the tissue at the distance x from the ventricle and in the CSF, respectively; S is a proportionality constant; k_p is the capillary transfer coefficient with dimension t^{-1}; and D_w is the diffusion coefficient of the solute in water. Fenstermacher and Patlak (1975) deduced values of 0.046 $\min^{-1}$ for water, 0.0046 $\min^{-1}$ for urea and 0.04 $\min^{-1}$ for ethylene glycol, penetrating the caudate nucleus of the dog. Later Fenstermacher and Davson (1982) found a value of 0.02 $\min^{-1}$ for cycloleucine penetrating the rabbit's brain.

Active Transport of Ions

As we have indicated earlier, the composition of the CSF may well be similar to that of the extracellular fluid of the brain. Furthermore, there is no doubt, from the ionic composition of the CSF compared with that of blood plasma, that the CSF must be regarded as a secretion involving the active transport of Na^+, in the first place, and probably of many other ions such as K^+, Mg^{2+} and Cl^-.

The concentration of Na^+ in CSF is maintained by active processes, as demonstrated most strikingly by Davson and Segal (1970) in their study of inhibitors of Na^+ transport, while Wright's 1970) study of the isolated amphibian choroid plexus provided electrochemical evidence for active processes. It might be argued that the high concentration of Cl^- was a passive consequence of the active Na^+ transport; however, there is no doubt from the study of Bourke *et al.* (1970) and Abbott *et al.* (1971) that the concentration of Cl^- in the CSF is controlled by specific mechanisms that ensure that other anions do not take the place of Cl^- in the CSF.

For example Saito and Wright (1987) measured the internal concentration of Cl^- in choroidal epithelial cells at the same time as the potential difference across the apical membrane and showed that the concentration of Cl^- was greater than that demanded by an equilibrium distribution between CSF and internal contents, having regard to the potential difference; in other words, the concentration and potential indicated a force driving Cl^- from the stroma of the choroid plexus to the CSF.

Osmolality

The CSF, as finally secreted, is approximately isosmolal with blood plasma; and the choroidal epithelium has been likened to the epithelium of the proximal renal tubule, which transports an isosmotic fluid from the glomerular filtrate into the blood. As with the tubular epithelium, the clefts between adjacent cells exhibit the characteristic junctional complexes; these are located in the apical region of the cells, and include the zonula occludens, or tight junction, that effectively seals the intercellular space and restricts the permeability of the epithelium as a whole to lipid-insoluble molecules and ions.

So far as the analogy between renal tubular epithelium and choroidal epithelium is concerned, we must note that transport of fluid from the renal tubule is from the apical side of the epithelial cells to the basal, or serosal, side, whereas the flow of fluid in the choroid plexus takes place from the basal, or serosal, side to the apical side. According to the Diamond–Bossert (1967) model of active fluid transport, it is the intercellular cleft, sealed by the tight junction, that occupies an important role in both processes. In the case of fluid absorption, as with the renal tubule, Na^+ was actively transported into the cleft close to the tight junction, while with secretory epithelia, such as the choroidal epithelium, Na^+ was pumped out of the clefts into the cells, creating a flow of fluid in the opposite direction.

The Flow of Cerebrospinal Fluid

We may now consider in a little detail the mechanisms involved in control over the ionic composition of the CSF and, thus, of the extracellular fluid of the brain. If we concentrate, first, on the choroid plexus–CSF system, we must appreciate that the ionic transport mechanisms are closely related to the directed flow of fluid from the plasma side of the choroidal epithelial cell to the ventricular side. If the flow of fluid is to be induced osmotically, then Na^+ with its accompanying anions, Cl^- and HCO_3^- must be driven into the epithelial or 'barrier' cell and ejected into the ventricle, either directly across the ventricle-facing epithelial membrane, or less directly through the intercellular clefts. The driving force for bringing Na^+ into the cell will be the concentration gradient and also the membrane potential, both favouring flux from extracellular fluid to the cell interior. In addition, there is the active Cl^- influx described by Saito and Wright (1987). Flux out of the cell is presumably governed by the Na^+–K^+-ATPase-activated pump that is inhibited by cardiac glycosides, a process that, in effect, provides the energy for the movement of ions and fluid across the choroidal epithelium.

Inhibition

Because the flow of CSF is intimately linked with the active processes controlling ion movements across the choroid epithelium, inhibitors of the ionic movements will be reflected in changes in rate of secretion of the fluid as a whole.

Cardiac Glycosides

Of particular interest is the demonstration that the secretion of the CSF is inhibited by cardiac glycosides (Davson and Segal, 1970), drugs that are well established as inhibitors of the Na^+–K^+-ATPase complex involved in control over the Na^+–K^+ balance of the cell.

Localization

In many secretory epithelia this enzyme is localized to the basolateral membrane of the secreting cell (Ernst, 1975), i.e. to those parts of the cell membrane that are separated from the apex by tight junctions. Moreover, it has been further localized to the cytoplasmic side of the plasma membrane, conformably with the involvement of K^+-sensitive hydrolysis involved in the release of K^+ into the cytoplasm during the Na^+–K^+ exchange process. So far as the choroidal epithelium is concerned, however, there is little doubt, from the studies of Quinton *et al.* (1973) and Masuzawa *et al.* (1981) that the enzyme is located on the apical membranes. Thus, ^{3}H-labelled ouabain was found attached to the microvilli of choroidal epithelial cells after incubating the tissue in a medium containing radioactive probe.

Carbonic Anhydrase Inhibitors
A similar degree of inhibition of CSF secretion is given by the carbonic anhydrase inhibitor acetazolamide, or Diamox. This is associated with an inhibition of transport of ^{24}Na from blood to CSF. These effects have been attributed by Maren (1977) to the diminished rate of formation of bicarbonate ion, one of the components of the CSF. However, it has been suggested (e.g. Davson, 1967) that acetazolamide interferes with the active transport of Cl^- by its effect on the carriers responsible for this, rather than on any interference with synthesis of bicarbonate. Furosemide and bumetanide, also inhibitors of carbonic anhydrase, have smaller effects on the rate of CSF secretion (Vogh and Langham, 1981), which have been attributed to their less powerful inhibitory action on carbonic anhydrase.

Na$^+$-coupled Chloride Transport
The co-transport of Na^+ and an anion, such as Cl^-, is involved in the concentrating process of urine in the kidney loop of Henle, and so-called 'loop diuretics', such as bumetanide and furosemide, exert their action through an inhibition of the co-transporter involved in this process. Thus, although inhibitors of carbonic anhydrase, they most probably exert their effects on CSF production by an inhibition of transport of Na^+ and Cl^- into the choroidal epithelial cell. Johanson *et al.* (1990), working with isolated rat choroid plexuses, showed that bumetanide decreased uptake of Na^+ and Cl^- by the plexus by a maximal 45%; furosemide was nearly as effective. Acetazolamide significantly reduced uptake of Na^+ but not that of Cl^-, suggesting a different mechanism of action (Figure 1.58a, b).

Anion Exchange
We have already seen that the first transporter molecule to be isolated was that involved in the exchange of anions across the erythrocyte. This type of facilitated transport is by no means peculiar to the erythrocyte; its presence in any system is demonstrated by the inhibitory action of stilbenes, SITS and DIDS. Johanson *et al.* (1985) showed that SITS caused the choroidal epithelium to lose Cl^- and HCO_3^-, and later Deng and Johanson (1989) studied the effect of DIDS on anion fluxes in the choroid plexus of the intact rat. DIDS reduced the rate of flow of CSF by 29% and this was associated with a diminution of anion fluxes into the plexus. According to Saito and Wright (1987), the chloride ion is not at electrochemical equilibrium within the choroid plexus cell, being accumulated some two to three times above the level demanded by the concentration gradient and membrane potential. Apparently this accumulation process is inhibited by

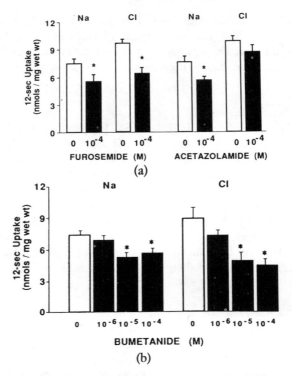

Figure 1.58 (a) Effect of bumetanide, an inhibitor of co-transport, on rate of uptake of Na and Cl by *in vitro* rat choroid plexus. Uptake is corrected for extracellular distribution. Open bars are vehicle (<1% ethanol) controls for drug (solid bars). Values are means ± s.e. for 7 or 8 CP tissues. *$P < 0.05$, bumetanide vs. vehicle control, by multiple-range test. Effects at 10^{-4} M are not statistically different from those at 10^{-5} M. (b) Effect of furosemide and acetazolamide on choroid plexus uptake of Na and Cl. Uptake is corrected for extracellular distribution. Open bars at controls; filled bars are 10^{-4} M drug in artificial cerebrospinal fluid (aCSF). Values are means ± s.e. for 7–9 tissues. *$P < 0.05$, drug vs. control by Student's *t* test. From Johanson *et al.* (1990)

furosemide applied to the basolateral side of the cell, emphasising the importance of the coupled cation plus anion transporter, while the inhibition due to disulphonic stilbenes, such as DIDS, reflects the inhibition of anion exchange.

Amiloride

This pyrazine diuretic was shown by Davson and Segal (1970) to inhibit rate of secretion of CSF and transport of ^{24}Na from blood to CSF. The mechanism of this action has been discussed by Murphy and Johanson (1989), the question at issue being whether a specific $Na^+–H^+$ exchange process was being inhibited or whether a less specific blocking of Na^+ channels in the cell membrane was responsible. They confirmed the inhibition of blood–CSF transport and showed that the Na^+ content of the cell was reduced. Because high doses were necessary to induce inhibition of transport (Davson and Segal had to administer the drug by close arterial injection to obtain effects), they concluded that amiloride was acting primarily on a Na^+-H^+ exchange transporter.

Acid–Base Changes

Alkalosis, either metabolic or respiratory, was long ago shown to reduce rate of secretion of CSF (Oppelt *et al.*, 1963), whereas acidosis had no effect. The significance of these results has been questioned, however, by Murphy and Johanson (1990), who have demonstrated an acidosis-induced decrease in transport into the choroid plexus from blood, attributable to an effect on Na^+-H^+ exchange, while Vogh *et al.* (1985) and Zloković *et al.* (1987a) have shown that the directly measured rate of secretion of CSF in rats and rabbits, using ventriculo-cisternal perfusion, can be reduced by about 10% if the artificial CSF perfusing the ventricles is acidified by addition of $AlCl_3$. Again, Murphy and Johanson (1989) have shown that acidosis reduces rate of transport of ^{22}Na into brain and CSF of rats by 18–25%, according to the severity of the acidosis.

Transposition to the Blood–Brain Barrier

Control of Extracellular Fluid

It is reasonable to assume that essentially the same mechanisms of control of ion concentrations pertain to both CSF and brain extracellular fluid, but the experimental study of the latter fluid is by no means easy. With microelectrodes it is possible to establish the concentration of, say, K^+ in the extracellular space of brain and this is, indeed, comparable with that in CSF, while the studies of Bradbury and Stulcova (1970) and Bradbury *et al.* (1972) indicate that the processes governing transport of K^+ into CSF are essentially similar to those governing transport into the extracellular fluid.

Sodium

Of fundamental importance is the control of sodium transport; so far as the CSF is concerned, there is no doubt that an active process, in which an ATPase is concerned, is involved, so that some 60% inhibition of secretion is achieved with ouabain. Whether the remaining transport is a passive one of filtration from the choroid plexus capillaries, and passive diffusion across the choroidal epithelium, is purely a matter of surmise; alternatively it has been argued that the remaining 40% is a fluid derived from the brain, i.e. it is brain extracellular fluid derived from the brain capillaries (Pollay and Curl, 1967). Studies of transport of ^{24}Na from blood to brain give equivocal results. In an early study Davson (1955) showed that the isotope infused into the plasma equilibrated with CSF and brain extracellular fluid at virtually identical rates; the passage of ^{24}Na into the CSF could be equated with secretion of CSF, in the sense that the rate of turnover of the CSF, measured as a turnover constant, or fractional renewal in unit time, was equal to the transfer coefficient of ^{24}Na for transport from blood to CSF, i.e. both had the value of 0.0041 min^{-1}. Treatment of the animal with ouabain or acetazolamide, both inhibitors of CSF secretion, reduced the rate of turnover of ^{24}Na in the expected fashion, so far as the CSF was concerned, but had practically no effect on turnover of ^{24}Na in the brain. Thus, there is a fundamental difference in the control mechanisms for CSF and brain, but this does not mean that the turnover of ^{24}Na in the brain is a purely passive affair; rather it may mean that the transport of the isotope, ^{24}Na, from blood to brain extracellular space is not accompanied by significant water movement, whereas the transport to CSF is. Thus, the transport from blood to brain may be a simple exchange of ^{24}Na for ^{23}Na, requiring no movement of water; by contrast, we know that the transport of ^{24}Na from blood to CSF is not associated with any exchange with ^{23}Na. On this view the brain extracellular fluid is virtually (but not completely: Cserr *et al.*, 1981) a stagnant fluid by contrast with the CSF, which flows at an easily measurable rate.

The fact that it is is nearly stagnant by no means indicates, however, that its composition is not controlled by active processes: a similar situation applies in most cells; their internal concentration of Na$^+$ is controlled by an active transport that 'pumps' the ion out of the cell as fast as it enters by passive diffusion, but there is no flow of fluid out of the cell because no osmotic changes need occur. Thus, once again, the analogy of the brain capillary membrane with a cell membrane becomes manifest, the extracellular fluid of brain being analogous with the intracellular fluid of a cell, but in this case the extracellular fluid has a high concentration of Na$^+$ rather than the high concentration of K$^+$ that is found in most cells. As the extracellular fluid of brain is the environment of neurons, the low concentration of K$^+$ and high concentration of Na$^+$ are, of course, necessary for development of resting and action potentials.

Chloride

We have seen that the transport of Cl$^-$ into the CSF is controlled by specific mechanisms. In a recent study Smith and Rapoport (1984) have shown that transport of Cl$^-$ across the blood–brain barrier of the rat followed Michaelis–Menten kinetics when the plasma level of Cl$^-$ was reduced to different values by intraperitoneal dialysis with the Cl$^-$ substitute isethionate. From their kinetics they deduced a K_m of 43 mM and a V_{max} of 2.5×10^{-3} μmol s^{-1} g^{-1}, while the transfer coefficients for unidirectional penetration of the brain were 2.0 and 5.8×10^{-5}/s at plasma concentrations of 120 and 0 mM, respectively.

Potassium

The concentration of this ion in the CSF is only some 60% of the plasma concentration, indicating that the active transport of Na^+ into the fluid from blood is associated with an active transport of K^+ in the opposite direction. By analogy, we may expect a similar system operating across the blood–brain barrier, leading to a relatively low concentration of K^+ in the brain extracellular space; determination of the actual concentration with K^+-sensitive electrodes has confirmed this [Note 7], while Bradbury and his colleagues have demonstrated essentially similar active processes taking place across the choroid plexuses and brain capillaries (Bradbury *et al.*, 1972).

Electrical Resistance

An essential feature of a membrane that enables efficient control over passage of electrolytes across it is that the permeability to the ions be held low, as otherwise the active process is dissipated by leakage through the membrane. The electrical resistance reflects this low permeability to ions, and it is interesting that the brain capillary has a very high resistance, namely $1300\ \Omega\ cm^2$ (Crone and Olesen, 1981), comparing with the frog mesenteric capillary endothelium of 1–$2\ \Omega\ cm^2$.

Isolated Capillaries

So far as the brain capillary is concerned, the work of Eisenberg and Suddith (1979) and Goldstein (1979) demonstrated an ouabain-sensitive transport of K^+ by isolated brain microvessels, and cytochemically ATPase was localized to the antiluminal border of the endothelial cell (Firth, 1977; Betz *et al.*, 1980; Vorbrodt *et al.*, 1982). In a quantitative study Harik *et al.* (1985) found the values of B_{max} and K_d given in Table 1.5 for the binding of labelled ouabain to brain microvessels and to cerebral cortex homogenate. In the choroid plexuses of the pig they found a B_{max} of 23.0 ± 3.8; this probably belonged to the epithelium, so that the specific activity of the enzyme in this tissue must be very large.

Table 1.5

	B_{max} (pmol/mg protein)	K_d (mM)
Cerebral cortex	38.3 ± 3.5	31.1 ± 6.0
Microvessels	10.6 ± 0.3	46.7 ± 3.4

Combined Model

Johanson *et al.* (1989) have presented a model (Figure 1.59) of the ion transport mechanisms across a 'barrier cell', which can be the choroidal epithelial cell or the brain capillary endothelial cell. On the apical side of the choroid plexus cell or the abluminal side of the capillary cell is located the Na^+–K^+-ATPase, sensitive to ouabain, while the three postulated Na^+ or Cl^- transporters are located on the basolateral or luminal sides of the cell. The extent to which the analogy between

CSF and brain extracellular fluid can be applied requires considerably more studies on the blood–brain barrier, either in the intact animal or on isolated brain capillaries or explants.

More General Model

The model presented by Johanson illustrated by Figure 1.59 indicates the mechanisms controlling the ionic composition of, primarily, the CSF, but since this fluid, because of its close diffusional relations with the extracellular fluid of the central nervous tissue, must have a similar constitution to this, the model describing control of the composition of the CSF must, necessarily, represent a model of the control of the composition of the extracellular fluid of the nervous tissue, exerted, this time, by the capillaries of this tissue whose membranes are typical of epithelium. A model designed to represent the factors operating across the blood–brain barrier, i.e. across the capillaries of the central nervous tissue, may therefore by appropriately presented here. Figure 1.60, from Betz *et al.* (1980), illustrates the location of a number of control mechanisms in the capillary of nervous tissue. The model emphasizes the asymmetry of the capillary membrane, the Na^+-dependent active process that transports alanine and other amino acids being located on the abluminal surface.

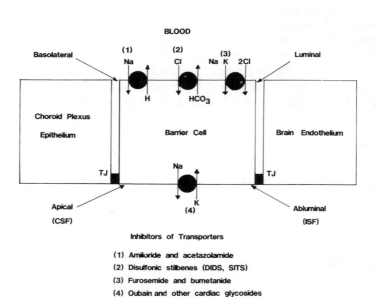

Figure 1.59 The ion transport systems at the blood–CSF (choroid plexus) and blood–brain barriers. Sodium is transported into the barrier cell by secondary active transport (1), is inhibited by amiloride and acetazolamide, (2) by DIDS and SIT, (3) by furosemide and bumetanide and (4) by oubain and other cardiac glycosides. TJ, tight junction; ISF, interstitial fluid. From Johanson *et al.* (1989)

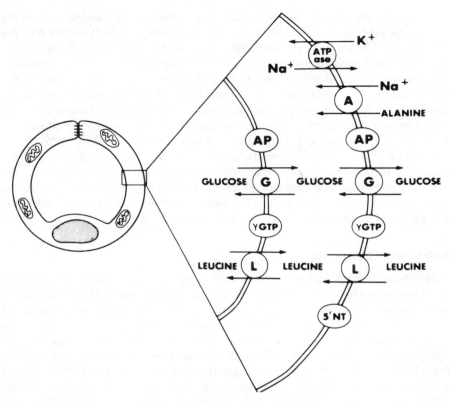

Figure 1.60 Polar model of brain capillary endothelial cell. The proposed distribution of enzyme and transport activities between the luminal and antiluminal membranes is shown in the expanded view of the capillary membrane. ATPase, Na^+, K^+-ATPase: A, A system for neutral amino acids; AP, alkaline phosphatase: G, glucose carrier: GTP, γ-glutamyl transpeptidase: L, L system for neutral amino acids; 5'-NT, 5'-nucleotidase. From Betz *et al.* (1980)

Cerebral Oedema

The control over the concentration of Na^+ in the extracellular fluid of the brain is of great interest, because movements of this ion, with its accompanying anions, govern the amount of water in any given compartment. In connective tissue there is no specific local control over the transport of this and similar ions into the extracellular spaces, because the capillaries are very highly permeable to non-colloidal solutes, and the control of the fluid balance between blood and connective tissue is brought about predominantly by the concentration of plasma proteins and the capillary pressure, according to the well-known Starling principle. Thus, oedema of connective tissue occurs when the balance between colloid osmotic and hydrostatic forces is disturbed; such a disturbance is not necessarily injurious to the tissue, so that quite large changes in volume can occur physiologically and reversibly. With the brain, enclosed in an indistensible box, the situation is different; and we may look on the control over electrolyte exchange across the brain capillaries as a necessary mechanism that permits the maintenance of a constant brain volume in spite of large fluctuations in the composition of the blood plasma. Thus, in the absence of control through low permeability and active transport, the free exchanges of Na^+ across the capillary endothelium of the brain would immediately set free the processes that allow easy changes in extracellular fluid volume through changes in plasma colloid–osmotic or capillary pressure.

Cerebral oedema does occur pathologically; and this can be attributed, not to a change in plasma composition or capillary pressure, but to a toxic action on the blood–brain barrier as a result of which the control over electrolyte movements from blood to extracellular space is impaired. In other words, cerebral oedema is due primarily to a *breakdown of the blood–brain barrier*.

Iodide and Thiocyanate

To continue with the analogy between control mechanisms across the blood–CSF and blood–brain barriers, we may recall that the choroid plexuses have been shown to be capable of active removal of solutes into the blood against gradients of concentration; this has been especially manifest with the iodide and thiocyanate ions. Isolated choroid plexuses will actually accumulate these ions (Welch, 1962a, b) from their external medium. Active transport across the capillaries of the brain has been harder to demonstrate, but the studies of Bito *et al.* (1966), Ahmed and Van Harreveld (1969) and Davson and Hollingsworth (1973) have left no doubt that the capillaries of the brain co-operate with the choroid plexuses in excluding iodide and thiocyanate, and, to a lesser extent, bromide, from access from the blood.

Amino Acids

The concentrations of most amino acids, especially those that exert a transmitter function, such as glycine and glutamic acid, are held at a low value in the CSF, and there is no doubt from studies with non-metabolizable amino acids, such as cycloleucine and AIBA, that these low concentrations are not due to utilization by the adjacent nervous tissue (Davson *et al.*, 1986). Definite proof that an amino acid, such as glycine, may be actively transported out of the brain across the brain capillaries has been difficult to establish; however, Davson *et al.* (1982) have shown that, when the ventricular system was perfused with a fixed concentration of [^{3}H]-glycine and the blood level of this labelled material was held above that in the perfusion fluid, absorption from the perfusion fluid was maintained (Figure 1.61). This was true of both glycine and cycloleucine, so that the low concentrations of amino acids in the CSF may well be the consequence of active processes that are primarily concerned with removing transmitters from the nervous tissue; because of the similarity in structure, a system designed to exclude these amino acids might

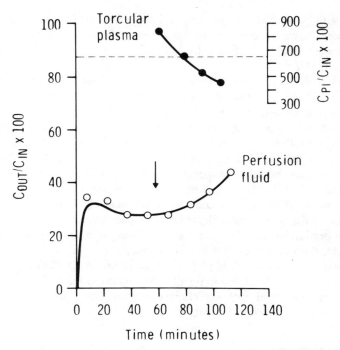

Figure 1.61 The effect of establishing a high activity of $[^3H]$-glycine in the plasma on clearance of $[^3H]$-glycine from the ventricles. At the arrow, the intracarotid infusion was begun. Left-hand ordinates: $C_{out}/C_{in} \times 100$. Right-hand ordinates: radioactivity in plasma as percentage of that in the entering perfusion fluid, C_{in}. Abscissae: time in min. The dashed line represents the value of $C_{out}/C_{in} \times 100$ expected in absence of clearance, determined by Blue Dextran. From Davson *et al.* (1982)

well fail to exclude other amino acids whose presence in the nervous tissue is not a nuisance. In fact, of course, all the amino acids that cannot be synthesized by the brain cells—the essential amino acids—must cross the blood–brain barrier and be present at suitable concentrations in the extracellular fluid. These concentrations, however, are lower than would be achieved by a purely passive diffusion across the blood–brain barrier, and this, we may imagine, is due to the presence of this excluding mechanism that keeps transmitter amino acids out of the brain, and, because of its failure to exhibit complete specificity to the amino acids that are to be excluded, tends to exclude the essential amino acids as well.

Glucose

The same situation may well prevail with regard to the very essential metabolite glucose. The concentration in the CSF is only some 65% of the plasma concentration, and it has been argued that this low concentration is due to utilization by the brain cells, so that transport from the blood to the brain cannot keep pace with the demands of the cells; the brain thus acts as a drain on the CSF. The evidence, however, does not favour this hypothesis, and there is little doubt that the glucose level in CSF is actively regulated at a lower concentration than that in plasma.

Thus, when discussing the relations between CSF and the brain extracellular fluid, Davson (1958) pointed out that, if the low concentration of glucose in the CSF were due to losses to the brain tissue because of utilization, the concentration in CSF should vary according to its position in the ventriculosubarachnoid system, being highest in the ventricles, where it is just formed with, presumably, a concentration equal to that in plasma, and falling as it passed through the ventricles into the subarachnoid spaces. Yet analyses of CSF taken from different locations along the CSF axis failed to reveal significant differences in concentration. Thus, we must assume that the concentration of glucose in CSF is about the same as that in the brain extracellular fluid, namely some 65% of that in plasma. The concentration in the brain extracellular fluid might well be low because of utilization by the brain cells, but the low concentration in the CSF cannot be a consequence of this; the choroid plexuses must be secreting a fluid with a glucose concentration some 65% of that in the plasma, and the studies of Deane and Segal (1985) on the perfused isolated choroid plexus have amply confirmed this hypothesis, as we shall see in Chapter 2.

Homoeostatic Mechanism

In discussing this problem, Davson (1976) suggested that the important feature of the glucose concentration in the extracellular fluid of brain was to maintain this constant, since the brain cells utilized glucose at a rate that was governed entirely by the concentration presented to them: a high concentration of glucose in the extracellular fluid would lead to an unnecessary glucose consumption; too low a concentration would lead to neuronal deficits. Thus, if a constant concentration must be maintained, the question becomes, what should the concentration be? When designing a water-bath that will maintain a constant temperature, the experimenter decides on a temperature that is some degrees different from the laboratory temperature; if he is employing a heating device to maintain constancy, then he chooses a temperature below the laboratory temperature, so that the effects of changed laboratory temperature are rapidly transmitted to the heating apparatus, and the disturbance from equilibrium is restored by onset of the heat. If cooling is the means of regulation, then a temperature above that of the laboratory is chosen, so that any increase in laboratory temperature is signalled rapidly and the cooling process is initiated. Choosing a bath temperature about equal to the usual laboratory temperature is not recommended, because a change in laboratory temperature takes a long time, now, to give the signal for a change in heat input or output.

If we transpose this analogy to the situation with respect to concentration of sugar in the CSF, and so in the brain extracellular fluid, it may well be that a better homoeostasis will be achieved if the steady level aimed at is either higher than, or lower than, the concentration in the plasma. With glucose it appears that a lower concentration has been chosen and the Michaelis–Menten parameters are such that changes in plasma concentration will have a strong influence on the flux coefficients. The situation may well be the same with amino acids, the level of each one in the CSF and extracellular fluid of the brain being governed by an active process holding the concentration at a lower level from that in plasma, but with influx and efflux coefficients governed by Michaelis–Menten affinity coefficients that allow of rapid adjustments of the influx or efflux rates, governed by fluctuations in plasma concentration.

Thus, in the kinetic treatment of fluxes of amino acids into the brain employed by Pardridge, Michaelis–Menten kinetics have been applied, but no thought has been given to the existence of active processes that determine the final steady-state level of the amino acid in the CSF or brain extracellular space. Clearly, there is room for a great deal of experimental research on the exchanges of amino acids, sugars and fatty acids between blood and CSF and blood and brain extracellular space—experiments that will assess the role of active transport, i.e. an asymmetrical mode of transport, in which passage from one side to the other may be different from passage in the opposite direction.

Enzymatic Contributions to the Blood–Brain Barrier

The basic mechanism of the blood–brain barrier consists in a restricted permeability to lipid-insoluble substances, associated with facilitated transport of certain preferred solutes, achieved by its specialized capillaries whose lining membranes behave like epithelia, their intercellular clefts being sealed by tight junctions. An additional barrier to passage from blood to nervous tissue could be provided by enzyme systems that altered the solutes in question, thereby reducing the chance of their reaching the nervous tissue.

Transmitters

Thus, the barrier to transmitters such as noradrenaline or dopamine is high, owing to their low lipid-solubility; this barrier is enhanced, however, by enzymatic degradation within the capillary endothelial cells. The enzymes, namely monoamine oxidase (MAO) and catechol-O-methyl transferase (COMT), are present in the capillary endothelial cells (Hardebo *et al.*, 1980), and, by breaking down any monoamine entering them from the blood side, contribute to the barrier. When these enzymes are inhibited, the capillary endothelial cells accumulate noradrenaline.

L-DOPA Trapping Mechanism

L-DOPA is a lipid-soluble precursor of dopamine and, as such, it can cross the blood–brain barrier. However, there is an enzymatic trapping mechanism that restricts its passage from blood to nervous tissue. Bertler and his colleagues (Bertler *et al.*, 1963, 1966) showed that, because of the presence of amino acid decarboxylase in the endothelial cells of the brain capillary, intravenously administered L-DOPA was converted to the lipid-insoluble dopamine, where it was trapped.

Parkinsonism

Clinically it has been found desirable to transport dopamine from blood to the central nervous system, as in the treatment of Parkinsonism; dopamine is prevented from crossing the blood–brain barrier directly by its low permeability, but, because its precursor, L-DOPA, crosses the barrier easily, this has been administered, but, as we have seen above, the trapping mechanism in the brain capillaries represents an obstacle. Hardebo *et al.* (1979) made use of the fact that intravenously administered carbidopa (α-methyl-DOPA hydrazine), a decarboxylase inhibitor, inhibited the enzyme, amino acid decarboxylase in the blood vessels, thereby allowing L-DOPA to pass through the blood–brain barrier unchanged; it did not inhibit the enzyme in the tissue, however, so that, having crossed the blood–brain barrier as L-DOPA, it was converted to dopamine, where it could exert its action. The high concentration of the decarboxylase in the brain microvessels was demonstrated by Hardebo *et al.* (1980); there was significant MAO and COMT activity in these vessels too, but by no means so great as in whole brain, in contrast to the situation with the aromatic L-amino acid decarboxylase.

Xenobiotic Enzymes

Recently it has been shown that isolated brain microvessels contain certain drug-metabolizing enzymes. Gherst-Egea *et al.* (1988) compared the activities in whole brain and in isolated brain microvessels of four lipophilic xenobiotic metabolizing enzymes, i.e. enzymes that inactivated lipophilic drugs that penetrated the blood–brain barrier easily. Of the four studied, epoxide hydroxylase had five times the activity of whole brain tissue in the isolated brain microvessels, and the activity of 1-naphthol-UDP-glucuronyl transferase in the microvessels was some fifteen times that in the whole brain tissue. The authors suggested that these enzymes might protect the nervous tissue from the deleterious action of extraneous lipophilic substances.

Breakdown of the Blood–Brain Barrier

The breakdown of the barrier under pathological or experimental conditions was described by the classical workers by a staining of the brain tissue by intravenously administered trypan blue; and essentially the larger number of more recent studies have involved the same basic principle, substituting for trypan blue Evans blue-labelled plasma albumin, if light-microscopic studies were undertaken, or horseradish peroxidase if electron microscopy was involved. These essentially qualitative studies relied, consequently, on a gross change in permeability of the brain capillary, so gross as to permit the diffusion of very large molecules across its endothelium. More subtle alterations would have to be measured by changes in the permeability coefficients to smaller molecules or ions, as in the studies of Bakay and Lindberg (1949) on ^{32}P-labelled inorganic phosphate, and Cameron *et al.* (1969) on ^{14}C-labelled sucrose.

Modes of Breakdown

The insults to the brain that cause a breakdown of the barrier and that have been employed experimentally are numerous; chief among these has been the 'cold lesion' involving application of intense cold to the brain surface through a cryogenic probe; the induction of anoxia by unilateral ligation of the blood supply to the brain; and, most recently, the intravenous injection of a hypertonic solution of a non-penetrant solute, such as L-arabinose or mannitol. This last method is of most practical interest, since the breakdown of the barrier—the so-called 'opening of the barrier'—is reversible, and it has been assumed that the cause of the breakdown is the shrinkage of the endothelial cells of the brain capillary that leads to an opening of the previously closed intercellular clefts, i.e. opening of tight junctions as illustrated by Figure 1.62, from Rapoport *et al.* (1972).

Osmotic Opening of the Barrier

The phenomenon is of practical interest, since it is possible to introduce drugs that would not normally cross the blood–brain barrier into the brain by a preliminary hyperosmolal injection. Neuwelt and Rapoport (1983) have discussed the possible

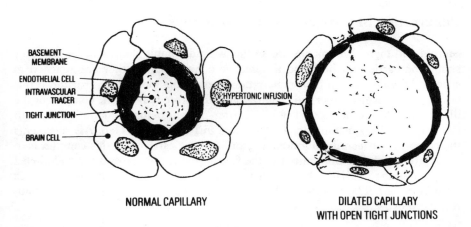

NORMAL CAPILLARY

DILATED CAPILLARY WITH OPEN TIGHT JUNCTIONS

Figure 1.62 Illustrating opening of tight junctions of the blood–brain barrier through hyperosmolal solutions. From Rapoport *et al.* (1972)

value of the technique in introducing chemotherapeutic drugs into the brain tissue; and we may quote the work of Greig *et al.* (1988) in which interferon-alpha was caused to penetrate the brain of the rat by previous injection of hypertonic arabinose. A great advantage provided by this technique is that the breakdown of the barrier is reversible, so that the drug, introduced into the brain-tissue, becomes 'locked in', owing to the returning impermeability of the blood–brain barrier.

Hypertensive Breakdown

Experimental hypertension induced by, for example, intracarotid injection of blood (Rapoport, 1976) causes a transient breakdown of the blood–brain barrier; in rats the mean pressure had to be raised to 180 mmHg (Hardebo and Nilsson, 1981); the rise in pressure must be abrupt (Häggendal and Johansson, 1972), and the critical pressure to obtain breakdown varies with the species. Ziylan (1984) found a pressure of 160 mmHg for the rabbit, compared with 240 mmHg in cats and dogs. It is likely that the cause of breakdown is opening of interendothelial clefts, as with osmotically induced breakdown, since the effects were additive (Hardebo, 1980).

Morphology of Breakdown

The morphological interpretation of the barrier opening suggested by Rapoport has, however, been questioned (Brightman, 1977; Farrell and Shivers, 1984) and, before discussing the matter further, it would be profitable to consider the possibility that large lipid-insoluble molecules, such as proteins and peptides, may, indeed, cross the blood–brain barrier normally. The matter will be dealt with more thoroughly in Chapter 3; here we need only consider it in general terms.

Penetration of Carrier-bound Hormones

Steroid and thyroid hormones are so highly lipid-soluble that, in order that they should be carried in the blood in effective concentrations, they are attached to specific proteins, so that their penetration through the blood–brain barrier, if this occurs, must involve either the penetration of the protein–hormone complex or the dissociation of the hormone from its carrier-protein before penetration through the brain capillary membrane, as illustrated in Figure 1.63. Here AL represents the complex between the hormone (ligand) and the carrier (A); this complex is in equilibrium with free hormone, L_F; the free hormone then crosses the endothelial cell membrane (BBB), when it may then be taken up by appropriate cells (sequestration). The binding of A to L is measured by the dissociation constant, K_d, given by

$$K_d = \frac{[A]\,[L]}{[AL]} \qquad (1.52)$$

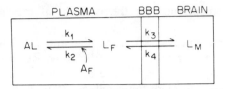

Figure 1.63 A compartmental model portrays the transport of protein-bound ligands into brain *in vivo* during passage of the bolus tracer. The brain endothelial wall, i.e. the BBB, separates the plasma and brain compartments. AL, protein–ligand complex; L_F, free ligand in the plasma compartment; L_M, free ligand in the brain compartment. Since plasma proteins do not cross the BBB, the transport of protein-bound ligands into the brain occurs via a free intermediate mechanism which involves an obligatory dissociation of protein-bound ligand into the free intermediate state before transmembrane transport. From Pardridge and Landaw (1984)

Thus, the greater the value of K_d the greater will be the concentration of free A for any given concentrations of binding protein and hormone.

In vitro and *in vivo* K_d

It has usually been assumed that the dissociation constant, measured *in vitro* by dialysing the carrier-plus-hormone against an aqueous medium through a membrane impermeable to the carrier complex, would apply to the situation *in vivo*, i.e. that passage through the capillaries did not affect K_d. The systematic studies of Pardridge and his colleagues (1979–1981; 1984; 1987), in which the effects of carrier-protein were varied, permitted estimates of K_d from the *in vivo* measurements, and it appeared that the dissociation constants were higher *in vivo* than *in vitro*; apparently some change in the character of the carrier took place in the capillary which allowed the ligand to free itself from the carrier and be available for transport across the endothelial membrane. Some comparisons are shown in Table 1.6, where it will be seen that the differences can be very great and, if

Table 1.6 Comparison of plasma protein dissociation constants *in vivo* in the brain capillary and *in vitro*. From Pardridge and Landaw (1984)

Plasma protein	Ligand	In vitro $K_d{}^a$ (μM)	In vivo $K_d{}^b$ (μM)
Albumin	Propranolol	290 ± 30	220 ± 40
	Testosterone	53 ± 1	$2,520 \pm 710$
	Corticosterone	260 ± 10	$1,330 \pm 90$
	Dihydrotestosterone	53 ± 6	830 ± 140
	Oestradiol	23 ± 1	710 ± 100
	T_3	4.7 ± 0.1	46 ± 4
Orosomucoid	Propranolol	3.3 ± 0.1	19 ± 4

[a] Data are mean $\pm$ s.e.
[b] Estimates $\pm$ s.e. from case I non-linear regression fits.

correct, of obvious importance for the carriage of the hormones across the blood–brain barrier.

In assessing the apparent K_d, K_d^a, Pardridge and Landaw (1984) applied the equation for capillary permeability derived by Kety, Renkin and Crone in their studies [Note 8], namely $E = 1 - e^{PS/F}$, where E is the extraction of the solute from the plasma during a pass through the capillary, PS is the permeability $\times$ surface area product, and F is the blood flow. Their equivalent equation was

$$E_t = 1 - e^{\dfrac{-k_3\bar{t}}{1 + A_F/K_d^a}} \tag{1.53}$$

where E_t is the unidirectional extraction constant of the hormone, k_3 is the rate-constant (s^{-1}) for hormone transport through the blood–brain barrier in the direction blood-to-brain, $\bar{t}$ is the mean brain capillary transit time and A_F is the concentration of unoccupied carrier-binding sites. When there is no plasma binding, the equation becomes

$$E = 1 - e^{-k_3 t} \tag{1.54}$$

where $k_3\bar{t} = PS/F$, since, by definition, $PS = k_3 V_p$ and $F = V_p/\bar{t}$, where V_p is the capillary volume (ml per gram brain).

To test the hypothesis that K_d was different from the *in vitro* K_d, Equation (1.53) was fitted to the curves relating extraction versus carrier-protein concentration by regression analysis, assuming that K_d was variable, and again when K_d was fixed by the *in vitro* determination. The better fit was obtained using the *in vivo* values of K_d which were equated with the ratio k_1/k_2 of Figure 1.63.

Penetration of Large Molecules

Facilitated transport that permits the passage of highly lipid-insoluble molecules to cross biological membranes is, as we have seen, a feature of the blood–brain barrier, permitting the passage of amino acids, sugars and fatty acids, among other metabolities, from blood to brain parenchyma. The special channels available for this form of transport are comparable in diameter with those of the penetrating molecules, so that it is unlikely that the same mechanism would be available for much larger molecules, such as proteins and polysaccharides.

Transcytosis

When a dissociation reaction is not available to enable a compound to enter the cell and pass through it, then a process of engulfment of the large molecule by an invagination of the cell membrane—*endocytosis*—may take place. The endocytosed molecule is carried in the vesicle formed by pinching off the invaginated membrane, and finally ejected from the cell by the opposite process of *exocytosis* (Figure 1.64). The extent to which this process takes place, if at all, across the central nervous tissue is a matter of dispute.

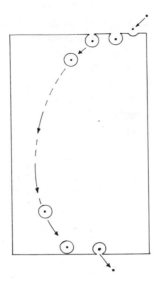

Figure 1.64 A model of transcytosis. The molecule is engulfed by an invagination of the cell membrane—endocytosis. The molecule is then carried across the cytoplasm in a vesicle formed by the pinching off of the invaginated membrane. The vesicle then fuses with the opposite side of the cell and is ejected—exocytosis

An alternative mechanism might be the formation of transcellular pores by the fusion of vesicles, themselves formed by endocytosis. These pores would be transient and thus difficult to envisage ultrastructurally. The subject has been critically reviewed by Broadwell (1989), who has emphasized the weakness of a great deal of the evidence supposedly favouring either the formation of transient channels or the actual transport of large molecules through the capillary endothelial cells by transcytosis.

Endocytosis

The phenomenon of endocytosis by animal cells has long been established and various modes have been differentiated. Thus, we have a purely non-specific endocytosis, as seen when an amoeba engulfs a solid particle, such as a latex bead, a process that requires no specific 'recognition' of the particle to be absorbed. Experimentally this may be studied by the endocytosis of the iron particle, ferritin, which is sufficiently electron-dense to be demonstrable by the electron microscope, or, if radioactively labelled, by autoradiography. Another class, described as *adsorptive endocytosis*, relies on an adsorptive interaction between the particle and the surface of the cell membrane; thus, cell membranes contain glycoproteins on their surface, and it is found that certain lectins [Note 9] have affinity for the sugar residues on these glycoproteins. For example, the lectin wheat-germ agglutinin (WGA) has an affinity for the neuraminic acid residues, while another lectin, ricin, has an affinity for the D-galactose residue, and phytohaemagglutinin for the *N*-acetylgalactosamine residue. These lectins are internalized by endocytosis, a process that can be followed in the electron microscope by labelling the lectins with horseradish peroxidase, which, by an appropriate chemical reaction, can be localized as an electron-dense material. Finally, there is a more specific form of endocytosis involving specific receptors for the endocytosed molecule, receptors that are located in the cell membrane and accumulate in clathyrin-coated pits in this membrane. An example is provided by the iron-carrying protein, transferrin; the iron required for synthesis of haemoglobin, for example, is absorbed by reticulocytes by virtue of their transferrin receptors in the coated pits. The pinched-off 'coated vesicles' are then passed on to the synthetic machinery and Golgi apparatus, and the receptor, plus the transferrin, are recycled (Goldstein *et al.*, 1985).

Exocytosis

In special instances, as with a liver cell, the endocytosed molecule may have to be passed out of the cell intact into a bile canaliculus; in which case the process involves the opposite to endocytosis, namely exocytosis. Thus, the complete process is described as *transcytosis*.

Connective Tissue Capillaries

Passage of large molecules across the capillaries of connective tissue is considered to represent passage through large pores constituted by the interstitium of the intercellular clefts, although it was argued for many years by Palade that the transport of proteins and fluid through the capillary involved engulfment of plasma into vesicles, which are apparently numerous in connective tissue capillaries, with their subsequent exocytosis at the abluminal, or tissue face of the capillary. This hypothesis, of doubtful credibility from the first, has now been finally abandoned, and the more obvious alternative, namely a passage between the capillary endothelial cells along their intercellular clefts, has been accepted (Frokjaer-Jensen, 1980; Bundgaard *et al.*, 1983). Where very large molecules are concerned, such as beta-lipoprotein, with a molecular weight of some 1 300 000, there is a definite escape from the connective tissue capillary, since the protein is found in lymph. These large molecules might escape through exceptionally large pores, but transport by transcytosis is a possibility. Certainly, when ferritin particles are injected into the blood, they are seen in vesicles within the capillary cell cytoplasm (Bruns and Palade, 1968).

The Central Nervous System Capillary

As we have seen, the central nervous system capillary differs fundamentally from that of connective tissue, the intercellular clefts being sealed by true tight junctions, so that small peptide or protein molecules, such as horseradish peroxidase or microperoxidase, are held up at the junctions and accumulate on the luminal side of the capillary cleft. If it may be shown that there is a significant transport of a protein, such as transferrin or insulin, across the blood–brain barrier, then it is reasonable to postulate a transcytotic mechanism of transport, passage through intercellular clefts being forbidden by the tight junctions. The evidence relating to the transport of large molecules, such as immunoglobulins, from blood to brain tissue will be discussed in its appropriate context (Chapter 3), so we need mention here only a few findings supporting the general concept.

Binding to Capillary Membrane

If, say, insulin is transported by a specific transcytotic mechanism, we may expect to measure a specific binding of this polypeptide to the brain capillary membrane. Frank and Pardridge (1987) have shown just such a binding of labelled insulin to isolated brain capillaries, a binding that was reduced competitively by adding unlabelled insulin to the medium: the K_a for this high-affinity binding was 2.3 ± 0.3 mM^{-1}. Half-maximal reduction in binding was achieved at 1.7 nM insulin. Pardridge *et al.* (1985) isolated a membrane-bound protein with molecular weight of 127 kD from brain capillaries which may have been responsible for this specific adsorption. Evidence for a process of exocytosis by isolated capillary could not be obtained, perhaps because the process requires metabolic energy which the isolated capillary cannot supply (Pan and Johnstone, 1984). By infusing labelled insulin and albumin into the carotid artery of the rabbit and subsequent analysis of brain, together with radioautography to assess the location of any protein taken up, Duffy and Pardridge (1987) showed that a preferential passage of insulin, as opposed to serum alubumin, occurred from blood into brain. Thus, a transport across the blood–brain barrier was demonstrated, but of course a transcytotic mechanism was not.

Wheat-germ Agglutinin–Horseradish Peroxidase

Broadwell *et al.* (1988) profited by the known adsorptive endocytosis of lectins into cells; they labelled wheat-germ agglutinin (WGA) with horseradish peroxidase and, after intravenous injection, examined the capillary endothelium of brain taken from different regions. The brain endothelial cells endocytosed the complex, transporting it in vesicles to the Golgi complex where it appeared in the cytoplasmic region described by Novikoff *et al.* (1975) as GERL (Golgi-Endoplasmic-Reticulum-Lysosomes), an acid-phosphatase reactive structure, which Novikoff considered to be a specialized region of the smooth endoplasmic recticulum, continuous with the rough-surfaced endoplasmic reticulum, and concerned with the formation of lysosomes. If Griffiths and Simons (1986) are correct, this region is better described as part of the Golgi complex and independent of the endoplasmic reticulum. As illustrated by Figure 1.65, it represents the final locus of processing of proteins synthesized by the endoplasmic reticulum, and may be called the trans-Golgi network (TGN). As the final region of the Golgi membrane system involved in packaging proteins ready for transport elsewhere, it might well be involved in any transcytotic process. Thus, the

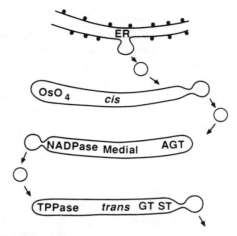

Figure 1.65 Prevailing model of the Golgi complex. The major feature is the presence of three compartments through which transit proteins move sequentially. The cytochemical activities and the specific functions ascribed to the compartments are shown. The model proposes that proteins move from one station to the next by vesicular transport. AGT, *N*-acetylglucosamine-transferase I; GT, galactosyl transferase; ST, sialyl transferase; OsO_4, reduced osmium tetroxide; NADPase, nicotinamide adenine dinucleotide phosphatase; TPPase, thiamine pyrophosphatase. From Griffiths and Simons (1986)

membranous vesicles that are available for transporting material synthesized by the cell might also be used as vehicles for material adventitiously introduced into the cell by endocytosis; hence, this region might well be the region for equipping the endocytosed material for exocytosis.

Golgi Vesicles

That the Golgi vesicles involved in exocytosis of previously synthesized protein may also be involved in the exocytosis of previously endocytosed material was demonstrated by Fishman and Fine (1985), who were able to segregate endocytotic and exocytotic vesicles in the hepatocyte by differential sedimentation, and they showed that transferrin, previously endocytosed into the hepatic cell from the blood, was present in the same coated vesicles that contained newly synthesized acetylcholinesterase. Later Stoorvogel *et al.* (1988) localized the joint pathway in the trans-Golgi reticulum or network (TGN). Figure 1.66 illustrates some of the possible mechanisms by which endocytosed material may cross the endothelial cell.

Capillary Depletion Technique

When attempting to measure transcytosis quantitatively, one is confronted with the problem as to whether the small amounts of protein or other solute are, indeed, transported into the brain tissue, or whether they are merely taken into the brain capillaries. Triguero *et al.* (1990) have shown that measurable amounts of cationized albumin and IgG are carried into the brain tissue by infusing the protein

BRAIN

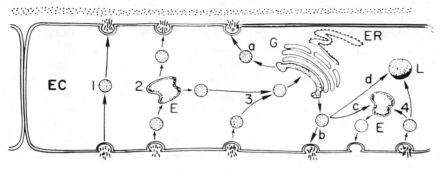

BLOOD

Figure 1.66 Hypothetical transcytotic pathways for blood-borne macromolecules through the non-fenestrated, cerebral endothelial cell (EC) include the following pathways: 1, endocytic vesicles may ferry molecules directly from the luminal to the abluminal side of the endothelium; 2, endocytic vesicles derived from the luminal surface membrane are directed to endosomes (E) that give rise to exocytic vesicles directed to the abluminal membrane; 3, vesicles from the luminal plasmalemma or endosomes are channelled to the inner Golgi saccule (G). Transport vesicles from the inner Golgi saccule may engage in exocytosis at the abluminal (pathway a) and luminal (pathway b) cell surfaces, or they may represent primary lysosomes charged with delivering acid hydrolases to endosomes (pathway c) and secondary lysosomes (L; pathway d). Internalized cell surface membrane that may or may not contain receptor sites is usually directed to secondary lysosomes or to endosomes; the latter may recycle membrane harbouring receptor sites to the cell surface (pathway 4). These four intracellular pathways may apply to blood-borne ligands internalized within cerebral endothelia by receptor-mediated endocytosis. Because endocytosis appears not to occur at the abluminal side, the blood–brain barrier may be polarized with regard to the transcytosis of protein. ER, endoplasmic reticulum. From Broadwell *et al.* (1988)

into the perfused isolated rat head and, after an appropriate time, e.g. 10 min, homogenizing the brain and measuring uptake into the homogenate, and then centrifuging away the capillary fraction, and measuring the amount in the supernatant and in the centrifuged pellet. Uptake into the 'capillary depleted homogenate' was considerable and the computed value of PS for cationized albumin was 3.5 μl min^{-1} g^{-1}, compared with 3.8 μl min^{-1} g^{-1} reported earlier by Takasato *et al.* (1984).

Cationization
The cell surface is usually, if not always, negatively charged, owing to the presence of acidic residues exposed to the extracellular space; an adsorptive interaction between the cell surface and a protein, such as serum albumin, would be prevented or retarded by this electrical charge, since most proteins at physiological pH are also negatively charged. Conversion of a protein into a positively charged molecule, by covalent reaction with an amine, might be expected to favour

adsorption and thus endocytosis. Griffin and Giffels (1982) prepared cationized serum albumin by coupling it with hexamethylene diamine, and showed that it penetrated from blood to CSF after intravenous administration much more rapidly than normal albumin. Later, Kumagai *et al.* (1987) showed that isolated brain capillaries bound cationized albumin, a binding that was not reversed by washing with acid, and thus suggesting that binding had been followed by endocytosis. Beta-endorphin does not cross the blood–brain barrier at a significant rate; however, when this was linked to cationized serum albumin, Kumagai *et al.* found that it was taken up by isolated brain capillaries *in vitro*. When given by intracarotid infusion, penetration into the substance of the brain was demonstrated by autoradiography. This work is of great interest in so far as it indicates the possibility of introducing drugs, etc., into the brain which would have been held up by the blood–brain barrier. Moreover, the introduction of immune globulins into the brain by a similar process of cationization, described by Triguero *et al.* (1989), opens up the possibility of immune therapy.

Histones

Histones are basic proteins and thus cationic at normal pH; Pardridge *et al.* (1989) considered the possibility that histones could act as natural carriers for other molecules during transcytosis across the blood–brain barrier, similar to transferrin and insulin. They showed that isolated bovine microvessels took up [125I]-histone in a saturable manner, with a K_d of 15.2 ± 2.8 μM. Protamine and polylysine competitively inhibited; *in vivo* intracarotid infusion showed a more rapid uptake than that of albumin. This process, whereby a non-transportable peptide or protein, such as beta-endorphin, is coupled covalently with a transportable peptide vector, such as insulin, transferrin or cationized albumin, has been described as *chimeric peptidization.*

Dynorphin Analogue

Dynorphin (1–8) and Dynorphin (1–13) are naturally occurring opioid peptides in the central nervous system (Cuello, 1983). An analogue of these, E-2078, is not hydrolysed by endopeptidases in the blood and, hence, is used instead of the dynorphins. It was found by Terasaki *et al.* (1989) to bind to isolated brain capillaries, the amount increasing with time to reach a steady-state cell-to-medium ratio of some 58. About a quarter was removed by acid, this presumably representing that bound to the surface, the remaining, acid-stable, fraction presumably being intracellular. Pretreatment of the capillaries with an endocytosis inhibitor, phenylarsine oxide, completely suppressed the acid-resistant absorption but not the acid-removable. E-2078 is positively charged at pH 7.4, and the inhibition of endocytosis by polylysine suggests that the endocytosis is similar to that of cationized albumin, a type called by Terasaki *et al.* 'adsorptive-mediated endocytosis', by contrast with receptor-mediated endocytosis, as with transferrin and insulin.

Polarity of the Capillary Membrane

Broadwell (1989) has emphasized an apparent polarity in the brain capillary membrane, in the sense that the endocytosis of such materials as horseradish peroxidase is only observed on the luminal surface of the capillary membrane; thus, presentation of the marker by way of the extracellular space, as during perfusion through the ventricles, does not give rise to endocytosis. Hence, transcytosis of large molecules, if it occurs, must be one-way, from blood to tissue.

Protein-plus-ligand Penetration

It has been suggested (Weisiger *et al.*, 1981; Ockner *et al.*, 1983) that some highly lipid-soluble metabolites, such as fatty acids, carried in the blood bound to plasma protein, are transmitted to their cells of destination by a specific binding of the protein complex to the cells of destination. Bilirubin is highly lipid-soluble and is bound to serum albumin, a binding that effectively prevents its access to most cells of the body. It is removed from the circulation by the liver and, according to the theory of Ockner *et al.*, this removal is assisted by the specific binding of albumin to receptors on the hepatocyte membrane. However, Stollman *et al.* (1983) showed that albumin did not facilitate the uptake of [^{3}H]-bilirubin by the perfused liver, so that there was no delay in the transit time of bilirubin through the perfused liver if albumin was added at the same time. That there are no specific receptors on the capillaries of the brain that might act in the manner suggested by Ockner *et al.* was shown by Pardridge *et al.* (1985), in both *in vivo* studies of extraction of [^{3}H]-albumin from the rat's brain circulation and direct studies on binding at the surface of isolated brain capillaries. Such binding of albumin as occurred was not saturable by concentrations between 1.5 and 735 μM, and was presumably a non-specific binding to the glycocalyx of the endothelial cells.

Summary

In general, then, as we shall see in Chapter 3, the transport of large peptides across the blood–brain barrier can occur by a preliminary binding of the peptide to receptors on the brain capillary surface. The binding is followed by endocytosis, which is a spontaneous process not requiring energy (Solenski and Williams, 1985); the subsequent exocytosis, which presumably occurs, is harder to demonstrate, since the usual preparation for study, namely the isolated brain capillary, lacks the ATP required for the process, which requires energy. The subject has been reviewed critically by Broadwell (1989), who emphasizes that the commonly observed engulfment of horseradish peroxidase by cerebral capillary, endothelial cells represents a digestive process by which the protein is taken up into lysosomes, and is not a sign of transcytosis. He concluded that the 'literature is replete with over-interpreted and misinterpreted data with the results of unwarranted conclusions . . . , etc.'

The Broken-down Barrier

We may now revert to the situation where large molecules such as serum albumin escape from the bloodstream into the brain tissue, a situation described by breakdown of the blood–brain barrier. The route of escape can be the opening of formerly tight junctions between capillary membrane cells, or by some transcytotic mechanism. The study of the osmotic opening of the blood–brain barrier, by virtue of its simple and reproducible establishment by the intra-arterial infusion of hyperosmotic arabinose, and the reversible nature of the changes evoked, is doubtless of most value, although the changes produced under these conditions are not necessarily common to all situations in which the barrier is broken down.

Osmotic Opening

So far as the interpretation of the osmotic opening of the barrier is concerned, it would seem from the measurements of Rapoport and his colleagues (Ziylan *et al.*, 1983, 1984; Armstrong *et al.*, 1987), made on the simultaneous permeability to pairs of solutes of different molecular weight, e.g. sucrose and inulin, or sucrose and dextran, that the permeability coefficients, measured immediately after the osmotic insult and during the period of recovery, could be explained most plausibly by the initial opening of large pores which subsequently closed up. They pointed out that the recovery from breakdown was manifest as a relatively larger decrease in permeability for the larger molecule (Figure 1.67), which would

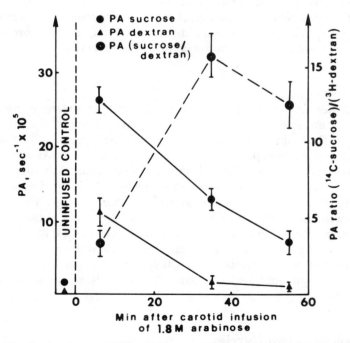

Figure 1.67 Regional permeability-surface area (PA) products and ratios for left-sided occipital lobe for [^{14}C]-sucrose and [^{3}H]-dextran after 30 s left-sided carotid infusion of 1.8 molal arabinose. From Ziylan *et al.* (1984)

suggest a gradual closure of the pores, so that the larger molecule would encounter the greater obstruction to diffusion. A careful analysis of the kinetics, on the basis largely of Renkin's (1954) analysis of porous membranes, showed that the situation was more complex, so that the influx of the solutes was governed partly by a simple diffusive process, when relative rates would be governed by the molecular weights [Note 10], and partly by a bulk flow of fluid, in which case, provided reflexion coefficients were sufficiently low, i.e. the pores were large, the different solutes would be carried in at approximately the same rate. Thus the ratio between the permeabilities, shown on the graph of Figure 1.67, passes through a maximum, and it was considered that during the later stages of recovery the changes in the ratio could be determined by the bulk flow. That bulk flow from blood to brain takes place after this type of osmotic insult was demonstrated practically in that, after the initial decrease in brain water due to the osmotic extraction of water, the water content of brain actually rose above normal by 1–2%. Such an increase is to be expected if some of the intravenously infused arabinose crosses the blood–brain barrier into the extracellular fluid. When the barrier returns to normal, the arabinose is trapped and makes the extracellular fluid hypertonic to the blood, with the consequent penetration of water.

Limited Breakdown

The descriptions of the opening of the blood–brain barrier presented in the literature have suggested that the barrier is broken down fairly uniformly, so that, therapeutically, drugs that formerly failed to pass from blood to brain would be able to do so after an osmotic insult. A recent study of Somjen *et al.* (1992) cast doubt on this simple view, since simultaneous injections of K^+ along with the hyperosmotic material failed to produce the physiological effects expected of a raised extracellular brain concentration of this ion. It seems, therefore, that osmotic breakdown of the barrier is a somewhat localized response, and this is confirmed by the patchiness of the staining of brain tissue by Evans Blue after the osmotic insult.

Transcytosis and Tubules

An alternative explanation of the escape of large molecules from the blood into the nervous tissue has been that the initial trauma promotes a process of transcytosis whereby plasma proteins are carried across the capillary membrane (Westergaard *et al.*, 1977; Hansson and Johansson, 1980; Houthoff *et al.*, 1982). The kinetic studies of Rapoport and his colleagues led them to reject this hypothesis. The evidence adduced in favour of transcytosis, or another hypothesis, namely the formation of tubular structures stretching across the cytoplasm of the capillary endothelial cell, has been based on thin-section electron microscopy; by the use of high-voltage electron microscopy thicker sections have been studied which, it is claimed have permitted a more accurate assessment of the three-dimensional nature of the structures being examined; and finally freeze-fracture studies of the cell membrane, especially in the neighbourhood of the intercellular junctions, have given clues as to the existence of vesicular structures related to the cell membrane. It is out of the question to review this evidence critically here, the more so as it requires someone with lengthy experience in interpreting electron microscopic sections. Suffice it to say that, with the osmotically opened barrier, Farrell and Shivers (1984) found horseradish peroxidase located in vesicles of 40–200 nm diameter within the endothelial cells; the tight junctions on freeze-fracture showed no basic difference from normal, but chains of cytoplasmic vesicles could be seen stretching through the cytoplasm in thin sections, while in the freeze-fractured material craters apparently formed by these vesicles, while attached to the cell membrane, were observed. Finally, actual tubular structures, apparently stretching across the endothelial endoplasm, formed of fused vesicles, were described, as illustrated by Figure 1.68. This study, and one of Lossinsky *et al.* (1983) employing a cold-lesion to induce breakdown of the barrier, have emphasized, not only the formation of apparently tubular structures, derived from the endothelial plasma membrane, but also the marked tendency of the brain capillary to form cytoplasmic vesicles, which are normally absent from central nervous capillaries, a feature of blood–brain barrier breakdown that had been earlier emphasized by Westergaard *et al.* (1976) and Joó (1971).

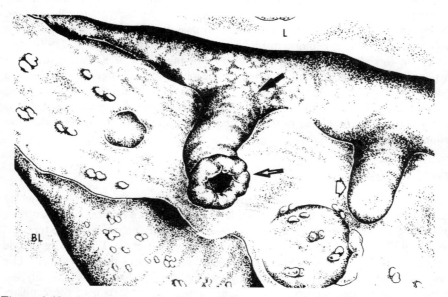

Figure 1.68 Artist's conception of the complete transendothelial channel. The lettering and arrows used denote the origin of the channel from the luminal plasmalemma (black arrow) and the abluminal opening (white on black arrow) on the channel on the opposite side of the cell. Open arrow identifies an elongated pinocytotic invagination of the luminal plasmalemma. BL, basal lamina; L, lumen of capillary. From Farrell and Shivers (1984)

Digestive Process

To what extent the presence of the foreign marker molecule, e.g. horseradish peroxidase, contributes to this reaction remains to be seen. In an earlier study Lossinsky *et al.* (1981) described tubular structures containing horseradish peroxidase making direct connections with dense bodies of lysosomes, presumably visualizing a digestive process of the foreign material, and we must note that Balin *et al.* (1987) have emphasized that the uptake of horseradish peroxidase by brain capillary endothelial cells is a *non-specific digestive process* of foreign material, so that the tubular profiles filled with this marker are, in fact, *vesicles* carrying ingested peroxidase to secondary lysosomes.

Summary

To summarize a somewhat vexed problem as to the extent to which transcytosis may occur in normal and abnormal brain capillaries, we must emphasize the great difficulties in interpretation of thin-section transmission electron micrographs. The vesicles described in the normal capillary by Palade and his collaborators have been interpreted by Frokjaer-Jensen (1984) as cross-sections of tubular invaginations of the plasma membrane, while the demonstration of a continuous transendothelial channel requires for its validation serial sections over large distances compared with the thinness of the sections, a process beautifully described by Tripathi and Tripathi (1974) in the arachnoid villi. The processes of both endocytosis and exocytosis in a variety of cells have been established, and the factors controlling them are becoming well understood, but the identification of the same processes, and their control, in the brain capillary is a matter for future intensive research.

Tumours

It has been long known that the blood–brain barrier in a cerebral tumour is abnormal, so that the tumour may be identified by the escape of X-ray-opaque material from blood. The tissue adjacent to the tumour also shows barrier abnormality which may be due to the abnormal mechanical pressure exerted by the tumour, since the breakdown can be mimicked by injection of space-occupying material. Long (1970) described the histology of the capillaries in a human astrocytoma; some capillaries appeared normal, whereas others had no tight junctions and others had no astroglial sheath. In the adjacent tissue, however, the capillaries appeared quite normal, so that lanthanum failed to pass through the tight junctions. In the case of an artificial astrocytoma induced by implantation of C 6 cells, Shivers *et al.* (1984) found extravasation of horseradish peroxidase into the tumour but not into the surrounding neuropil. In both situations, according to them, the capillary tight junctions were normal, while in the tumour the usual chains of vesicles and tubules were identified; in the peritumour tissue, however, there was no extravasation of horseradish peroxidase, so presumably the engulfment was indicative of a digestive process rather than transcytosis.

The Glial Sheath

In looking for some unifying concept that might form the basis for the primary cause of the increased barrier permeability manifest in the variety of insults that have been employed in demonstrating the phenomenon, it may well be worth focusing attention on the glial sheath. Many years ago Clemente and Holst (1954) made an attempt to ascertain the function of the glial sheath in the blood–brain barrier, arguing that the effects of X-irradiation, which causes a breakdown of the barrier, might be specifically confined to a class of cells. They found, indeed, that irradiation of the monkey's head led to a specific degeneration of the astroglia, and argued that the glial sheath was responsible for the barrier. In reviewing the matter Davson (1967) rejected the possibility, but the real significance of the experiment may have escaped notice, namely that the X-rays, by damaging the astrocytes, caused the brain capillaries to lose their barrier characteristics, just as happens in cultured endothelium if not co-cultured with astrocytes. Whether osmotic breakdown of the barrier, which is rapidly reversible, could be included in the general mechanism is doubtful, although the claim of Farrell and Shivers (1984) that the tight junctions in the opened barrier are normal might well demand a reconsideration of the simple mechanical hypothesis suggested by Rapoport.

Steady-State CSF Concentrations

We have seen that, with certain slowly penetrating substances, the steady-state concentration in the CSF is less than that in the plasma, i.e. R_{CSF} is less than unity. In general terms, this failure to achieve the expected diffusion equilibrium may be expressed by the statement that K_{in} is less than K_{out}, since at the steady state we have

$$C_{CSF}/C_{pl} = K_{in}/K_{out} \tag{1.40}$$

$$= \frac{rK_f + K_d}{K_f + K_d} \tag{1.48}$$

where K_f is the rate of flow of CSF, r is the fraction of the plasma concentration that enters with the fluid and K_d is the component entering the CSF by diffusion from the nervous tissue after crossing the blood–brain barrier.

Because the flow of CSF out of the system is unrestricted, in the sense that it takes place through large water-filled channels offering no barrier to the passage of solutes up to very large dimensions, we may say that the value of R_{CSF} will be determined by K_{in}, which varies with different solutes according to the degree of impediment the choroidal epithelium and the capillaries of the brain offer to the passage of solute from blood. Thus, we may expect that, with solutes of decreasing permeability through the blood–CSF and blood–brain barriers, the values of R_{CSF} should decrease in parallel. Felgenhauer (1974) applied this concept to the proteins of the CSF, arguing that, if the proteins had to pass through a system of

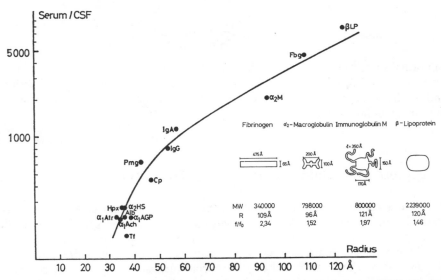

Figure 1.69 Correlation between serum/CSF concentration ratios and hydrodynamic radii. Inset: overall dimensions of the four largest human serum proteins and their relevant molecular parameters. MW, molecular weight; R, hydrodynamic radius; f/f_0, frictional ratio; βLP, β-lipoprotein; Fbg, fibrinogen; α_2-M, α_2-macroglobulin; IgA, immunoglobulin A; IgG, immunoglobulin G; Pmg, plasminogen; Cp, ceruloplasmin; α_2-HS, α_2-HS-glycoprotein; Hpx, haemopexin; Alb, albumin; α_1-AGP, α_1-acid glycoprotein; α_1-Atr, α_1-antitrypsin; α_1-Ach, α_1-antichymotrypsin; Tf, transferrin. From Felgenhauer (1974)

leaky pores the value of R_{CSF}, or its reciprocal, Q, should be simply related to the dynamic radii of the proteins. Figure 1.69 illustrates the results; where very large proteins are concerned, such as fibrinogen and beta-lipoprotein, some allowance must be made for the marked asymmetry of the molecules in attempting to assess a notional molecular radius corresponding to a sphere. Examples of this asymmetry are indicated in Figure 1.69; fibrinogen has the lowest molecular weight of the four asymmetrical proteins but its hydrodynamic volume is greater than that of alpha$_2$-macroglobulin, and it is therefore more retarded than the more compact alpha$_2$-macroglobulin. A study of this kind is valuable, since it permits an insight into the probable source of a given protein in the CSF; thus, if its quotient, Q, is very different from that predicted by the curve of Figure 1.69, we may look for an additional mechanism of entry to the simple passive passage through pores in the choroidal epithelium and the blood capillaries of the brain. Thus, Tibbling *et al.* (1977) considered the concentrations of two proteins of different size and normally occurring in the CSF, namely serum albumin and immunoglobulin G (IgG). On the basis of a simple passage through pores, the realtive values of R_{CSF} or its reciprocal, Q, for the two proteins should remain constant from one individual to another, and Tibbling *et al.* computed an *IgG index*, given by the ratios of Q for IgG over that for albumin, i.e.:

$$\text{IgG index} = \frac{Q_{IgG}}{Q\text{alb}} = \frac{R_{CSF, \, alb}}{R_{CSF, \, IgG}}$$

In normal subjects the quotient varied from 0.051 to 0.183; it was considered that deviations from this range would be due to a change in the nature of the barriers and/or the presence of protein not derived from the plasma, as with synthesis of immunoglobulins within the brain.

Complete Morphology of the Blood–Brain Barrier

We have agreed that the primary site of the blood–brain barrier is the capillary endothelium; however, we have also seen that the brain and spinal cord are in close apposition to cerebrospinal fluid and that ready diffusion across the lining membranes of the ventricles and CSF takes place. Thus, to some extent the blood–CSF barrier, constituted by the choroid plexuses in the first place, must also be regarded as part of the system that insulates the nervous tissue from the blood circulation. The CSF is contained, also, in the subarachnoid spaces, which are lined by the pia-glial layer on the surface of the brain and cord, and the arachnoid membrane, which itself is closely apposed to the dura mater. Passage from blood to the subarachnoid CSF is restricted, and this restriction is imposed, first, by the blood–brain barrier, so that escape from blood across the pia-glia is restricted; second, it is imposed by the arachnoid membrane, a necessary restraint owing to the high permeability of the dural capillaries. Thus, Goldmann, in his classical experiments, observed that intraparenterally injected trypan blue stained the dura but not the underlying CSF.

This meningeal barrier has been described in detail by Nabeshima *et al.* (1975), and they have delineated a *barrier layer* of arachnoid cells whose intercellular spaces are closed by tight junctions. Thus, between the innermost layer of the dura mater and the arachnoid mater there is traditionally described the *subdural space*, although, according to Nabeshima *et al.*, the border between the two meninges is not well defined, so that when the dura splits from the arachnoid, this takes place in the layer of *border cells*, belonging to the dura. Next to the border layer there are two or three layers of flattened cells tightly packed together, the spaces between them being closed by tight junctions and gap junctions, and it is these layers that have been described as the barrier layer, insulating the dura proper from the subarachnoid space. This layer had been called by Andres (1967) the *subdural neurothelium*, equivalent to the perineurium of peripheral nerve, which, in a similar fashion, acts as a diffusion barrier restricting access to the endoneurium of the nerve from the epineurium, which may be considered the analogue of the dura. The pia mater closely invests the spinal and cerebral parenchyma, its cells being analogous with those of the arachnoid but not linked by tight junctions, so that we may expect free access from the parenchyma to the subarachnoid fluid. Beneath the pia there is a so-called glial layer, so that it is customary to speak of the pia-glial

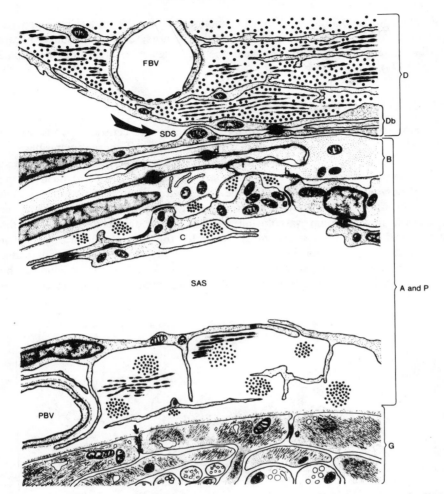

Figure 1.70 Summary diagram showing layers of cells in the meninges, types of cells in these layers and types of junctions between them. Only features applicable to all of the species of animals studied are included. Large arrow at upper left indicates widening of the subdural space which is actually intradural, produced during preparation of the tissue. Small arrow below indicates astrocytic border junction. The sizes of desmosomes (d), hemidesmosomes (h), tight junctions (t) and gap junctions (g) are exaggerated. Arachnoid trabeculae, extending from the inner to the outer layer of arachnoid cells, have been omitted for clarity. A and P, arachnoid-pia; B, arachnoid barrier layer; C, arachnoid cistern; D, dura; Db, dural border layer; FBV, fenestrated blood vessel in dura; G, marginal glia of brain; PVB, pia-arachnoid blood vessel; SAS, subarachnoid space; SDS, subdural space. From Nabeshima *et al.* (1975)

lining of the brain and cord. According to Brightman and Reese (1969), this layer consists of a network of interlacing sheet-like processes lined by a basement membrane; lying next to this are the mesothelial cells of the pia, adjacent mesothelial cells being linked by gap junctions, as are the underlying astrocytic processes; these gap-junctions are permeable to horseradish peroxidase. Figure 1.70 summarizes the relations between the meninges as described by Nabeshima *et al.* (1975).

The Circumventricular Organs

Classical studies on the uptake of trypan blue in the central nervous system showed that certain regions lacked a barrier to this dyestuff; these regions, because of their close association with the ventricles of the brain, have been described as circumventricular organs (CVO). They are specialized tissues atypical of the central nervous system; and include the area postrema, protruding into the IVth ventricle, the median eminence, the neurohypophysis, the pineal gland or epiphysis, the organum vasculosum of the lamina terminalis (OVLT), the subfornical organ or intercolumnar tubercle, the subcommissural organ or paraphysis, and the choroid plexuses (Figure 1.71). In general, the defective barrier in these regions is due to the absence of tight junctions occluding the interendothelial cell clefts; and the physiological significance of the absence of a

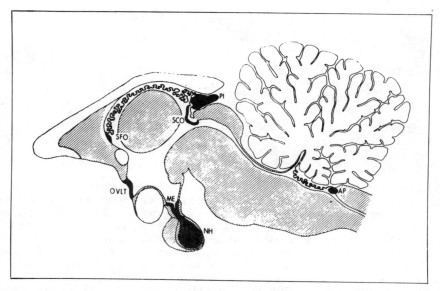

Figure 1.71 Section through squirrel monkey brain in median sagittal plane. Most parts of ventricular walls are covered by ciliated ependyma. Specialized non-ciliated ependymal cells cover circumventricular organs. These, and similarly non-ciliated epithelium of the choroid plexus, are outlined in black. Located around the IIIrd ventricle are the following circumventricular organs: median eminence (ME); neurohypophysis (NH); pineal body (Pl); organum vasculosum of the lamina terminalis (OVLT); subfornical organ (SFO); subcommissural organ (SCO). Area postrema (AP) is found at transition of IVth ventricle into central canal. From Weindl and Joynt (1973)

barrier must be sought in the special functions of the organs. For example, the choroid plexuses are the site of secretion of the CSF, and the capillaries in these organs must produce a filtrate from plasma which is subsequently 'processed' by the choroidal epithelium, which acts as a barrier between blood and CSF, as we have seen. Thus, the ependyma covering the choroid plexuses has become specialized, not only serving to secrete CSF, but also acting as a barrier to prevent 'leaks' from blood into the nervous tissue. In a similar fashion, it appears that the ependymal linings of the other circumventricular organs have to some extent become specialized, reducing leaks that would otherwise occur in these non-barrier regions; this is certainly true of the median eminence, the ependymal cells adjacent to this region being sealed by tight junctions (Reese and Brightman, 1968). The absence of a barrier in the median eminence is of obvious significance, since it is here that the portal system of capillaries receives the releasing hormones secreted by the hypothalamus, and transmits them to the anterior pituitary; these releasing hormones must have ready access to the portal system of capillaries, so that the absence of a barrier here is understandable. The significance of the absence of a barrier in some other organs is not always obvious, but, in general, it could be that the specialized cells in these organs, such as the pineal, need to 'sample' the circulating blood; thus, the area postrema is closely related anatomically to the vomiting centre, which must react to changes in blood composition.

References

Abbott, N.J., Davson, H., Glen, I. and Grant, N. (1971). Chloride transport and potential across the blood–CSF barrier. *Brain Res.*, **29**, 185–193

Ahlskog, J.E. *et al.* (1989). Cerebrospinal fluid indices of blood–brain barrier permeability following adrenal–brain transplantation in patients with Parkinson's disease. *Exp. Neurol.*, **105**, 152–161

Ahmed, N. and Van Harreveld, A. (1969). The iodide space in rabbit brain. *J. Physiol.*, **204**, 31–50

Andres, K.H. (1967). Uber die Feinstruktur der Arachnoidea und Dura mater von Mammalia. *Z. Zellforsch..*, **79**, 272–295

Armstrong, B.K., Robinson, P.J. and Rapoport, S.I. (1987). Size-dependent blood–brain barrier opening demonstrated with [^{14}C] sucrose and a 200,000-Da [^{3}H] dextran. *Exp. Neurol.*, **97**, 686–696

Aronson, P.S. (1978). Energy-dependence of phlorizin-binding to isolated renal microvillus membranes. *J. Membrane Biol.*, **42**, 81–98

Ashcroft, G.W., Dow, R.C. and Moir, A.T.B. (1968). The active transport of 5-hydroxyindole-3-acetic acid and 3-methoxy-4-hydroxyphenylacetic acid from a recirculating perfusion system of the cerebral ventricles of the unanaesthetized dog. *J. Physiol.*, **199**, 397–425

Ashwell, G. and Morell, A.G. (1974). The role of surface carbohydrates in the hepatic recognition and transport of circulating glycoproteins. *Adv. Enzymol.*, **41**, 99–128

Audus, K.L. and Borchardt, R.T. (1986). Characteristics of the large neutral amino acid transport system of bovine microvessel endothelial cell monolayers. *J. Neurochem.*, **47**, 484–488

Bakay, L. and Lindberg, O. (1949). Studies on the role of the cerebrospinal fluid in brain metabolism as measured with radioactive phosphate. *Acta Physiol. Scand.*, **17**, 179–190

Balin, B.J., Broadwell, R.D. and Salcman, M. (1987). Tubular profiles do not form transendothelial channels through the blood–brain barrier. *J. Neurocytol.*, **16**, 721–735

Baly, D.L. and Horuk, R. (1988). The biology and biochemistry of the glucose transporter. *Biochem. Biophys. Acta*, **947**, 571–590

Baños, G., Daniel, P.M., Moorhouse, S.R. and Pratt, O.E. (1973). The influx of amino acids into the brain of the rat *in vivo*: the essential compared with some non-essential amino acids. *Proc. Roy. Soc. B*, **183**, 59–70

Barondes, S.H. (1988). Bifunctional properties of lectins: lectins redefined. *Trends Biochem. Sci.*, **13**, 480–482

Beck, D.W., Roberts, R.L. and Olson, J.J. (1986). Glial cells influence membrane-associated enzyme activity at the blood–brain barrier. *Brain Res.*, **381**, 131–137

Beck, D.W., Vinters, H.V., Hart, M.N. and Cancilla, P.A. (1984). Glial cells influence polarity of the blood–brain barrier. *J. Neuropathol. Exp. Neurol.*, **43**, 219–224

Bertler, A., Falck, B., Owman, C. and Rosengren, C. (1966). The localization of monoaminergic blood–brain barrier mechanisms. *Pharmacol. Rev.*, **18**, 369–385

Bertler, A., Falck, B. and Rosengren, E. (1963). The direct demonstration of a barrier mechanism in the brain capillaries. *Acta Pharmacol. Toxicol.*, **20**, 317–321

Bertossi, M., Ribatti, D., Nico, B., Virginntino, D., Mancini, L. and Roncali, L. (1989). Computerized three-dimensional reconstruction of the developing blood–brain barrier. *Acta Neuropathol.*, **79**, 48–51

Betz, A.L., Firth, J.A. and Goldstein, G.W. (1980). Polarity of the blood–brain barrier: distribution of enzymes between the luminal and antiluminal membranes of brain capillary endothelial cells. *Brain Res.*, **192**, 17–28

Betz, A.L. and Goldstein, G.W. (1978). Polarity of the blood–brain barrier: neutral amino acid transport into isolated brain capillaries. *Science*, **202**, 225–227

Birnbaum, M.J., Haspel, H.C. and Rosen, O.M. (1986). Cloning and characterization of a cDNA encoding the rat brain glucose-transporter protein. *Proc. Natl Acad. Sci. USA*, **83**, 5784–5788

Bito, L.Z., Bradbury, M.W.B. and Davson, H. (1966). Factors affecting the distribution of iodide and bromide in the central nervous system. *J. Physiol.*, **185**, 323–354

Bito, L.Z. and Davson, H. (1966). Local variations in cerebrospinal fluid composition and its relationship to the composition of the extracellular fluid of the cortex. *Exp. Neurol.*, **14**, 264–280

Bito, L.Z. and Davson, H. (1974). Carrier-mediated removal of prostaglandins from cerebrospinal fluid. *J. Physiol.*, **236**, 39P–40P

Bito, L.Z., Davson, H. and Salvador, E.V. (1976). Inhibition of *in vitro* concentrative prostaglandin accumulation by prostaglandins, prostaglandin analogues and by some inhibitors of organic anion transport. *J. Physiol.*, **256**, 257–271

Blasberg, R.G., Fenstermacher, J.D. and Patlak, C.S. (1983). Transport of α-aminoisobutyric acid across brain capillary and cellular membranes. *J. Cereb. Blood Flow Metab.*, **3**, 8–32

Bourke, R.S., Gabelnick, H.L. and Young, O. (1970). Mediated transport of chloride from blood into cerebrospinal fluid. *Exp. Brain Res.*, **10**, 17–38

Bowman, P.D., Ennis, S.E., Rarey, K.E., Betz, A.L. and Goldstein, G.W. (1983). Brain microvessel endothelial cells in tissue culture: a model of blood–brain barrier permeability. *Ann. Neurol.*, **14**, 396–402

Bradbury, M.W.B. (1979). *The Concept of a Blood–Brain Barrier*. Wiley, Chichester

Bradbury, M.W.B. and Cole, D.F. (1980). The role of the lymphatic system in drainage of cerebrospinal fluid and aqueous humour. *J. Physiol.*, **299**, 353–365

Bradbury, M.W.B., Cserr, H.E. and Westrop, R.J. (1981). Drainage of cerebral interstitial fluid into deep cervical lymph of the rabbit. *Am. J. Physiol.*, **240**, F329–F336

Bradbury, M.W.B. and Kleeman, C.R. (1967). Stability of the potassium content of cerebrospinal fluid and brain. *Am. J. Physiol.*, **213**, 519–528

Bradbury, M.W.B. and Sarna, G.S. (1977). Homeostasis of the ionic composition of the cerebrospinal fluid. *Exp. Eye Res.*, **25** (Suppl), 249–257

Bradbury, M.W.B., Segal, M.B. and Wilson, J. (1972). Transport of potassium at the blood–brain barrier, *J. Physiol.*, **221**, 617–632

Bradbury, M.W.B. and Stulcova, B. (1970). Efflux mechanism contributing to the stability of the potassium concentration in cerebrospinal fluid. *J. Physiol.*, **208**, 415–430

Bradbury, M.W.B., Villamil, M. and Kleeman, C.R. (1968). Extracellular fluid, ionic distribution and exchange in isolated frog brain. *Am. J. Physiol.*, **214**, 643–651

Brendel, K., Meezan, E. and Carlson, E.C. (1974). Isolated brain microvessels: a purified metabolically active preparation from bovine cerebral cortex. *Science*, **185**, 953–955

Brightman, M.W. (1965). The distribution within the brain of ferritin injected into cerebrospinal fluid compartments. *Am. J. Anat.*, **117**, 193–220

Brightman, M.W. (1977). Morphology of blood–brain interfaces. *Exp. Eye Res.*, **25** (Suppl), 1–25

Brightman, M.W. and Reese, T.S. (1969). Junctions between intimately apposed cell membranes in the vertebrate brain. *J. Cell Biol.*, **40**, 648–677

Broadwell, R.D. (1988). Absence of a blood–brain barrier within transplanted brain tissue? *Science*, **241**, 473–474

Broadwell, R.D. (1989). Transcytosis of macromolecules through the blood–brain barrier: a cell biological perspective and critical appraisal. *Acta Neuropathol.*, **79**, 117–128

Broadwell, R.D., Balin, B.J. and Selcman, M. (1988). Transcytotic pathway for blood-borne protein through the blood–brain barrier. *Proc. Natl Acad. Sci. USA*, **85**, 632–636

Bruns, R.R. and Palade, G.E. (1968). Studies on blood capillaries. I. and II. *J. Cell Biol.*, **37**, 244–299

Bugge, J. (1974). The cephalic arteries of hystriomorph rodents. *Symp. Zool. Soc. London*, **34**, 61–68

Bundgaard, M., Hagman, P. and Crone, C. (1983). The three-dimensional organization of plasmalemmal vesicular profiles in the endothelium of rat heart capillaries. Microvasc. Res., **25**, 358–368

Cameron, I.R., Davson, H. and Segal, M.B. (1969). The effect of hypercapnia on the blood–brain barrier to sucrose in the rabbit. *Yale J. Biol. Med.*, **42**, 241–247

Campbell, P.N. and Davson, H. (1948). Absorption of 3-methylglucose from the small intestine of the rat and cat. *Biochem. J.*, **43**, 426–429

Cardelli-Cangiano, P. *et al.* (1987). Isolated brain microvessels as *in vitro* equivalent of the blood–brain barrier: selective removal by collagenase of the A-system of neutral amino acid transport. *J. Neurochem.*, **47**, 1667–1678

Carter-Su, C., Pessin, J.E., Mora, R., Gitomer, W. and Geeh, M.P. (1982). Photoaffinity labelling of the human erythrocyte D-glucose transporter. *J. Biol. Chem.*, **257**, 5419–5425

Carter-Su, C., Pillion, D.J. and Czech, M.P. (1980). Reconstituted D-glucose transport from the adipocyte plasma membrane. *Biochemistry*, **19**, 2374–2385

Chen, C.-C. *et al.* (1986). Human erythrocyte glucose transporter: normal asymmetric orientation and function in liposomes. *Proc. Natl Acad. Sci. USA*, **83**, 2652–2656

Christensen, H.N. (1969). Some special kinetic problems of transport. *Adv. Enzymol.*, **32**, 1–31

Christensen, H.N. (1979). Exploiting amino acid structure to learn about membrane transport. *Adv. Embryol. Related Areas Mol. Biol.*, **49**, 41–101

Christensen, H.N. *et al.* (1965). The use of N-methylation to direct the route of mediated transport of amino acids. *J. Biol. Chem.*, **240**, 3609–3636

Christensen, H.N., Handgloten, M.E., Lam, I., Tager, S. and Zand, R. (1969). A bicyclic amino acid to improve discriminations among transport systems. *J. Biol. Chem.*, **244**, 1510–1520

Christensen, H.N. and Liang, M. (1966). Transport of diamino acids into the Ehrlich cell. *J. Biol. Chem.*, **241**, 5542–5551

Christensen, H.N., Oxender, D.L., Liang, M. and Vatz, K.A. (1965). The use of

N-methylation to direct the route of mediated transport of amino acids. *J. Biol. Chem.*, **240**, 3609–3616

Clemente, C.D. and Holst, E.A. (1954). Pathological changes in neurons, neuroglia and blood–brain barrier induced by X-irradiation of heads of monkeys. *Arch. Neurol. Psychiat.*, **71**, 66–79

Collander, R. (1949). The permeability of plant protoplasts to small molecules. *Physiol. Plant.*, **2**, 300

Collander, R. and Barlund, H. (1933). Permeabilitatsstudien an *Chara Ceralophylla. Acta. Bot. Fenn.*, **11**, 1–14

Courtice, F.S. and Simmonds, W.J. (1951). The removal of protein from the subarachnoid space. *Aust. J. Exp. Biol. Med. Sci.*, **29**, 255–263

Crane, R.K. (1977). The gradient hypothesis and other models of carrier-mediated active transport. *Rev. Physiol. Biochem. Pharmacol.*, **78**, 99–159

Crane, R.K., Forstner, G. and Eicholz, A. (1965). An effect of Na^+ concentration on the apparent Michaelis constant for intestinal sugar transport *in vitro. Biochim. Biophys. Acta*, **109**, 467–477

Cremer, J.E., Heath, D.F., Teal, H.M., Woods, M.S. and Cavanagh, J.B. (1975). Some dynamic aspects of brain metabolism in rats given portocaval anastomosis. *Neuropathol. Appl. Neurobiol.*, **1**, 293–311

Crone, C. (1961). *Om diffusionen af nogle organiske non-elektrolyter fra bold til hjernevaev.* Ejnar Munksgaard, Kobenhaven

Crone, C. (1963). The permeability of capillaries in various organs as determined by the use of the 'Indicator Diffusion' method. *Acta Physiol. Scand.*, **58**, 292–305

Crone, C. (1965). Facilitated transfer of glucose from blood into brain tissue. *J. Physiol.*, **181**, 103–113

Crone, C. and Olesen, P. (1981). The electrical resistance of brain capillary endothelium. *J. Physiol.*, **182**, 53P–54P

Cserr, H.F., Cooper, D.N., Suri, P.K. and Patlak, C.S. (1981). Efflux of radiolabeled polyethylene glycols and albumin from rat brain. *Am. J. Physiol.*, **240**, F319–F328

Cuello, A.C. (1983). Cerebral distribution of opioid peptides. *Br. Med. Bull.*, **39**, 11–16

Curry, F.E. and Michel, C.C. (1980). A fiber matrix model of capillary permeability. *Membrane Res.*, **20**, 96–99

Davson, H. (1955). A comparative study of the aqueous humour and cerebrospinal fluid in the rabbit. *J. Physiol.*, **129**, 111–133

Davson, H. (1956). *Physiology of the Ocular and Cerebrospinal Fluids.* Churchill, London

Davson, H. (1958). Some aspects of the relationship between the cerebrospinal fluid and the central nervous system. In *The Cerebrospinal Fluid.* Ciba Foundation Symposium. Churchill, London, pp. 189–203

Davson, H. (1967). *Physiology of the Cerebrospinal Fluid.* Churchill, London

Davson, H. (1976). The blood–brain barrier. Review Lecture, Physiological Society. *J. Physiol.*, **255**, 1–28

Davson, H., Begley, D.J., Chain, D.G., Briggs, F.O. and Shepherd, M.T. (1986). Steady-state distribution of cycloleucine and α-aminoisobutyric acid between plasma and cerebrospinal fluid. *Exp. Neurol.*, **91**, 163–173

Davson, H. and Danielli, J.F. (1942). *The Permeability of Natural Membranes.* Cambridge University Press, Cambridge

Davson, H. and Hollingsworth, J.G. (1973). Active transport of ^{131}I across the blood–brain barrier. *J. Physiol.*, **233**, 327–347

Davson, H., Hollingsworth, J.G., Carey, M.B. and Fenstermacher, J.D. (1982). Ventriculo-cisternal perfusion of twelve amino acids in the rabbit. *J. Neurobiol.*, **13**, 293–318

Davson, H., Kleeman, C.R. and Levin, E. (1961). Blood–brain barrier and extracellular space. *J. Physiol.*, **159**, 67P–68P

Davson, H., Kleeman, C.R. and Levin, E. (1963). The blood–brain barrier. In *Drugs and Membranes.* (Proc. 1st. Int. Congr. Pharmacol. Stockholm). Pergamon, Oxford, pp. 71–94

Davson, H. and Oldendorf, W.H. (1967). Transport in the central nervous system. *Proc. Roy. Soc. Med.*, **60**, 326–328

Davson, H. and Pollay, M. (1963). The turnover of ^{24}Na in the cerebrospinal fluid and its bearing on the blood–brain barrier. *J. Physiol.*, **167**, 247–255

Davson, H. and Segal, M.B. (1970). The effects of some inhibitors and accelerators of sodium transport on the turnover of ^{22}Na in the cerebrospinal fluid. *J. Physiol.*, **209**, 131–153

Davson, H. and Spaziani, E. (1959). The blood–brain barrier. *J. Physiol.*, **149**, 135–143

Davson, H. and Spaziani, E. (1960). The fate of substances injected into the anterior chamber of the eye. *J. Physiol.*, **151**, 202–215

Davson, H. and Welch, K. (1971). The permeation of several materials into the fluids of the rabbit's brain. *J. Physiol.*, **218**, 337–351

Davson, H., Welch, K. and Segal, M.B. (1987). *Physiology and Pathophysiology of the Cerebrospinal Fluid.* Churchill Livingstone, London

Deane, R. and Segal, M.B. (1985). The transport of sugars across the perfused choroid plexus of the sheep. *J. Physiol.*, **362**, 245–260

DeBault, L.E. and Cancilla, P.A. (1980). γ-glutamyl transpeptidase in isolated brain endothelial cells and induction by glial cells *in vitro. Science*, **207**, 653–655

Dehouck, M.-P., Méresse, S., Delorme, P., Fruchart, J.-C. and Cecchelli, R. (1990). An easier, reproducible, and mass production method to study the blood–brain barrier *in vitro. J. Neurochem.*, **54**, 1798–1801

Deng, Q.-S. and Johanson, C.E. (1989). Stilbenes inhibit exchange of chloride between blood, choroid plexus and cerebrospinal fluid. *Brain Res.*, **501**, 183–187

Diamond, J.M. and Bossert, W.H. (1967). Standing gradient osmotic flow. A mechanism for coupling of water and solute transport in epithelia. *J. Gen. Physiol.*, **50**, 2061–2083

Dick, A.P.K., Harik, S.I., Klip, A. and Walker, D.M. (1984). Identification and characterization of the glucose transporter of the blood–brain barrier by cytochalasin B binding and immunological reactivity. *Proc. Natl Acad. Sci. USA*, **81**, 7233–7237

Duffy, K.R. and Pardridge, W.M. (1987). Blood–brain barrier transcytosis of insulin in developing rabbits. *Brain Res.*, **420**, 32–38

Eisenberg, H.M. and Suddith, R.L. (1979). Cerebral vessels have the capacity to transport sodium and potassium. *Science*, **206**, 1083–1085

Elsworth, J.D., Redmond, D.E. and Roth, R.H. (1982). Plasma and cerebrospinal fluid 3-methoxy-4-hydroxyphenylethylene glycol (MHPG) as indices of brain norepinephrine metabolism in primates. *Brain Res.*, **235**, 115–124

Ernst, S.A. (1975). Transport ATPase cytochemistry: ultrastructural localization of potassium-dependent phosphatase activities in rat kidney cortex. *J. Cell Biol.*, **66**, 586–608

Farrell, C.L. and Shivers, R.R. (1984). Capillary junctions in the rat are not affected by osmotic opening of the blood–brain barrier. *Acta Neuropathol.*, **63**, 179–188

Felgenhauer, K. (1974). Protein size and cerebrospinal fluid. *Klin. Wchschr.*, **52**, 1158–1164

Fenstermacher, J.D. and Davson, H. (1982). Distribution of two model amino acids from cerebrospinal fluid to brain and blood. *Am. J. Physiol.*, **242**, F171–F180

Fenstermacher, J.D. and Patlak, C.S. (1975). The exchange of material between cerebrospinal fluid and brain. In Cserr, H.F., Fenstermacher, J.D. and Fencl, J.D. (Eds), *Fluid Environment of the Brain.* Academic Press, New York, pp. 201–214

Fenstermacher, J.D., Patlak, C.S. and Blasberg, R.G. (1974). Transport of material between brain extracellular fluid, brain cells and blood. *Fed. Proc.*, **33**, 2070–2074

Firth, J.A. (1977). Cytochemical localization of the K^+ regulation interface between blood and brain. *Experientia*, **33**, 1093–1094

Fishman, J.B. and Fine, R.E. (1985). A Golgi-derived exocytic coated vesicle can contain both newly synthesized acetylcholinesterase and internalized transferrin. *J. Cell Biol.*, **101**, 423a

Frank, H.J.L. and Pardridge, W.M. (1987). A direct *in vitro* demonstration of insulin binding to isolated brain microvessels. *Diabetes*, **30**, 757–761

Fremont-Smith, F., Dailey, M.E., Merritt, H.H. and Carroll, M.P. (1931). The composition of the human cerebrospinal fluid and blood plasma in meningitis. *Arch. Neurol. Psychiat.*, **25**, 1290–1296

Frokjaer-Jensen, J. (1980). Three-dimensional organization of plasmalemmal vesicles in endothelial cells. An analysis by serial sectioning of frog mesenteric capillaries. *J. Ultrastruct. Res.*, **73**, 9–20

Frokjaer-Jensen, J. (1984). The plasmalemmal vesicular system in striated muscle capillaries and in pericytes. *Tissue and Cell*, **16**, 31–42

Gerhart, D.Z., LeVasseur, R.J., Broderius, M.A. and Drewes, L.R. (1989). Glucose transporter localization in brain using light and electron immunocytochemistry. *J. Neurosci. Res.*, **22**, 464–472

Gherst-Egea, J.-F., Minn, A. and Siest, G. (1988). A new aspect of the protective function of the blood–brain barrier: activation of four drug-metabolizing enzymes in isolated brain microvessels. *Life Sci.*, **42**, 2515–2523

Gjedde, A. and Crone, C. (1975). Induction processes in blood–brain transfer of ketone bodies during starvation. *Am. J. Physiol.*, **229**, 1165–1169

Glynn, I.M., Hara, Y. and Richards, D.E. (1984). The occlusion of sodium ions within the mammalian sodium–potassium pump: its role in sodium transport. *J. Physiol.*, **351**, 531–547

Glynn, I.M. and Richards, D.E. (1982). Occlusion of rubidium ions by the sodium–potassium pump: its implications for the mechanism of potassium transport. *J. Physiol.*, **330**, 17–43

Glynn, I.M., Richards, D.E. and Hara, Y. (1985). The properties and role of occluded ion forms of the Na,K-ATPase. In Glynn, I.M. and Ellory, C. (Eds), *The Sodium Pump*. The Company of Biologists, Cambridge

Goldmann, E.E. (1909). Die äussere und innere Sekretion des gesunden und kranken Organismus im Lichte der 'vitalen Färbung'. *Beitr. Klin. Chir.*, **64**, 192–265

Goldmann, E.E. (1913). Vitalfärbung am Zentralnervensystem. *Abh. Preuss. Akad. Wiss. Phys.-Math. Kl.*, No. 1, 1–60

Goldstein, G.W. (1979). Relation of potassium transport to oxidative metabolism in isolated brain capillaries. *J. Physiol.*, **286**, 185–195

Goldstein, G.W. (1988). Endothelial cell–astrocyte interactions. A cellular model of the blood–brain barrier. *Ann. N.Y. Acad. Sci.*, **529**, 31–39

Goldstein, G.W. and Betz, A.L. (1983). Recent advances in understanding brain capillary function. *Ann. Neurol.*, **14**, 389–395

Goldstein, G.W., Betz, A.L. and Bowman, P.D. (1984). Use of isolated brain capillaries and cultured endothelial cells to study the blood–brain barrier. *Fed. Proc.*, **43**, 191–195

Goldstein, J.L. *et al.* (1985). Receptor-mediated endocytosis: concepts emerging from LDL receptor system. *Ann. Rev. Cell Biol.*, **1**, 1–39

Greig, N.H., Fredericks, W.R., Holloway, H.W., Sonerant, T.T. and Rapoport, S.I. (1988). Delivery of human interferon-alpha to brain by transient osmotic blood–brain barrier modification in the rat. *J. Pharmacol.*, **245**, 581–586

Griffin, D.E. and Giffels, J. (1982). Study of protein characteristics that influence entry into cerebrospinal fluid of normal mice and mice with encephalitis. *J. Clin. Invest.*, **70**, 289–295

Griffiths, G. and Simons, K. (1986). The trans Golgi network: sorting at the exit side of the Golgi complex. *Science*, **234**, 438–443

Häggendal, E. and Johansson, B. (1972). Effect of increased intravascular pressure on the blood–brain barrier to protein in dogs. *Acta Neuropathol. Scand.*, **48**, 271–275

Hammes, G.G. (1982). Unifying concept for the coupling between ion pumping and ATP hydrolysis or synthesis. *Proc. Natl Acad. Sci.*, **79**, 6881–6884

Hansson, H.-A. and Johansson, B.B. (1980). Induction of pinocytosis in cerebral vessels by acute hypertension and by hyperosmolar solutions. *J. Neurosci. Res.*, **5**, 183–190

Hardebo, J.E. (1980). A time study in rat on the opening and reclosure of the blood–brain barrier after hypertensive or hypertonic insult. *Exp. Neurol.*, 70, 155–166

Hardebo, J.E., Emson, P.C., Falck, B., Owman, C. and Rosengren, E. (1980). Enzymes related to monoamine transmitter metabolism in brain microvessels. *J. Neurochem.*, 35, 1388–1393

Hardebo, J.E., Falck, B., Owman, C. and Rosengren, E. (1979). Studies on the enzymatic blood–brain barrier: quantitative measurements of DOPA decarboxylase in the wall of microvessels as related to the parenchyma in various CNS regions. *Acta Physiol. Scand.*, 105, 453–460

Hardebo, J.E. and Nilsson, B. (1981). Opening of the blood–brain barrier by acute elevation of the intracarotid pressure. *Acta Physiol. Scand.*, 111, 43–49

Harik, S.I., Doull, G.H. and Dick, A.P.K. (1985). Specific ouabain binding to brain microvessels and choroid plexus. *J. Cereb. Blood Flow Metab.*, 5, 156–160

Hawkins, R.A., Mans, A.M. and Biebuyck, J.F. (1982). Amino acid supply to individual cerebral structures in awake and anesthetized rats. *Am. J. Physiol.*, 242, E1–E11

Hawkins, R.A., Mans, A.M., Davis, D.W., Hibbard, L.S. and Lu, D.M. (1983). Glucose availability to individual cerebral structures is correlated to glucose metabolism. *J. Neurochem.*, 40, 1013–1018

Hediger, M.A., Coady, M.J., Ikeda, T.S. and Wright, E.M. (1987a). Expression cloning and a cDNA sequencing of the Na^+/glucose co-transporter. *Nature*, 330, 379–381

Hediger, M.A., Coady, M.J., Ikeda, T.S. and Wright, E.M. (1987b). Expression cloning and cDNA sequencing of the Na^+/glucose co-transporter. *Nature*, 330, 379–381

Heinemann, U. and Lux, H.D. (1977). Ceiling of stimulus induced rises in extracellular potassium concentration in the cerebral cortex of the cat. *Brain Res.*, 120, 231–249

Heisey, S.R., Held, D. and Pappenheimer, J.R. (1962). Bulk flow and diffusion in the cerebrospinal fluid of the goat. *Am. J. Physiol.*, 203, 775–781

Hibbard, L.S. and Hawkins, R.A. (1984). Three-dimensional reconstitution of metabolic data from quantitative autoradiography of rat brain. *Am. J. Physiol.*, 247, E412–E419

Hjelle, J.T., Baird-Lambert, J., Cardinale, G., Spector, S. and Udenfriend, S. (1978). Isolated microvessels: the blood–brain barrier *in vitro*. *Proc. Natl Acad. Sci. USA*, 75, 4544–4548

Hofstee, B.H.J. (1959). Non-inverted versus inverted plots in enzyme kinetics. *Nature*, 184, 1296–1298

Hollingsworth, J.G. and Davson, H. (1973). Transport of sulfate in the rabbit's brain. *J. Neurobiol.*, 4, 389–396

Hopfer, U. and Groseclose, R. (1980). The mechanism of Na^+-dependent D-glucose transport. *J. Biol. Chem.*, 255, 4453–4462

Houthoff, H.J., Go, G.K. and Gerrito, P.O. (1982). The mechanism of blood–brain barrier impairment by hyperosmolar perfusion. *Acta Neuropathol.*, 56, 99–112

Iversen, L.L. and Neal, M.J. (1968). The uptake of [^{3}H]GABA by slices of rat cerebral cortex. *J. Neurochem.*, 15, 1141–1149

Jacobs, J.M. (1977). Penetration of systemically injected horseradish peroxidase into ganglion and nerves of the autonomic nervous system. *J. Neurocytol.*, 6, 607–618

Johanson, C.E., Parandoosh, Z. and Smith, Q.R. (1985). Cl–HCO_3 exchange in choroid plexus: analysis by the DMO method for cell pH. *Am. J. Physiol.*, 249, F478–F484

Johanson, C.E. *et al.* (1989). In *Intracranial Pressure*. VII. Ed. Hoff & Betz. Springer Verlag: Berlin.

Johanson, C.E., Sweeney, S.M., Parmelee, J.T. and Epstein, M.H. (1990). Cotransport of sodium and chloride by the adult mammalian choroid plexus. *Am. J. Physiol.*, 258, C211–C216

Johnson, D.C., Singer, S., Hoop, B. and Kazemi, H. (1987). Chloride flux from blood to CSF: inhibition by furosemide and bumetanide. *J. Appl. Physiol.*, 63, 159–160

Joó, F. (1971). Increased production of coated vesicles in the brain capillaries during enhanced permeability of the blood–brain barrier. *Br. J. Exp. Pathol.*, 52, 646–649

Joó, F. (1985). The blood–brain barrier *in vitro*: ten years of research on microvessels isolated from the brain. *Neurochem. Int.*, **7**, 1–25

Jørgensen, P.L. (1985). Conformational E_1–E_2 transitions in $\alpha\beta$-units related to cation transport by pure Na,K-ATPase. In Glynn, I.M. and Ellory, C. (Eds), *The Sodium Pump*. The Company of Biologists, Cambridge, pp. 83–96

Karlish, S.J.D., Yates, D.W. and Glynn, I.M. (1978). Conformational transitions between Na^+-bound and K^+-bound forms of $(Na^+ + K^+)$-ATPase, studied with formicin nucleotides. *Biochim. Biophys. Acta*, **525**, 252–264

Karnovsky, M.J. (1967). The ultrastructural basis of capillary permeability studied with peroxidase as a tracer. *J. Cell Biol.*, **35**, 213–236

Kasanicki, M.A., Cairns, M.T., Davies, A., Gardiner, R.M. and Baldwin, S.A. (1987). Identification and characterization of the glucose-transport protein of the bovine blood–brain barrier. *Biochem. J.*, **247**, 101–108

Katzman, R. and Leiderman, P.H. (1953). Brain potassium exchange in normal adult and immature rats. *Am. J. Physiol.*, **175**, 263–270

Kessler, M. and Semenza, G. (1983). The small intestinal Na^+, D-glucose cotransporter: an asymmetric gated channel (or pore) responsive to $\Delta\psi$. *J. Membrane Biol.*, **76**, 27–56

Kety, S.S. (1951). The theory and application of the exchange of inert gas at the lungs and tissues. *Pharmacol. Rev.*, **3**, 1–41

Krogh, A. (1946). The active and passive exchanges of inorganic ions through the surfaces of living cells and through living membranes generally. *Proc. Roy. Soc. B*, **133**, 140–200

Kromphardt, H., Grobecker, H., Ring, K. and Heinz, E. (1963). Über den Einfluss von Alkali-ionen auf den Glycintransport in Ehrlich-Ascites Tumorzellen. *Biochim. Biophys. Acta*, **74**, 549–551

Kumagai, A.K., Eisenberg, J.B. and Pardridge, W.M. (1987). Absorptive mediated endocytosis of cationized albumin and a β-endorphin-cationized albumin chimeric peptide by isolated brain capillaries. *J. Biol. Chem.*, **262**, 15214–15219

Kyte, J. and Doolittle, R.F. (1982). A simple method of displaying the hydropathic character of a protein. *J. Mol. Biol.*, **157**, 105–132

Lai, F.M., Udenfriend, S. and Spector, S. (1975). Presence of norepinephrine and related enzymes in isolated brain microvessels. *Proc. Natl Acad. Sci. USA*, **72**, 4622–4625

LeFevre, P.G. (1962). Rate and affinity in human red blood cell sugar transport. *Am. J. Physiol.*, **203**, 286–290

Levin, V.A., Fenstermacher, J.D. and Patlak, C.A. (1970). Sucrose and inulin space measurements of cerebral cortex in four mammalian species. *Am. J. Physiol.*, **219**, 1528–1533

Lewandowsky, M. (1900). Zur Lehre der Cerebralspinalflüssigkeit. *Z. Klin. Med.*, **40**, 480–494

Lin, J.-T., Swarc, K., Kinne, R. and Jung, C.Y. (1984). Structure state of the Na^+/D-glucose cotransporter in calf kidney brush-border enzymes. Target size analysis of the Na^+-dependent phlorizin binding and Na^+-dependent D-glucose transport. *Biochim. Biophys. Acta*, **777**, 201–208

Long, D.M. (1970). Capillary ultrastructure and the blood–brain barrier in human malignant brain tumors. *Neurosurgery*, **32**, 127–144

Lossinsky, A.S., Vorbrodt, A.W. and Wisniewski, H.M. (1983). Ultracytochemical studies on vesicular and canalicular transport structures in the injured mammalian blood–brain barrier. *Acta Neuropathol.*, **61**, 239–245

Lossinsky, A.-S., Vorbrodt, A.W., Wisniewski, H.M. and Iwanowski, L. (1981). Ultra-cytochemical evidence for endothelial channel–lysosome connections in mouse brain following blood–brain barrier changes. *Acta Neuropathol.*, **53**, 197–202

Lucchesi, K.J. and Gosselin, R.E. (1990). Mechanism of L-glucose, raffinose and inulin transport across intact blood–brain barrier. *Am. J. Physiol.*, **258**, H695–H705

Lund-Andersen, H. (1979). Transport of glucose from blood to brain. *Physiol. Rev.*, **59**, 305–352

Lux, H.D. and Naher, E. (1973). The equilibration time course of $(K^+)_0$ in cat cortex. *Exp. Brain Res.*, **17**, 190–205

McComb, J.G. and Hyman, S. (1990). Lymphatic drainage of cerebrospinal fluid in the primate. In Johansson, B.B., Owman, C. and Widner, H. (Eds), *Pathophysiology of the Blood–Brain Barrier*. Elsevier, Amsterdam

Madrazzo, I. *et al.* (1987). Open neurosurgical autograft of adrenal medulla to the right caudate nucleus in two patients with intractable Parkinson's disease. *New Engl J. Med.*, **316**, 831–834

Maren, T.H. (1977). Ion secretion into cerebrospinal fluid. *Exp. Eye Res.*, **25** (Suppl), 157–159

Masuzawa, T., Saito, T. and Sato, F. (1981). Cytochemical studies on enzyme activity associated with cerebrospinal fluid secretion in the choroid plexus and ventricular ependyma. *Brain Res.*, **222**, 309–322

Michaelis, L. and Menten, M.L. (1913). Die Kinetik der Invertinwirkung. *Biochem. Z.*, **49**, 333–369

Miller, L.P. and Oldendorf, W.H. (1986). Regional kinetic constants for blood–brain barrier pyruvic acid transport in conscious rats by the monocarboxylic acid carrier. *J. Neurochem.*, **46**, 1412–1416

Miller, L.P., Pardridge, W.M., Braun, L.D. and Oldendorf, W.H. (1985). Kinetic constants for blood–brain barrier amino acid transport in conscious rats. *J. Neurochem.*, **45**, 1427–1432

Mueckler, M. *et al.* (1985). Sequence and structure of a human glucose transporter. *Science*, **229**, 941–945

Murphy, V.A. and Johanson, C.E. (1989). Alteration of sodium transport by the choroid plexus with amiloride. *Biochim. Biophys. Acta*, **979**, 187–192

Murphy, V.A. and Johanson, C.E. (1990). Na^+–H^+ exchange in choroid plexus and CSF in acute metabolic acidosis or alkalosis. *Am. J. Physiol.*, **258**, F1528–F1537

Nabeshima, S., Reese, T.S., Landis, D.M.D. and Brightman, M.W. (1975). Junctions in the meninges and marginal glia. *J. Comp. Neurol.*, **164**, 127–170

Neame, K.D. and Richards, T.G. (1972). *Elementary Kinetics of Membrane Carrier Transport*. Blackwell, Oxford

Neuwelt, E.A. and Rapoport, S.I. (1983). Modification of the blood–brain barrier in the chemotherapy of malignant brain tumors. *Fed. Proc.*, **43**, 214–219

Nieh, M., Kunz, U. and Koepsell, K. (1987). Identification of D-glucose-binding polypeptides which are components of the renal Na^+-D-glucose cotransporter. *J. Biol. Chem.*, **262**, 10718–10727

Nishimura, M., Johnson, D.C. and Kazemi, H. (1988). Effects of inhibitors on chloride outflux from cerebrospinal fluid. *J. Appl. Physiol.*, **64**, 2183–2189

Norby, J.C., Klodos, I. and Christiansen, N.O. (1983). Kinetics of Na-ATPase activity by the Na-K-pump. Interactions of the phosphorylated intermediates with Na^+, $Tris^+$, and K^+. *J. Gen. Physiol.*, **82**, 725–759

Novikoff, A.B., Yam, A. and Novikoff, P.M. (1975). Cytochemical study of secretory process in transplantable insulinoma of Syrian golden hamster. *Proc. Natl Acad. Sci. USA*, **72**, 4501–4505

Ockner, R.K., Weisiger, R.A. and Gollan, J.L. (1983). Hepatic uptake of albumin-bound substances: albumin receptor concept. *Am. J. Physiol.*, **245**, G13–G18

Oldendorf, W.H. (1971). Brain uptake of radiolabeled amino acids, amines, and hexoses after arterial injection. *Am. J. Physiol.*, **221**, 1629–1639

Oldendorf, W.H. (1971/2). Blood–brain barrier permeability to lactate. *Eur. Neurol.*, **6**, 49–55

Oldendorf, W.H. (1973). Carrier-mediated blood–brain barrier transport of short-chain monocarboxylic acids. *Am. J. Physiol.*, **224**, 1450–1453

Oldendorf, W.H. and Davson, H. (1967). Brain extracellular space and the sink action of the cerebrospinal fluid. *Arch. Neurol.*, **17**, 196–205

Oppelt, W.W., Maren, T.H., Owens, E.S. and Rall, D.P. (1963). Effects of acid–base alterations on cerebrospinal fluid production. *Proc. Soc. Exp. Biol. Med.*, *N.Y.*, **114**, 86–89

Orlowski, M. (1963). *Arch. Immun. Exp. Ther.*, **11**, 1 (quoted by Orlowski *et al.*, 1974)

Orlowski, M., Sessa, G. and Green, J.P. (1974). γ-Glutamyl transpeptidase in brain capillaries: possible site of a blood–brain barrier for amino acids. *Science*, **184**, 66–68

Pan, B.-T. and Johnstone, R.M. (1983). Fate of the transferrin receptor during maturation of sheep reticulocytes *in vitro*: selective externalization of the receptor. *Cell*, **33**, 967–977

Pan, B.-T. and Johnstone, R.M. (1984). Selective externalization of the transferrin receptor by sheep reticulocytes *in vitro*. Response to ligands and inhibition of exocytosis. *J. Biol. Chem.*, **259**, 9776–9782

Pappenheimer, J.R. (1953). Passage of molecules through capillary walls. *Physiol. Rev.*, **33**, 387–423

Pappenheimer, J.R., Heisey, J.R. and Jordan, E.F. (1961). Active transport of Diodrast and phenolsulfonaphthalein from cerebrospinal fluid to blood. *Am. J. Physiol.*, **200**, 1–10

Pardridge, W.M. (1977). Kinetics of competitive inhibition of neutral amino acid transport across the blood–brain barrier. *J. Neurochem.*, **28**, 103–108

Pardridge, W.M. (1979). Carrier-mediated transport of thyroid hormones through the blood–brain barrier: primary role of albumin-bound hormone. *Endocrinology*, **105**, 605–612

Pardridge, W.M. (1981). Transport of protein-bound hormones into tissues *in vivo*. *Endocrinol. Rev.*, **2**, 103–123

Pardridge, W.M. (1984). Transport of nutrients and hormones through the blood–brain barrier. *Fed. Proc.*, **43**, 201–204

Pardridge, W.M. (1987). Plasma protein-mediated transport of steroid and thyroid hormones. *Am. J. Physiol.*, **252**, E157–E164

Pardridge, W.M., Eisenberg, J. and Cefalu, W.T. (1985). Absence of albumin receptor on brain capillaries *in vivo* or *in vitro*. *Am. J. Physiol.*, **249**, E264–E267

Pardridge, W.M. and Landaw, E.M. (1984). Tracer kinetic model of blood–brain barrier transport of plasma protein-bound ligand. *J. Clin. Invest.*, **74**, 745–752

Pardridge, W.M. and Mietus, L.J. (1979). Transport of steroid hormone through the rat blood–brain barrier. *J. Clin. Invest.*, **64**, 145–154

Pardridge, W.M. and Mietus, L.J. (1980). Effect of progesterone-binding globulin versus a progesterone antiserum on steroid hormone transport through the blood–brain barrier. *Endocrinology*, **106**, 1137–1141

Pardridge, W.M. and Mietus, L.J. (1981). Enkephalin and blood–brain barrier: studies of binding and degradation in isolated brain microvessels. *Endocrinology*, **109**, 1138–1143

Pardridge, W.M. and Oldendorf, W.H. (1975a). Kinetics of blood–brain barrier transport of hexoses. *Biochim. Biophys. Acta*, **382**, 377–392

Pardridge, W.M. and Oldendorf, W.H. (1975b). Kinetic analysis of blood–brain barrier transport of amino acids. *Biochim. Biophys. Acta*, **401**, 128–136

Pardridge, W.M., Triguero, D. and Buciak, J. (1989). Transport of histone through the blood–brain barrier. *J. Pharmacol.*, **251**, 821–826

Pardridge, W.M., Triguero, D., Yang, J. and Cancilla, P.A. (1990). Comparison of *in vitro* and *in vivo* models of drug transcytosis through the blood–brain barrier. *J. Pharmacol.*, **253**, 884–891

Pardridge, W.M., Yang, J. and Eisenberg, J. (1985). Blood–brain barrier protein phosphorylation and dephosphorylation. *J. Neurochem.*, **45**, 1141–1147

Patlak, C.S., Blasberg, R.G. and Fenstermacher, J.D. (1983). Graphical evaluation of blood-to-brain transfer constants from multiple-time uptake data. *J. Cereb. Blood Flow Metab.*, **3**, 1–7

Patlak, C.S. and Fenstermacher, J.D. (1975). Measurements of blood–brain transfer constants by ventriculocisternal perfusion. *Am. J. Physiol.*, **229**, 877–884

Peerce, B.E. and Wright, E.M. (1984a). Conformational changes in the intestinal brush-border sodium–glucose cotransporter labeled with fluorescein isothiocyanate.

Proc. Natl Acad. Sci. USA, **81**, 2223–2226

Peerce, B.E. and Wright, E.M. (1984b). Sodium-induced conformational changes in the glucose transporter of intestinal brush-borders. *J. Biol. Chem.*, **259**, 14105–14112

Peerce, B.E. and Wright, E.M. (1985). Evidence for tyrosyl residues at the Na^+ site on the intestinal Na^+/glucose cotransporter. *J. Biol. Chem.*, **260**, 6026–6031

Peerce, B.E. and Wright, E.M. (1986). Distance between substrate sites on the Na-glucose cotransporter by fluorescent energy transfer. *Proc. Natl Acad. Sci. USA*, **83**, 8092–8096

Perlow, M.J., Freed, W.J., Hoffer, B.J., Seiger, A., Olson, L. and Wyatt, R.J. (1979). Brain grafts reduce motor abnormalities produced by destruction of nigrostriatal dopamine system. *Science*, **204**, 643–647

Pollay, M. (1966). Cerebrospinal fluid transport and the thiocyanate space of brain. *Am. J. Physiol.*, **210**, 275–279

Pollay, M. and Curl, F. (1967). Secretion of cerebrospinal fluid by the ventricular ependyma of the rabbit. *Am. J. Physiol.*, **213**, 1031–1038

Pollay, M. and Davson, H. (1963). The passage of certain substances out of the cerebrospinal fluid. *Brain*, **86**, 137–150

Preston, J.E., Segal, M.B., Walley, G.J. and Zloković, B.V. (1989). Neutral amino acid uptake by the isolated perfused sheep choroid plexus. *J. Physiol.*, **408**, 31–43

Prince, D.A., Lux, H.D. and Naher, E. (1973). Measurement of extracellular potassium activity in cat cortex. *Brain Res.*, **50**, 489–495

Quinton, P.M., Wright, E.M. and Tormey, J. McD. (1973). Localization of sodium pumps in the choroid plexus epithelium. *J. Cell Biol.*, **58**, 724–730

Quiocho, F.A. and Vyas, N.K. (1984). Novel stereospecificity of the L-arabinose-binding protein. *Nature*, **310**, 381–386

Rall, D.P., Oppelt, W.W. and Patlak, C.S. (1962). Extracellular space of brain as determined by diffusion of inulin from the ventricular system. *Life Sci.*, **2**, 43–48

Rapoport, S.I. (1976). Opening of the blood–brain barrier by acute hypertension. *Exp. Neurol.*, **52**, 467–479

Rapoport, S.I., Hori, M. and Klatzo, I. (1972). Testing of a hypothesis for osmotic opening of the blood–brain barrier. *Am. J. Physiol.*, **223**, 323–331

Rapoport, S.I., Ohno, K. and Pettigrew, K.D. (1979). Drug entry into the brain. *Brain Res.*, **172**, 354–359

Reese, T.S. and Brightman, M.W. (1968). Similarity in structure and permeability to peroxidase of epithelia overlying fenestrated cerebral capillaries. *Anat. Rec.*, **160**, 414 (abstract)

Reese, T.S. and Karnovsky, M.J. (1967). Fine structural localization of a blood–brain barrier to exogenous peroxidase. *J. Cell Biol.*, **34**, 207–217

Renkin, E.M. (1954). Filtration, diffusion and molecular sieving through porous cellulose membranes. *J. Gen. Physiol.*, **38**, 225–243

Renkin, E.M. (1959). Transport of potassium-42 from blood to tissue in isolated mammalian skeletal muscles. *Am. J. Physiol.*, **197**, 1205–1210

Riklis, E. and Quastel, J.H. (1958). Effects of cations on sugar absorption by isolated surviving guinea pig intestine. *Can. J. Biochem. Physiol.*, **36**, 347–362

Roncali, L., Nico, B., Ribatti, D., Bertossi, M. and Mancini, L. (1986). Microscopical and ultrastructural investigation on the development of the blood–brain barrier in the chick embryo optic tectum. *Acta Neuropathol.*, **70**, 193–201

Rosenberg, I.H., Goldman, A.L. and Rosenberg, L.E. (1965). The role of sodium ion in the transport of amino acids by the intestine. *J. Biochim. Biophys. Acta*, **102**, 101–171

Rosenberg, T. and Wilbrandt, W. (1955). The kinetics of membrane transport involving chemical reactions. *Exp. Cell Res.*, **9**, 49–67

Rosenstein, J.R. and Brightman, M.W. (1986). Alterations of the blood–brain barrier after transplantation of autonomic ganglia into the mammalian central nervous system. *J. Comp. Neurol.*, **250**, 339–351

Rothstein, A. and Ramjeesingh, M. (1980). The functional arrangement of the anion channel of red blood cells. *Ann. N.Y. Acad. Sci.*, **358**, 1–12

Saito, Y. and Wright, E.M. (1987). Regulation of intracellular chloride in bullfrog choroid plexus. *Brain Res.*, **417**, 267–272

Schatzmann, H.J. (1953). Herzglykoside als Hemmungstoffe fur die aktiven Kalium- und Natriumtransport durch die Erythrocytenmembran. *Helv. Physiol. Pharmacol. Acta*, **11**, 346–354

Semenza, G., Kessler, M., Hosang, M., Weber, J. and Schmidt, U. (1984). Biochemistry of the Na^+, D-glucose cotransporter of the small intestinal brush-border membrane. The state of the art in 1984. *Biochim. Biophys. Acta*, **779**, 343–379

Sen, A.K. and Widdas, W.F. (1962). Variations of the parameters of glucose transfer across the human erythrocyte membrane in the presence of inhibitors of transfer. *J. Physiol.*, **160**, 404–416

Shivers, R.R., Edmonds, C.L. and Del Maestro, R.F. (1984). Microvascular permeability in induced astrocytomas and peritumor neuropil of rat brain. *Acta Neuropathol.*, **64**, 192–202

Skou, J.C. (1989). Sodium–potassium pump. In *Membrane Transport* (Ed. Tosteson, D.C.), Amer. Physiol. Soc., Bethesda, Md., pp. 155–185

Smith, Q.R. and Rapoport, S.I. (1984). Carrier-mediated transport of chloride across the blood–brain barrier. *J. Neurochem.*, **42**, 754–763

Solenski, N.J. and Williams, S.K. (1985). Insulin binding and vesicular ingestion in capillary endothelim. *J. Cell Physiol.*, **124**, 87–95

Somjen, G.G., Segal, M.B. and Herreras, O. (1992). Osmotic hypertensive opening of the blood–brain barrier in rats does not necessarily provide access for potassium to cerebral intracranial fluid. *J. Physiol.* (in press)

Spector, R. (1986). Nucleoside and vitamin homeostasis in the mammalian central nervous system. *Ann. N.Y. Acad. Sci.*, **481**, 221–230

Stern, L. and Gautier, R. (1921). Rapports entre le liquide céphalorachidien et la circulation sanguine. *Arch. Int. Physiol.*, **17**, 138–192

Stern, L. and Gautier, R. (1922). Les rapports entre le liquide céphalo-rachidien et les éléments nerveux de l'axe cérébrospinal. *Arch. Int. Physiol.*, **17**, 391–448

Stewart, P.A. and Wiley, M.J. (1981). Developing nervous tissue induces formation of blood–brain barrier characteristics in invading endothelial cells: a study using quail chick transplantation chimeras. *Devel. Biol.*, **84**, 183–192

Stollman, Y.R., Gartner, U., Theilman, L., Ohmi, N. and Wolkoff, A.W. (1983). Hepatic bilirubin uptake in the isolated perfused rat liver is not facilitated by albumin binding. *J. Clin. Invest.*, **72**, 718–723

Stoorvogel, W., Geuze, H.J., Griffith, J.M. and Strous, G.J. (1988). The pathways of endocytosed transferrin and secretory protein in the *trans*-Golgi reticulum. *J. Cell Biol.*, **106**, 1821–1829

Szentesvanyi, I., Patlak, C.S., Ellis, R.A. and Cserr, H.F. (1984). Drainage of interstitial fluid from different regions of rat brain. *Am. J. Physiol.*, **246**, F835–F844

Takasato, Y., Rapoport, S.I. and Smith, Q.R. (1984). An *in situ* brain perfusion technique to study cerebrovascular transport in the rat. *Am. J. Physiol.*, **247**, H484–H493

Tao-Cheng, J.-H., Nagy, Z. and Brightman, M.W. (1987). Tight junctions of brain capillaries *in vitro* are enhanced by astroglia. *J. Neurosci.*, **7**, 3293–3299

Taverna, R.D. and Langdon, R.G. (1973). Reversible association of cytochalasin B with the human erythrocyte membrane. *Biochim. Biophys. Acta*, **323**, 207–219

Terasaki, T., Ken-Ichihirai, Sato, H., Kang, Y.S. and Tsuji, A. (1989). Absorptive-mediated endocytosis of a dynorphin-like analgesic peptide, E-2078, into the blood–brain barrier. *J. Pharmacol.*, **251**, 351–357

Tibbling, G., Link, H. and Ohman, S. (1977). Principle of albumin and IgG analyses in neurological disorders. I. Establishment of reference values. *Scand. J. Clin. Lab. Invest.*, **37**, 385–390

Triguero, D., Buciak, J. and Pardridge, W.M. (1990). Capillary depletion method for quantification of blood–brain barrier transport of circulating peptides and plasma proteins. *J. Neurochem.*, **54**, 1882–1888

Triguero, D., Buciak, J.B., Yang, J. and Pardridge, W.M. (1989). Blood–brain barrier transport of cationized immunoglobulin G: enhanced delivery compared to native protein. *Proc. Natl Acad. Sci. USA*, **86**, 4761–4765

Tripathi, R.J. and Tripathi, R.C. (1974). Vacuolar transcellular channels as a drainage pathway for cerebrospinal fluid. *J. Physiol.*, **239**, 195–206

Vogh, B.P., Godman, D.R. and Maren, T.H. (1985). Aluminium and gallium arrest formation of cerebrospinal fluid by the mechanism of OH^- depletion. *J. Pharmacol.*, **233**, 715–721

Vogh, B.P. and Langham, M.R. (1981). The effect of furosemide and bumetanide on cerebrospinal fluid function. *Brain Res.*, **221**, 171–183

Vorbrodt, A.W., Lossinsky, A.S. and Wisniewski, H.M. (1982). Cytochemical localization of ouabain-sensitive, K^+-dependent p-nitro-phenylphosphatase (Transport ATPase) in the mouse central and peripheral nervous systems. *Brain Res.*, **243**, 225–234

Weindl, A. and Joynt, R. (1973). Barrier properties of the subcommissural organ. *Arch. Neurol.*, **29**, 16–22

Weisiger, R.J., Gollan, J. and Ockner, R. (1981). Receptor for albumin on the liver cell surface may mediate uptake of fatty acids and other albumin-bound substances. *Science*, **211**, 1048–1051

Welch, K. (1962a). Active transport of iodide by choroid plexus of rabbit *in vitro*. *Am. J. Physiol.*, **202**, 757–760

Welch, K. (1962b). Concentration of thiocyanate by the choroid plexus of the rabbit *in vitro*. *Proc. Soc. Exp. Biol. Med.*, **109**, 953–954

Welch, K. (1969). A model for the distribution of materials in fluids of the central nervous system. *Brain Res.*, **16**, 453–468

Westergaard, E., Go, G., Klatzo, I. and Spatz, M. (1976). Increased permeability of cerebral vessels to horseradish peroxidase induced by ischemia in Mongolian gerbils. *Acta Neuropathol.*, **35**, 307–325

Westergaard, E., Van Deurs, B. and Brøndsted, H.E. (1977). Increased vesicular transfer of horseradish peroxidase across cerebral endothelium evoked by acute hypertension. *Acta Neuropathol.*, **37**, 141–152

Whittam, R. (1962). The asymmetrical stimulation of a membrane adenosine triphosphatase in relation to active cation transport. *Biochem. J.*, **84**, 110–118

Widdas, W.F. (1952). Inability of difusion to account for placental glucose transfer in the sheep and consideration of the kinetics of a possible carrier transfer. *J. Physiol.*, **118**, 23–39

Widdas, W.F. (1954). Facilitated transfer of hexoses across the human erythrocyte membrane. *J. Physiol.*, **125**, 163–180

Wolff, J. (1963). Beiträge zur Ultrastruktur der Kapillaren in der normalen Grosshirnrinde. *Z. Zellforsch.*, **73**, 174–191

Wright, E.M. (1970). Ion transport across the frog posterior choroid plexus. *Brain Res.*, **23**, 302–304

Yudilevich, D.L. and De Rose, N. (1971). Blood–brain transfer of glucose and other molecules measured by rapid indicator dilution. *Am. J. Physiol.*, **220**, 841–846

Yudilevich, D.L., De Rose, N. and Sepulveda, F.V. (1972). Facilitated transport of amino acids through the blood–brain barrier of the dog studied on a single capillary pass. *Brain Res.*, **44**, 569–578

Ziylan, Y.Z. (1984). Pathophysiology of the opening of the blood–brain and blood–cerebrospinal fluid barriers in acute hypertension. *Exp. Neurol.*, **84**, 18–28

Ziylan, Y.Z., Robinson, P.J. and Rapoport, S.I. (1983). Differential blood–brain permeability to [^{14}C] sucrose and [^{3}H] inulin after osmotic opening in the rat. *Exp. Neurol.*, **79**, 845–857

Ziylan, Y.Z., Robinson, P.J. and Rapoport, S.I. (1984). Blood–brain barrier permeability and sucrose and dextran after osmotic opening. *Am. J. Physiol.*, **247**, R634–R638

Zloković, B.V., Begley, D.J., Djuricić, B.M. and Mitrović, D.M. (1986). Measurement of solute transport across the blood–brain barrier in the perfused guinea pig brain: method and application to *N*-methyl-alpha-aminoisobutyric acid. *J. Neurochem.*, **46**, 1444–1459

Zloković, B.V. Davson, H., Preston, J.E. and Segal, M.B. (1987a). The effects of aluminium chloride on the rate of secretion of the cerebrospinal fluid. *Exp. Neurol.*, **98**, 436–452

Zloković, B.V. *et al.* (1987b). Neuropeptide transport mechanisms in the central nervous system. In *Peptide and Amino Acid Transport Mechanisms in the Central Nervous System* (Eds Rakić, L., Begley, D.J., Davson, H. and Zloković, B.V.), Macmillan, London

Zloković, B.V., Lipovac, M.N., Begley, D.J., Davson, H. and Rakić, L. (1988). Slow penetration of thyrotropin releasing hormone across the blood–brain barrier of *in situ* perfused guinea pig brain. *J. Neurochem.*, **51**, 252–257

Notes

[1] The permeability of muscle to glucose is sensitive to insulin, by contrast with that of the erythrocyte or brain, and it is interesting that the transporter protein seems to be the same for both processes.

[2] Baly and Horuk (1988) have reviewed the biology and biochemistry of the glucose transporter. They distinguish three types—namely the bacterial permease, where entry is at the expense of ATP, etc.; Na^+- or H^+-dependent entry; and facilitated diffusion, the latter being divided into categories of insulin-dependence, as with adipocytes and muscle, and insulin-independence, as with brain, liver and the erythrocyte.

[3] A more general model describing the coupling between ion pumping and ATP hydrolysis or synthesis has been presented by Hammes (1982).

[4] The bonding of sugar molecules to a protein involved in active transport of this sugar into, say, a bacterial cell must be highly specific for the structure of sugar molecules, so that only certain sugars are taken up and metabolized. The actual arrangement of atoms in the binding site for arabinose in *E. coli* bacteria has been elucidated by Quiocho and Vyas (1984), using X-ray analysis with very high resolution (1.7 Å). The protein had a bilobate form and the sequestering site for sugar was in a cleft between the two lobes, an arrangement postulated on theoretical grounds to account for the specific uptake of a sugar by a transporter and its translocation through the membrane cleft as a result of a conformational or hinge-binding motion.

[5] By the term *hydropathy* is meant the tendency of a molecule, or part of a molecule, to dissolve in water; thus, molecules fall into two main classes—the hydrophilic, or water-soluble, and the hydrophobic, or lipophilic, types. Those combining these features, notably the lipids of the plasma membrane, which have strongly lipophilic hydrocarbon chains with polar end-groups, are described as *amphipathic*. A protein embedded in a lipid bilayer, such as the postulated transporters, must have a strongly lipophilic region, or regions, in its amino acid sequence, that permit this close association with lipid; and Kyte and Doolittle (1982) have devised a mode of displaying the hydropathic features of a protein, determined by assigning probable degrees of hydropathy to the individual amino acids in a sequence, using a scale ranging from -4.5 for the strongly hydrophilic arginine to $+4.5$ for the lipophilic isoleucine. Thus, with a suitable computer program that continuously determines the average hydropathy of a moving segment of polypeptide sequence as it advances through the amino acid sequence of a protein, from its amino terminal to its carboxy terminal, a graphic visualization of the peaks in hydropathy may be made, as in Figure 1.32. The best-understood membrane protein that has regions spanning the lipid

membrane is bacterial rhodopsin, involved in transduction of the light stimulus to the metabolic apparatus of the light-sensitive cell. This has seven membrane-spanning segments, of known amino acid sequence. There was excellent agreement between the plotted regions of hydropathy and the known location of the transmembrane fragments, and it was concluded that an average hydropathy, taken over segments containing 19 amino acids of greater than $+1.6$, indicated a probability that it would be one of the sequences spanning the membrane.

[6] Enzymes that break down amine transmitters, such as monoamine oxidase and COMT, are present in brain capillaries (Lai *et al.*, 1975; Hardebo *et al.*, 1980); the monolayers grown by Audjus and Borchadrt likewise contained these in concentrations comparable with those in homogenates of grey matter. Bowman *et al.* (1983) have described the culture technique, identifying the cells as true endothelial cells by containing factor VIII/von Willebrand antigen. The overlap regions contained junctions which, on freeze-fracture, revealed the usual anastomizing arrays of particles seen in normal brain capillaries. In a Ca^{2+}-free medium the cells retract reversibly; in the retracted condition the permeability of the monolayer to sucrose is increased by 120%. Hypertonic arabinose 'opened the barrier' (p. 111) by increasing sucrose permeability by 40%. More recently Dehouck *et al.* (1990) have described a 'mass production' technique for preparing co-cultures of endothelium and astrocytes.

[7] There have been a number of studies on the effects of changes in concentration of K^+ in the extracellular space of brain on the resting potentials of brain cells (e.g. Lux and Naher, 1973; Prince *et al.*, 1973; Heinemann and Lux, 1977) and they agree on a value of about 3 meq/l for the extracellular fluid concentration; unfortunately they do not give values for plasma levels, but if we take the value of 4.35 meq/kg H_2O found by Bito and Davson (1966) for the non-anaesthetized cat, this indicates a value closer to the CSF than the plasma.

[8] The equation was derived by Crone in his 1963 paper on capillary permeability in various tissues; similar equations were developed independently by Kety (1951) and Renkin (1959), so that the equation is generally named after Kety, Renkin and Crone.

[9] Lectins, as originally defined, are glycoproteins which, because of their two carbohydrate residues, are able to bind to carbohydrate residues on the surface of the erythrocyte, thereby linking two cells together and causing agglutination, i.e. clumping and precipitation from their suspension in plasma or saline. Barondes (1988) has argued that the early classification of lectins was on too narrow a basis, since other glycoproteins could link to *non-glycoside* sites. Thus, the receptor in the hepatocyte that is responsible for endocytosis of desialated glycoproteins in the blood attaches the desialated protein through its exposed galactose residue, and has been included in the enlarged definition; in this case its bipolarity is manifest first in the carbohydrate residue and second in the lipophilic region that permits integration into the cell membrane. Thus, the sialic acid on many glycoproteins is essential for their function, e.g. as a hormone, as with human chorionic gonadotrophin (HCG); when this is split off, the residue must be removed from the circulation by the liver cell, a removal that occurs by endocytosis following an initial attachment to the asialoglycoprotein receptor in the cell membrane (Ashwell and Morell, 1974).

[10] Actually, free diffusion would demand that rate was inversely proportional to the *square root* of molecular weight (Davson and Danielli, 1942).

Chapter 2

Transport of Glucose and Amino Acids in the Central Nervous System

Glucose

Source of Metabolic Energy

Glucose is the main source of energy for the central nervous system, so that the dynamics of its supply from blood are of great interest, especially since the central nervous tissue does not store glycogen to any great extent. Thus, the continuous metabolism of glucose must be adequately maintained by a continuous supply of the metabolite from the blood. Sugars, like amino acids, are highly water-soluble, and, being relatively large molecules, they are unlikely to penetrate the capillary membrane of nervous tissue to any extent in the absence of special mechanisms. That special mechanisms exist for both classes of metabolite has already been made clear, the transport from blood to nervous tissue being of the carrier-mediated, or facilitated, type, exhibiting Michaelis–Menten kinetics from which the two parameters, K_m and V_{max} may be derived, K_m being regarded as the reciprocal of the affinity of the molecule for the hypothetical carrier in the capillary membrane, or, more specifically, the concentration of the solute at which the carrier is half-saturated. V_{max} is the maximum rate of transport across the capillary, obtained by extrapolating the rate to zero solute concentration, and is an index to the number of carrier sites available to the solute.

The Steady-state Condition

Before considering the kinetics of the blood–brain barrier to glucose in detail, we must first consider the steady-state concentrations in the various compartments *vis-à-vis* the blood plasma. These compartments will be the extracellular and intracellular fluids of the nervous tissue, and, in parallel with these, the cerebro-spinal fluid, as illustrated in Figure 2.1. This last compartment comes into close relations with the extracellular fluid of the brain, from which it is separated by highly permeable membranes, the ependymal linings of the ventricles and the pia-glial surfaces. The composition of this fluid is of interest, since, as we have seen, this is probably very similar to that of the extracellular fluid of brain precisely because of the free diffusional communication between the two compartments, although the extent to which metabolism of glucose within the cells creates a sink favouring a loss of glucose from the extracellular space, forcing the concentration in the extracellular fluid below that in the CSF, creates some uncertainty. As will be evident from Figure 2.1, the actual concentrations in CSF, extracellular fluid

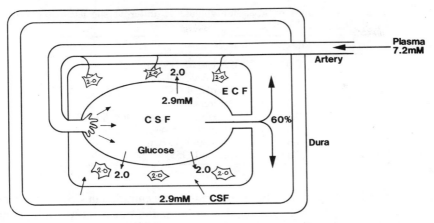

Figure 2.1   The steady-state distribution of glucose between the various compartments of the central nervous system. Values shown are in mM and arrows indicate net flux at steady state due to utilization by brain cells. Concentrations are approximate and refer to the rat (see text)

and intracellular fluid will be governed by the rate of utilization within the cells, indicated by the downward arrow, the rate at which the utilized glucose is replaced by diffusion from the extracellular space to cells, the rate at which the glucose lost from the extracellular space is replaced from the plasma, i.e. by the permeability of the blood–brain barrier, and finally by the rate at which any losses from the CSF to the extracellular fluid are replaced by renewal of the CSF. In general, the evidence indicates that the CSF concentration stays about equal to that in the extracellular fluid, a hypothesis based largely on the uniformity in concentration of glucose in the CSF when sampled from regions close to its origin (ventricles), the cisterna magna and more remote subarachnoid spaces (p. 108). From a metabolic point of view, furthermore, the CSF would be quite inadequate to supply glucose to the central nervous tissue in amounts that would significantly contribute to the amount utilized.

Thus, the brain must rely on its capillary circulation, some 5000 times greater than that of the choroid plexuses, for its glucose supplies. A knowledge of the relations between CSF and blood is nevertheless useful in the present context, since the CSF is easily accessible, and may most probably be considered as representative of brain extracellular fluid, at any rate under steady-state conditions.

Concentrations in CSF and Brain

Inspection of Table 2.1 indicates that the concentration of glucose in CSF of the rabbit is only some 60% of that in plasma–H_2O, i.e. R_{CSF} is 0.60. As Table 2.1 shows, this value of R_{CSF}, so much lower than unity, as would be expected of an uncharged non-electrolyte, is a general phenomenon, so far as mammalian species

Table 2.1 Values of R_{CSF} for glucose in different species. After Lund-Andersen (1979)

Species	R_{CSF}	Reference
Rat	0.3	Lewis *et al.* (1974)
	0.4	Feise *et al.* (1976)
Cat	0.6	Brøndsted (1970b)
	0.6	Davson (1967)
Sheep	0.6	Pappenheimer and Setchell (1973)
Dog	0.8	Atkinson and Weiss (1969)
Man	0.8	Brøndsted (1970a)
Rabbit	0.6	Davson (1955)

are concerned. As Figure 2.2 shows, where the concentration in CSF of the rat is plotted against plasma concentration, the concentration varies linearly with plasma concentration, so that, although its concentration depends on the metabolic state of the animal, the value of R_{CSF} is independent of this, suggesting a passive relation between the two fluids, at any rate so far as adjustments to change in plasma level are concerned. The fact that R_{CSF} is always less than unity, however, indicates the probable influence of an active process at the choroid plexuses by which the CSF level is held below that of plasma (Davson, 1976). If the low value in CSF were attributable to a metabolic sink in the adjacent tissue, the value of R_{CSF} might be expected to fall at low plasma levels when, as the middle curve shows, the tissue level falls to very low values, enhancing any sink action of the nervous tissue.

Concentration in Intracellular Water

The relative concentrations of glucose in the intracellular and extracellular compartments will be governed by utilization within the cell and the kinetics of passage across the cell membrane. If the transport rate exceeded the phosphorylation rate, the barrier across the cell membrane would not be significant, the rate of phosphorylation governing the transport into the cell, and free glucose would be found within the cell. If, on the other hand, the transport rate was less than that of phosphorylation, transport would be the rate-limiting factor for metabolism and free glucose would be absent. The human erythrocyte and liver cell are of the type in which transport rate exceeds phosphorylation and there is free glucose in them, while this is not true of muscle. Chemical analysis of brain tissue indicates the presence of glucose within the cells. Thus, Bryan *et al.* (1983) found a brain glucose content of 1.53 ± 0.04 μmol/g compared with a plasma level of 7.12 ± 0.53 μmol/g in unstressed unanaesthetized rats. On the assumption that the extracellular space of rat's brain is about 15% and that the concentration of glucose in the extracellular fluid is equal to that in the CSF (Davson, 1958; Brøndsted, 1970a), which, in the rat is 40% of the plasma value (Feise *et al.*, 1976), then we may compute an intracellular concentration of 1.8 mM, compared with 2.84 mM for the CSF; i.e. the intracellular concentration is less than that of

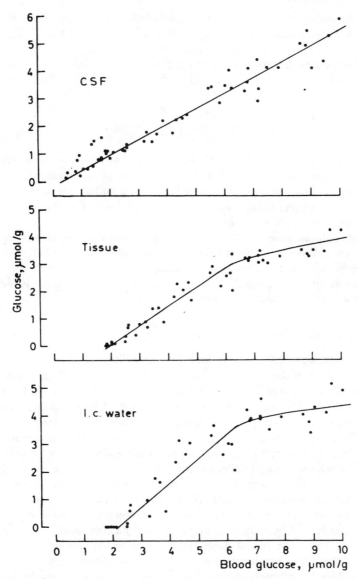

Figure 2.2 Glucose concentrations in CSF and brain tissue as a function of blood concentration. Intracellular concentrations were calculated on the basis of a blood volume of 3% and an extracellular space of 20%. Below blood-glucose concentrations of 1.7 μmol/g the tissue concentrations were close to zero and there was no intracellular glucose. From Lewis *et al.* (1974)

the CSF, as would be expected in view of the consumption by the brain cells.

Lund-Andersen (1979) deduced the internal glucose concentration from the Michaelis–Menten transport parameters and the steady-state glucose utilization.

Thus, at the steady state, the rate of glucose utilization is equal to the rate of the net glucose influx; a reasonable average of this is 0.4 µmol g^{-1} min^{-1}. T_{max} and K_t were taken as 1.5 µmol g^{-1} min^{-1} and 5 mM, respectively, and by assigning a plasma glucose concentration of 6 mM the brain's extracellular concentration was calculated to be 2.0 mM by substitution in the Michaelis–Menten formulation of facilitated transport:

$$J = \frac{T_m}{C_1 + K_t} \cdot C_1 - \frac{T_m}{C_2 + K_t} \, C_2$$

Here J is the net flux and C_1 and C_2 are the concentrations in extracellular and intracellular fluids, respectively. On the assumption of an extracellular space of 15% and a total brain glucose content of 1.7 µmol/g and a water content of 80%, the intracellular concentration was calculated at 2.2 mM, i.e. about equal to the extracellular concentration, as computed above.

Both calculations leave no doubt that transport into the cells is very rapid, and this has been confirmed by direct kinetic studies leading to the conclusion that, so far as the blood–brain barrier is concerned, the extracellular and intracellular compartments may be treated as the same, so that the system is described kinetically as a two-compartment one.

Concentration in Brain Extracellular Fluid

The ready exchange between CSF and the extracellular fluid of brain across the ependymal linings of the ventricles and across the pial lining of the subarachnoid spaces would suggest that the concentrations of various solutes might be the same in the two fluids (Davson, 1958; Bito and Davson, 1966), although metabolic consumption by the cells might cause the concentration in the extracellular fluid to be lower. The experimental measurement of this extracellular concentration is not easy; an initial attempt with regard to potassium and amino acids was made by Bito *et al.* (1966), who implanted collodion sacs, filled with saline, in the forebrain of the dog; after allowing some days for equilibration to take place, the sacs were removed and the contents analysed. With a chronic type of preparation like this, however, the sac becomes enveloped in a glial connective-tissue covering that effectively insulates it from the true extracellular fluid (Bito *et al.*, 1966; Beneviste and Diemer, 1987). In recent years, however, microdialysis probes have been constructed that allow estimates of extracellular concentrations to be carried out within less than 1 h of implantation. The technique and some results have been reviewed by Beneviste (1989); the probe developed by Tossman and Ungerstedt (1986) is illustrated in Figure 2.3(a) and that by Sandberg *et al.* (1986) in Figure 2.3(b). The former consists of a concentric arrangement of two tubes, one slightly shorter than the other, inserted into a dialysis membrane. Perfusion fluid enters by the top of the inner tube and leaves by the lower end of this through two holes in the wall. The fluid flows upwards in the space between the dialysis membrane and the inner tube, and diffusion between the fluid and the tissue takes place in this region. The perfusate leaves by way of a small tube at right angles from the probe.

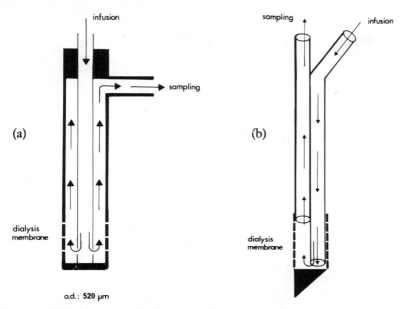

Figure 2.3 Microdialysis probes. (a) A radial section of the Tossman and Ungerstedt (1986) probe consisting of two concentric tubes, the outer one being inserted into a length of dialysis tubing sealed at one end. Fluid passes down the inner tube and fills the dialysis tubing, where exchange diffusion can occur. The dialysis tubing has a molecular weight 'cut off' of 20 000 and an external diameter of 520 μm. Fluid returns up the outer tube and is collected via the side arm. (b) A similar system developed by Sandberg *et al.* (1986) with two tubes side by side inserted into the dialysis tubing. The dialysis tubing has a molecular weight 'cut-off' of 3000 and an external diameter of 300 μm

The diameter of the probe is 520 μm, and the porosity of the membrane is such that molecules smaller than about 20 kD pass through. The apparatus in Figure 2.3(b) consists of a side-by-side arrangement of the tubes but is otherwise similar.

Calculation
The assessment of the true extracellular concentration of a given solute from measurements of the concentration in the outflowing fluid from the probe has been discussed in detail by Beneviste (1989) and her colleagues (Beneviste *et al.*, 1989; Beneviste and Hüttenmeir, 1990) and is fraught with difficulties due to uncertainties as to the correct diffusion coefficients to employ, the degree to which the solute is washed out of the tissue by the perfusion, and so on. So far as glucose is concerned, Lönnroth *et al.* (1987) varied the concentration of glucose in the perfusion fluid and measured the net increase in glucose concentration in the dialysate and extrapolated, as in Figure 2.4, to the point where there was no net exchange and therefore when the extracellular fluid and the perfusion fluid had the same concentration. Table 2.2 compares three estimates with the venous blood; the results suggest that the extracellular fluid reflects the venous plasma

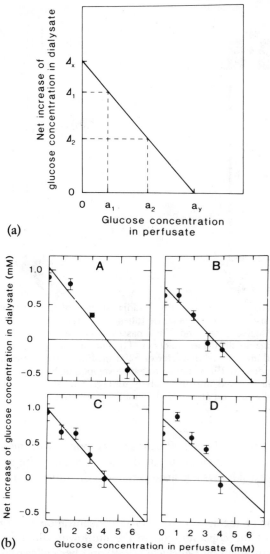

(a)

(b)

Figure 2.4 (a) Mathematical model for estimating dialysis recovery. When concentration gradient over dialysis membrane is altered by a change in glucose level in perfusate (a), a corresponding change in net increase of the concentration in the dialysate (open triangle) is recorded. By varying the concentration gradient repeatedly and by recording the net influx of the compound at every point, a linear relationship is established. Intercept on x-axis (a_y) indicates glucose concentration in perfusate at equilibrium with surrounding medium (= tissue concentration). Slope of line (Δ_x/a_y) gives the dialysis recovery of the compound. (b) *In vivo* dialysis of glucose from abdominal subcutaneous tissue in four subjects (A–D). Figures are means ± s.e. of two dialysis probes placed on each side of umbilicus. Blood/tissue glucose concentrations (mM) were 4.3/4.1 (A), 3.7/3.4 (B), 3.9/4.2 (C) and 4.4/4.6 (D). From Lönnroth *et al.* (1987)

Table 2.2 Estimated glucose concentrations in brain extracellular fluid and venous plasma. From Lönnroth *et al.* (1987)

	Estimated extracellular concentration (mM)	*Venous plasma concentration* (mM)
(1)	4.3 ± 0.4	4.3 ± 0.3
(2)	4.8 ± 0.5	5.0 ± 0.6
(3)	3.9 ± 0.3	4.1 ± 0.2

concentration, which was probably much less than the arterial plasma with which fluids are usually compared. Thus, had the comparison been made with the CSF, it seems likely that the concentrations would, indeed, have been approximately the same.

Transport into CSF

Although the concentration of glucose in the CSF probably bears little relationship to utilization by the brain parenchyma, the conditions controlling the glucose content of this fluid revealed by the nature of the blood–CSF barrier are worthy of study in so far as they increase our understanding of the relations between the blood and extracellular fluid of the brain, i.e. the blood–brain barrier, since we have seen that the sum total of factors affecting production of the CSF are very similar to those that affect the production of the extracellular fluid of the brain, the difference being only that the CSF is renewed rapidly and constitutes a true circulating medium, whereas the extracellular fluid is relatively stagnant.

Transfer Constant

Davson (1955) made the first quantitative study of transport of glucose across the blood–CSF barrier in the rabbit, computing a transfer constant of 0.0087 min^{-1}, indicating a high rate of transport for such a large lipid-insoluble molecule, being more rapid than that for thiourea with a constant of 0.0057 min^{-1}. This work was carried out before ^{14}C-labelled glucose was available, so that the measurements of influx were made by raising the plasma level of glucose several-fold through intravenous infusion. Under these conditions, as subsequent work has indicated, the influx is suppressed, owing to self-inhibition, since the transport has been shown to be carrier-mediated (Bradbury and Davson, 1964; Fishman, 1964; Brøndsted, 1970b).

Atkinson and Weiss (1969), working on dogs, deduced a K_m of 10 mM. This value is comparable with normal plasma concentration, so that the transport parameter, K_m, which tells us at what plasma level the carrier system will be half-saturated, is clearly adapted to the task of controlling rate of entry from blood to CSF, a condition of hypoglycaemia favouring penetration and so serving a homoeostatic role, and hyperglycaemia working in the opposite way.

The Perfused Choroid Plexus

Transport from blood to CSF occurs, as we have seen (p. 86), both directly in the freshly secreted fluid in the ventricles, and indirectly from blood in the brain parenchyma, whence the solute may diffuse into both ventricular and subarachnoid fluids. Thus, the demonstration of a carrier-mediated penetration from blood to CSF might be really a demonstration of a carrier-mediated transport across the blood–brain barrier associated with simple diffusion through the brain tissue. Pollay *et al.* (1972) developed a technique for perfusing the choroid plexuses of the lateral ventricles of the sheep *in situ*, so that when a solute of interest was incorporated into the artificial blood perfusing the plexus, its transport into an artificial CSF bathing the plexus could be deduced from the arteriovenous differences, the rate of secretion of CSF by the plexus being computed also from changes in concentration of Evans Blue-labelled albumin included in the artificial blood. Deane and Segal (1982, 1985) improved the technique and applied it to a detailed study of the kinetics of 3-methylglucose, a non-metabolized sugar that in a variety of studies had been shown to mimic accurately the behaviour of D-glucose. The system showed some asymmetry in that the K_m for blood-to-CSF flux was 3.9 mM, while that for CSF-to-blood flux was 0.42 mM; corresponding values of V_{max} were 121 and 89.3×10^{-3} µmol/min, respectively. Thus, the blood-to-CSF process is not saturated at normal plasma levels, whereas the CSF-to-blood process is. Fluctuations in plasma glucose will tend to be compensated, maintaining homoeostasis; however, fluctuations in CSF glucose will not. As we should expect, the system exhibited a net flux of glucose from blood to CSF consistent with a continuous secretion of newly formed fluid derived from the blood. From estimates of the net loss of D-glucose from the perfusing blood and the rate of secretion of newly formed CSF, the concentration in the newly formed fluid could be estimated, and, as Table 2.3 shows, it depended on the concentration in the blood. At a normal blood concentration of 5–9 mM it was less than that in plasma; a similar finding occurred with the non-metabolized 3-methylglucose.

Thus, the low concentration of glucose in the CSF compared with that in plasma, a feature of the CSF of all studied mammalian species, is not due to utilization by neighbouring brain tissue but is a consequence of the primary

Table 2.3 Estimated concentrations of sugar in newly secreted sheep CSF. From Deane and Segal (1985)

Sugar	Arterial sugar concentration (mM)	Net loss (µmol/min)	Secretion rate (µmol/min)	Estimated concentration (mM)
3-OMe Glucose	2.5	34	31	1.1
	5.0	80.6	34	2.4
D-Glucose	1.6	64	16.5	3.9
	4.9	97	32	3.1
	9.9	133	27	4.9

secretory process, a situation suggesting an active transport of glucose from CSF to blood.

The low concentration in CSF could, however, be ascribed to a molecular sieving at the choroid plexus, the glucose in the extracellular fluid of the plexus being carried in the stream of secreted CSF passively and prevented from achieving the same concentration in CSF as that in the filtrate by the low permeability of the choroidal epithelium to glucose, as illustrated in Figure 2.5. Thus, the plasma is filtered in the first place across the highly permeable fenestrated capillaries of the choroid plexus; the concentration in the filtrate will be the same as in plasma because of the highly permeable character of the choroidal capillaries. If the next stage in transport is a passive diffusion into the CSF across the epithelium, this process might not be rapid enough to ensure a concentration in the newly formed CSF equal to that in the filtrate; the glucose would be said to be 'sieved' on its way through the epithelium.

Nascent CSF

When the choroid plexus of a lateral ventricle is exposed and covered with a layer of oil, freshly secreted fluid may be collected (Ames *et al.*, 1965); and it may be assumed that its composition is unaffected by exchanges between it and the adjacent brain tissue by virtue of the layer of oil. Welch *et al.* (1970) employed this technique and showed that the concentration of glucose in the nascent CSF of the rabbit was, in effect, only 60% of that in plasma, varying linearly with the latter up to a plasma concentration of some 16 mM.

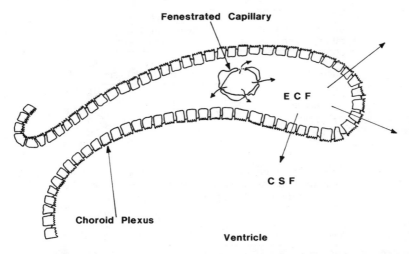

Figure 2.5   Molecular sieving by the choroid plexus. The capillaries of the choroid plexus, being fenestrated, will freely filter glucose, so the concentration in choroidal extracellular fluid will be the same as plasma. The transport processes across the choroidal epithelium are not rapid enough to ensure an equal concentration of glucose in the newly formed cerebrospinal fluid

Ventriculocisternal Perfusion

When the ventricles are perfused with an artificial CSF containing labelled sugars, these diffuse out of the fluid into the blood in the choroid plexuses and also into the blood of the brain tissue after crossing the ependymal lining of the ventricles. Thus, the measured 'clearance' of the sugar will not be a pure measure of transport across the choroid plexuses, although the relatively large area of exposed plexus probably ensures that a great deal of the transport occurs here. In this case the clearances may predominantly represent choroid plexus activity. Table 2.4, from Bradbury and Davson (1964), shows the clearances (K_{out}) and computed permeability coefficients for urea and three sugars. Permeability to D-glucose and D-xylose is high, and a carrier-mediated type of transport was indicated by reduction in clearance by adding inactive sugar to the perfusion medium. Table 2.5 shows the inhibition of clearance by reducing the Na^+ content of the medium or addition of ouabain. Bradbury and Brøndsted (1973) concluded that, in addition to the passive facilitated transport of sugars, there was a sodium-dependent active transport out of the CSF, but, of course, it could not be stated that this was due to activity at the choroid plexuses or the brain capillaries or both.

Blood-to-brain Transport

The Three Steps

As has frequently been emphasized, the nutrition of the brain cells relies

Table 2.4　Values of transfer constants. K_{out}, and permeability constants, P, for escape of solutes from the rabbit's ventricles. After Bradbury and Davson (1964)

Substance	K_{out} (ml/min $\times 10^3$)	P (cm/s $\times 10^5$)
Urea	4.9	1.8
D-Glucose	19.1	7.1
D-Xylose	14.7	5.5
D-Fructose	5.5	2.0

Table 2.5　Inhibition of extraction of sugars by low sodium or ouabain in ventriculocisternal perfusion. After Bradbury and Brøndsted (1973)

Sugar	Inhibition (%)	
	Low sodium	Ouabain
D-Glucose	24.0	28.3
α-Methylglucoside	37.5	60.0
3-O-Methylglucose	10.5	13.5
D-Galactose	9.0	20.5
2-Deoxyglucose	—	6.5

predominantly on transport from blood across the capillary membranes, transport from blood to CSF and thence to nervous tissue being quite inadequate, of itself, the capillary area of this tissue being some five thousand times that of the choroid plexuses. The dynamic processes with which we are concerned are (1) the passage of glucose across the central nervous capillary membrane; (2) the passage from the extracellular fluid into the tissue cells; and (3) the metabolic conversion of glucose to CO_2 and H_2O, the primary step in this last process being the phosphorylation of glucose catalysed by hexokinase. The dynamics of this process govern the rate of metabolism as a whole.

The kinetics of phosphorylation follow Michaelis–Menten kinetics, so that the rate of phosphorylation, $\mathcal{J}_h$, is given by:

$$\mathcal{J}_h = \frac{V_h}{C_{ex} + K_h} \cdot C_{ex} \qquad \text{(Step 3)}$$

where C_{ex} is the concentration in the extracellular fluid and K_h is the half-saturation constant for the enzyme.

As we have seen, transport across the brain capillary follows Michaelis–Menten kinetics, so that we have:

$$\mathcal{J}_g = \frac{V_g}{C_{pl} + K_g} \cdot C_{pl} - \frac{V_g}{C_{ex} + K_g} \cdot C_{ex} \qquad \text{(Step 2)}$$

The penetration from extracellular space into brain cells, i.e. step (2), may be expected to be governed by Michaelis–Menten kinetics, since it is a rapid process requiring a facilitation process in such a large lipid-insoluble molecule. A number of studies, based on *in vitro* penetration of brain slices, seemed to confirm this hypothesis, and K_m and V_{max} values were deduced by Bachelard (1971); thus, the value of K_m, the half-saturation concentration, was estimated at 5 mM, in the range of normal plasma levels. The K_h for hexokinase is about one-hundredth of this, about 0.04 mM, so that it was concluded that the rate of phosphorylation of glucose was governed by the rate of its transport into the cell. However, Lund-Andersen and Kjeldsen (1976) showed that estimates of kinetic parameters from measurements in tissue slices were fallacious, since the rate of passage of glucose, or its non-metabolizable analogue, 3-methyl glucose, across the cell membranes was so rapid that measurable changes in concentration in the suspension medium were governed by the rate of diffusion through this medium. Thus, the Michaelis–Menten parameters deduced from these studies on tissue slices had no kinetic meaning, the phosphorylation within the cells being the only component of the process taking place in the tissue slices that was governed by Michaelis–Menten kinetics; and this explains why no Michaelis–Menten kinetics were observed with the non-metabolized 3-methylglucose. In general, according to Lund-Andersen (1979), only when penetration of a sugar into the brain cells is very slow compared with diffusion through the tissue can Michaelis–Menten parameters have meaning so far as work on tissue slices is concerned.

Step (1). Blood-to-extracellular Space Transport

Because, as we have seen, transport from extracellular space into cells is very rapid, the extracellular space and intracellular space may be treated dynamically as a single compartment (Lund-Andersen, 1979), so that measurements of uptake by the brain are essentially measurements of transport across the blood–brain barrier. This will be especially true of measurements involving a single pass of blood through the capillaries, such as the indicator-dilution technique of Crone (1965) and Yudilevich and De Rose (1971), and the BUI technique of Oldendorf (1971).

Effects of Blood Concentration

As indicated earlier (Chapter 1), Pardridge and Oldendorf (1975) studied the effects of concentration on uptake of a number of hexoses and deduced values of K_m. They found values of 6 mM for 2-deoxyglucose, 9 mM for D-glucose, 10 mM for 3-O-methylglucose, 21 mM for D-mannose and 40 mM for D-galactose. All hexoses had about the same V_{max} of 1.56 μmol mg^{-1} min^{-1}, a constancy that can be attributed to the circumstance that the rate-limiting factor for transport is the rate of movement of the carrier–substrate complex across the membrane (or the equivalent conformational change), a rate that is not influenced by the nature of the substrate being carried. Expressed in more recent terminology, it would be said that the conformational change that effectively exposes the substrate to one or other side of the membrane does not depend on the substrate attached to the transporter protein. The fact that the half-saturation concentration for D-glucose is in the region of normal plasma levels means that the system is adapted for adjusting rate of transport to the physiological requirements, a state of hypoglycaemia leading to a higher permeability coefficient, and therefore more rapid transport to the tissue, than would be the case with a hyperglycaemic condition.

Maximum Speed of Equilibration

We have seen that an index to the speed of equilibration between two compartments is given by the value of the 'half-life', or $t_{1/2}$, which is related to the transfer coefficient by the equation

$$t_{1/2} = \log_e 2/K = c.\ 0.7/K$$

Under carrier-free conditions, when the concentration of glucose in the fluid perfusing the brain is negligibly small, the value of K is given by the ratio V_{max}/K_m.

With a V_{max} of 1.56 μmol mg^{-1} min^{-1} or 1560 μmol ml^{-1} min^{-1} and a K_m of 9 mM or 9 μm/ml, the ratio becomes 173 min^{-1}, giving a $t_{1/2}$ of about a quarter of a second, a very rapid process of equilibration. This, of course, is an ideal situation, so that with concentrations of glucose in the region of 10 mM, the half-life will be much longer, but there is no doubt that it will still be short. Thus, Crone obtained an extraction of 0.2 at normal blood glucose levels, and this was increased to about 0.5 at 30 mg/100 ml and, on extrapolation to zero concentration, would have been in the region of 0.3. As permeability is related to extraction, E, by the equation

$$P = -F/S \ln (1-E)$$

a change of extraction from 0.8 to 0.2 would mean a decrease in permeability by a factor of about 6. A reduction of this order would still leave the half-life of equilibration of glucose across the blood–brain barrier very short, and this accords with the experimental study of Buschiazzo *et al.* (1970), illustrated by Figure 2.6, which shows the course of equilibration of the non-metabolizable glucose analogue, 3-methylglucose, and of arabinose and mannitol with blood plasma when the plasma level in rats had been raised by a single bolus intravenous injection. The uptake of methylglucose is obviously rapid, and the authors concluded that equilibration would have occurred in just a few minutes.

Counterflow Acceleration
Uptake in fasting rats was more rapid, and a greater steady-state level was reached; the faster rate reveals the increase in permeability due to lowered substrate concentration, in accordance with the Michaelis–Menten relation, the normal blood glucose competing with methylglucose and reducing K_m. The increased steady-state level is of interest and may be explained on the basis of counterflow transport. Thus, the animals were studied in the steady state, so far as the distribution of glucose was concerned, hence, the level of glucose on the brain side of the blood–brain barrier was lower than in normal rats. Thus, as we have indicated earlier, we may envisage a situation in which the affinity of the carrier system is different on the two sides of the membrane if the concentration of a competing molecule is different on the two sides. A competing molecule on one side will reduce flux into the membrane but, on the other side, it will increase flux out of the membrane. The latter effect, namely the increased flux out of the membrane, has been called *counterflow acceleration*. In the particular situation depicted in Figure 2.6, the concentrations of glucose in the plasma of the normal rats were abnormally high, as they had been nephrectomized to prevent renal excretion of injected sugars. The fasting rats had lower blood glucose concentrations. If the changes in blood glucose were not completely reflected in corresponding changes in the glucose concentration in the extracellular fluid, the effect of, say, a rise in blood glucose would be to reduce the affinity for methyglucose on the blood side of the barrier in comparison with that on the brain side; thus, K_m on the blood side would rise in comparison with K_m on the brain side, and this would lead to a steady state in which the concentration in the brain would be higher. Buschiazzo *et al.* (1970) derived a function that permitted them to extrapolate the volume of distribution of 3-methylglucose to zero blood-glucose concentration; and the asymptote gave a brain space of 0.67 ml/g, which is not far from the space were methylglucose allowed to distribute itself evenly throughout the brain water.

Measurement of Regional Blood Flow and Solute Transport

Estimates of flux into the brain, employing the Crone and Oldendorf techniques, rely on the constancy of blood flow through the brain and, in order to derive a permeability coefficient, a knowledge of the actual value of the flow rate is necessary. Several methods of measuring simultaneously blood flow and solute uptake, or extraction, have been developed, notably by Pollay and Stevens (1979),

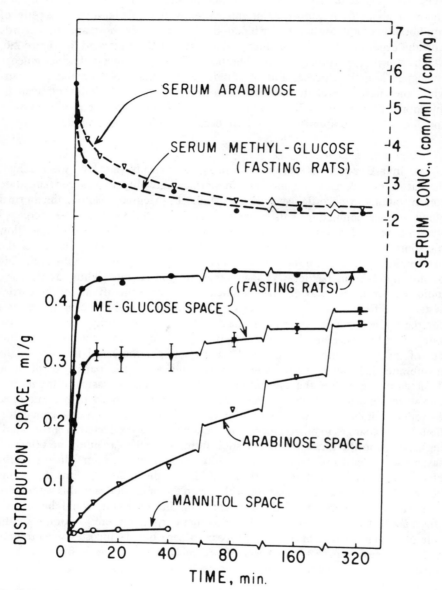

Figure 2.6 Time course of entry of sugar into brain of the rat. Lower four curves are brain/serum ratios (i.e. distribution space): upper curves are serum radioactivity concentrations divided by per-gram dose. Vertical lines through points are ±s.e.m. (n = 3). Points without standard errors were obtained from one or two tests. From Buschiazzo *et al.* (1970)

Gjedde *et al.* (1980), Sage *et al.* (1981) and Betz and Iannotti (1983). Essentially, the technique is based on the administration of a single intravenous bolus of a mixture of the flow indicator—i.e. of a substance whose escape into the brain is governed entirely by the rate of flow of blood through the tissue, such as butanol—and the solute whose extraction and permeability coefficient are required. The mathematical treatment is designed to permit the separate determination of blood flow through a part of the brain, on the basis of the extraction of the tracer whose escape is flow-limited, and the rate of flux of the other solute, such as labelled glucose, into the same part of the brain. The treatment of Gjedde *et al.* (1980) may be briefly summarized as follows.

Gjedde Treatment
Following introduction of the flow indicator into the circulation, it is taken up in accordance with the following equation:

$$\frac{dC_{br}(t)}{dt} = f^{bl}(C_a^{bl}(t) - C_v^{bl}(t)) \tag{2.1}$$

where $C_a^{bl}(t)$ and $C_v^{bl}(t)$ are the organ's arterial and venous blood concentrations at any time t. When equilibrium between blood and tissue occurs very rapidly, as with butanol or antipyrine, the equation can be modified as follows (Kety, 1951):

$$\frac{dC_{br}(t)}{dt} = f^{bl}\left(C_a^{bl}(t) - \frac{C_{br}(t)}{\lambda_{br}}\right) \tag{2.2}$$

in which λ_{br} is the tissue–blood partition coefficient (in ml/g) of the indicator. With f^{bl} constant during the period of measurement, Equation (2.2) is integrated to give

$$C_{br}(T) = f^{bl} \exp\left[-f^{bl}\frac{T}{\lambda_{br}}\right]\int_0^T C_a^{bl}(t) \exp\left[f^{bl}\frac{t}{\lambda_{br}}\right] dt \tag{2.3}$$

$E(T)$ the net extraction fraction of indicator is defined as

$$E(T) = 1 - \frac{\int_0^T C_v^{bl}(t)\, dt}{\int_0^T C_a^{bl}(t)\, dt} \tag{2.4}$$

From Equations (2.4) and (2.1) and integration we get the fundamental equation:

$$f^{bl} = \frac{C_{br}(T)}{E(T)\int_0^T C_a^{bl}(t)\, dt} \tag{2.5}$$

where f^{bl} is the blood flow per unit weight of brain, $C_{br}(T)$ is the indicator content per unit weight of brain at time T, $E(T)$ is the net extraction fraction at time T, and C_a^{bl} is the arterial blood concentration at any time, t.

Equation (2.5) applies to any organ as well as to the whole body; thus, for unit weight of another organ, indicated by the subscript, o:

$$C_o(T) = f_o^{bl}E_o(T)\int_0^T C_a^{bl}(t)\, dt \tag{2.6}$$

If C_a^{bl} is identical for the two, we have

$$f^{bl} = f_o^{bl} \frac{E_o(T) C_{br}(T)}{E(T) C_o(T)} \tag{2.7}$$

In the technique employed by Gjedde *et al.* (1980) and Sage *et al.* (1981) the reference 'organ' was the syringe into which arterial blood was drawn at the known rate, f_o, for the duration of the experiment, T. In this case $C_o(T)$ is given by $Q_o(T)$, the total amount of indicator in the syringe, and $E_o(T)$ equals 1. Thus, we have

$$f^{bl} = F_o^{bl} \frac{C_{br}(T)}{E(T) Q_o(T)} \tag{2.8}$$

and this is the operational form of the fundamental equation (2.5) employed by Gjedde *et al.* in their analysis of the experiments on rats, and by Betz and Iannotti (1983) on the gerbil.

For whole brain $E(T)$, the extraction fraction, can be determined from Equation (2.4) since venous concentration can be measured; for regional studies on brain, $E(T)$ could be determined by combining Equations (2.5) and (2.3), provided that the blood concentration during the course of the measurement was known.

The derived equation was:

$$E(T) = \frac{\exp\left[-f^{bl} \dfrac{T}{\lambda_{br}}\right] \displaystyle\int_0^T C_a^{bl}(t) \exp\left[f^{bl} \dfrac{t}{\lambda_{br}}\right] dt}{\displaystyle\int_0^T C_a^{bl}(t)\, dt} \tag{2.9}$$

To use this, the arterial concentration of the flow tracer was measured as a function of time after the intravenous injection of the bolus; a peak concentration was reached at time t', about 5 s, and then it declined exponentially with a constant, K.

Determination of Blood–Brain Glucose Transport
It was pointed out that Equations (2.4), (2.5) and (2.8) also applied to substances that penetrated into the extravascular compartment and only left in the venous blood, such as D-glucose. If there is no back-diffusion in time T, the extraction, $E(T)$, equals the unidirectionally extracted fraction of glucose in brain at time T, E_{glc}^*. If C_a^{pl} is the total arterial plasma concentration of glucose, Equation (2.8) gives

$$\mathcal{J}_{glc} = E_{glc}^* f^{pl} C_a^{pl} = C_a^{pl} F_o^{pl} \frac{C_{ev}^*(T)}{Q_o^*(T)} \tag{2.10}$$

where $\mathcal{J}_{glc}$ is the unidirectional glucose flux into brain, $C_{ev}^*(T)$ is the labelled glucose content of brain after allowing for any glucose remaining in the blood vessels at time of decapitation, and $Q_o^*(T)$ is the amount of label collected in the syringe.

On the basis of this analysis, Gjedde *et al.* (1980) obtained the values of blood–brain glucose transport, and regional blood flow, illustrated by Figure 2.7. While regional blood flow showed only small variations, the blood–brain transport showed larger; and this is especially manifest in the low value for cerebellum. The animals were under halothane anaesthesia, a condition known to increase blood flow, in contrast to barbiturate anaesthesia, which decreases this (Pollay and Stevens, 1979). Actual figures for blood flow, glucose influx and extraction fraction are shown in Table 2.6. We may note that the unidirectional glucose transport is about twice as high as that reported by Bachelard *et al.* (1973) and Pardridge and Oldendorf (1975), but agrees with that of Sokoloff *et al.* (1977) on uptake of 2-deoxy-D-glucose. The study of Pardridge and Oldendorf involved barbiturate anaesthesia.

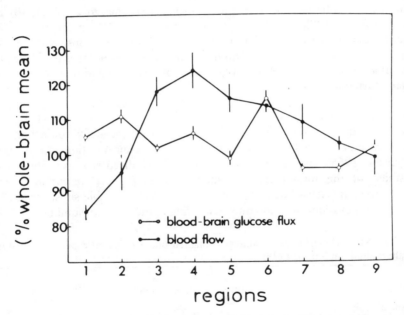

Figure 2.7 Gross regional brain blood flow and blood–brain glucose transfer rates in rat, expressed relative to whole brain means. Regions represent: 1, cerebellar hemisphere; 2, cerebellar vermis; 3, medulla and pons; 4, midbrain; 5, basal ganglia; 6, parietal cortex; 7, occipital lobe; 8, temporal lobe; 9, frontal lobe. Bars represent 2 s.e. From Gjedde *et al.* (1980)

Table 2.6 Whole-brain blood flow, blood–brain glucose flux and tracer glucose extraction. From Gjedde *et al.* (1980)

Blood flow (ml $(100\,\text{g})^{-1}\,\text{min}^{-1}$)	129 ± 7 (s.e.)
Glucose flux (μmol $(100\,\text{g})^{-1}\,\text{min}^{-1}$)	144 ± 13 (s.e.)
Extraction	0.21 ± 0.01 (s.e.)

Number of experiments, 5.

Variations in the Experimentally Determined Michaelis–Menten Parameters

Lund-Andersen (1979) drew attention to the quite large variations in estimates of K_m given by different authors (Table 2.7); differences for V_{max} were not so great. An important factor in determining these variations was undoubtedly the difference between steady-state and non-steady-state conditions that prevailed when assessing the effects of changed blood concentration on the unidirectional flux. Thus, a changed blood concentration of non-radioactive glucose, unless the animal has come to a steady state, will provide a situation in which the relative concentrations of inactive glucose will be varying during the measurement of changes in radioactivity in the brain due to penetration of labelled glucose. Thus, as Buschiazzo *et al.* (1970) had shown, an artificial asymmetry in the kinetic situation prevails, an asymmetry that varies with time and with the successive changes in plasma concentration required to assess K_m. When steady-state conditions are adhered to, as in the studies of Buschiazzo *et al.* (1970) and Bachelard *et al.* (1973) on the rat, Crowdon *et al.* (1971) on the mouse, and Pappenheimer and Setchell (1973) on sheep and rabbit, more consistent values, in the region of 7 mM, are obtained. Another factor to be considered is the choice of a mean value for the concentration of glucose, both labelled and unlabelled, in the capillary during its transit.

Mean Capillary Concentration

When the extraction fraction is converted into a permeability coefficient, two parameters are necessary, namely the mean capillary concentration and the blood flow (Crone, 1965); and there has been considerable discussion as to the correct assessment of the former factor, which assumes especial importance when assessing the Michaelis–Menten parameters of a metabolizable substrate such as glucose, when the concentration must fall owing to the local consumption (CMR).

Table 2.7 Michaelis–Menten parameters obtained under different experimental conditions (after Lund-Andersen, 1979)

Method	Animal	K_m (mM)	V_{max} (μmol g^{-1} min^{-1})	Blood glucose
Indicator diffusion				
Steady state	Dog	2	0.8	Low, normal high
Non-steady state	Dog	8.5	1.6	High
BUI				
Non-steady state	Rat	9–11	1.6	Normal
Non-steady state	Rat	22	—	High
Tissue uptake				
Steady state	Rat	7	—	Low, normal, high
Steady state	Mouse	6	2.1	Low, normal, high
Plasma-CSF model				
Steady state	Sheep	6	2.6	Low, normal, high
Steady state	Rabbit	5	2.8	Low, normal, high

Gjedde (1980) has analysed the kinetics on the basis of a simple model capillary, and has shown that, whereas the concentration of unlabelled glucose falls linearly along the length of the capillary, that of labelled glucose falls monoexponentially. The actual fall in concentration of unlabelled glucose along the capillary was shown to have little effect on the kinetic constants when they were measured with varying glucose concentration. Gjedde's equation relating extraction fraction, E, to K_m and T_{max} is similar to that derived by Crone (1963) for conversion of extraction to permeability: Crone's equation is

$$E_{glc} = 1 - \exp\left(-PS/f_{pl}\right)$$

while Gjedde's equation is

$$E_{glc}^* = 1 - \exp\frac{T_{max}}{f^{pl}(K_m + C_a^{pl})}$$

where PS, the permeability–surface area product, is equivalent to $T_{max}/(K_m + C_a^{pl})$. Thus, when this equation applies, a plot of $-f^{pl}\ln(1-E_{glc}^*)$ versus $-C_a^{pl}f^{pl}\ln(1-E_{glc}^*)$ is a straight line with slope $-K_m$ and ordinate intersection T_{max}. In his experimental study on the rat Gjedde (1980) obtained the graph of Figure 2.8, giving values of T_{max} and K_m of 253 ± 33 (s.e.) μmol $(100\ g)^{-1}$ min^{-1} and 5.9 ± 1.6 (s.e.) mM.

Brain Utilization and Supply

The concentration of glucose does not vary appreciably from one part of the brain

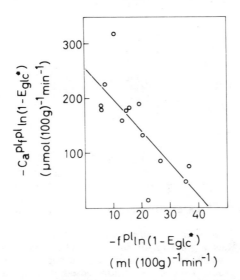

Figure 2.8   Estimate of the constants T_{max} and K_m for the transport of glucose from blood to brain by means of a double-logarithmic plot based on the mathematical treatment of blood–brain glucose transfer developed in the text. From Gjedde (1980)

to another although the rate of utilization does. Hawkins *et al.* (1979) found a value of 106 μmol min^{-1} (100 g)$^{-1}$ in frontal cortex of rats compared with 36 μmol min^{-1} (100 g)$^{-1}$ in the corpus callosum, a difference once again reflecting proportion of white to grey matter. In view of these variations, we would expect variations in the glucose influx correlating with variations in the other parameters.

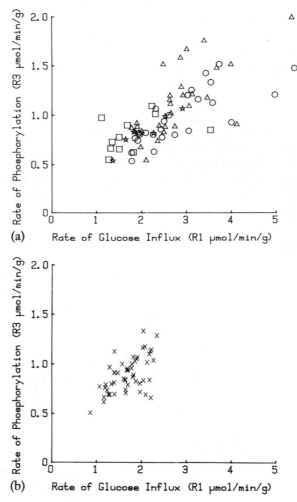

Figure 2.9 Rates of glucose influx and rates of glucose phosphorylation in brain regions of individual rats. (a) Rats in groups 2–5; (b) control rats. ×, group 1 (controls); △, group 2 = cismetrin-dosed, whole-body tremor; ○, group 3 = decamethonium-dosed, choreoathetosis; □, group 4 = decamethonium-dosed, fasted, choreoathetosis; fasting prevented rise in blood glucose but choreoathetosis remained; ☆, group 5 = decamethonium-dosed, hind-limb rigidity. Correlation coefficients for both figures were highly significant. From Cremer *et al.* (1981)

This was found by Cremer *et al.* (1981), who measured glucose influx and phosphorylation by sequential injections of $[^{14}C]$-glucose and $[^3H]$-deoxyglucose in rats, the rate of phosphorylation being assessed from the concentration of deoxyglucose in the tissue, since this sugar is phosphorylated by the hexokinase reaction but further stages in the oxidative pathway are blocked (Sokoloff *et al.*, 1977). As Figure 2.9 shows, there was a high correlation between the two parameters. Blood flow, also, varies regionally: (Reivick *et al.* (1969), working on awake cats, found values ranging from 0.21 ml g^{-1} min^{-1} in cerebral white matter to 1.74 ml g^{-1} min^{-1} in the inferior colliculus; in cerebral neocortex different regions had very similar blood flows, around 1.1 ml min^{-1} g^{-1}, and it is likely that regional variations are mainly determined by the proportions of grey to white matter. In general, as Des Rosier *et al.* (1974) and Lassen (1978) showed, blood flow and metabolic utilization are closely linked.

Since some authors failed to find a correlation between rate of penetration of glucose and metabolic utilization (Sokoloff *et al.*, 1977; Gjedde, 1980; Pardridge *et al.*, 1982), Hawkins *et al.* (1983) have re-examined the matter. They measured sugar influx, using quantitative autoradiography after a bolus injection of $[^{14}C]$-glucose and compared their regional influxes with the regional metabolic rates determined by Bryan *et al.* (1983). Figure 2.10 shows a definite, almost linear, relation between the two parameters, the curve being described by the equation

$$\text{clearance (ml min}^{-1}\text{ g}^{-1}) = 0.185 \ (r\text{CMR}_{glc})^{0.66}$$

Using this equation, they could predict, say, the change in influx rate or blood clearance, produced by pentobarbitone anaesthesia, which was shown by Hawkins *et al.* (1979) to reduce O_2 consumption from 0.75 to 0.28 μmol min^{-1} g^{-1}.

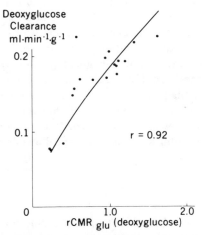

Figure 2.10 Correlation between deoxyglucose influx and rCMRglu determined using deoxyglucose. Plasma clearance of deoxyglucose was plotted against rCMRglu by region. All values were obtained from Sokoloff *et al.* (1977). The data are described by: clearance = 0.185(rCMRglu)$^{0.66}$. From Hawkins *et al.* (1983)

Inserting this in their equation, they predicted a change of 35% in rate of influx, which compares with Gjedde and Rasmussen's (1980) measurement of 33%.

Arterio–Venous Difference

An obvious explanation for the adaptation of glucose influx to metabolic usage might be sought in the strong correlation of blood flow with brain activity. An increased rate of flow through the capillaries would decrease the arterio–venous difference along the capillary, shifting the mean concentration towards the arterial value, but, since this difference is normally only in the region of 8%, such a shift could not make for large differences in uptake. Pollay and Stevens (1979) found a 20% increase in clearance when they doubled blood flow, whereas, on the basis of altered arterio–venous difference, the predicted change would be only some 4%. If Hawkins *et al.*'s equation applies, a 40% increase in clearance would be associated with the doubled blood flow and observed increase in metabolic utilization. Again, pentobarbitone anaesthesia decreased whole-brain glucose influx by 33% (Gjedde and Rasmussen, 1980); it decreases glucose metabolism by some 60% (Hawkins *et al.*, 1979), and, on the basis of the curve of Figure 2.10, a change of some 35% would be predicted for the rate of influx.

Opening of Capillaries

Thus, another mechanism in addition to changed arterio–venous difference must be sought, and this is probably the opening up of new capillaries, making more carriers available and thereby increasing V_{max}.

The Cerebellum

The cerebellum is relatively resistant to the effects of hypoglycaemia, so that the kinetics of glucose exchange in this region of the brain are of interest; LaManna and Harik (1985) measured simultaneous extraction of $[^{14}C]$-glucose and blood flow after a bolus injection, and found that the rate of influx was about the same as that to the cerebral cortex, despite the much greater blood flow in this latter region. Thus, it appears that the feature of the cerebellum that gives it its resistance to hypoglycaemia is the more favourable ratio between influx and blood flow, which means, essentially, that the cerebellum has a much greater safety factor where variations in blood glucose are concerned; it thus forms an exception to the close coupling of glucose utilization and rate of influx described by Hawkins *et al.* (1983).

The Glucose Carrier

We have seen that the membrane protein responsible for facilitated diffusion of glucose across the erythrocyte, adipocyte and hepatocyte, is a so-called band 4.5 polypeptide of molecular weight in the region of 45–50 kD; that isolated from a hepatoma cell was found to contain a sequence of 492 amino acid residues and was assigned the structure illustrated in Figure 1.23.

Cytochalasin B

The basis for isolation has been labelling with cytochalasin B, a compound that has a high affinity for the carrier and, by suitable treatment, can be made to bind with it covalently, thereby permitting its isolation and purification. Cytochalasin B was shown by Drewes *et al.* (1977) to inhibit glucose transport in the isolated perfused dog's head preparation, the K_i being 6.6 ± 1.9 μM. O_2 consumption by the brain was decreased following the decreased availability of glucose.

Isolated Protein

Dick *et al.* (1984) isolated a protein of molecular weight about 53 kD from a preparation of isolated cerebral microvessels; its binding to cytochalasin B had a K_d of 0.65–0.88 μM with a B_{max} of 60–80 pmol/mg protein. The K_d for binding was said to be similar to that for cytochalasin inhibition of 50% transport across the blood–brain barrier, and they showed that there was a good correlation between the ability of different sugars to displace cytochalasin B from the preparation and their *in vivo* K_m for hexose transport; they estimated that the cerebral microvessels could transport as much glucose as 10% of their wet weight per minute; and this makes them better endowed with carrier for glucose than any other tissue known, with the exception of human erythrocytes.

Membrane Localization

The location of the transporter to the plasma membrane was made very likely by its association with the enzyme gamma-glutamyl transpeptidase, an enzyme considered to represent a good label for plasma membranes generally. In a later paper (Dick and Harik, 1986) these findings were generally confirmed and amplified. As Table 2.8 shows, cerebral microvessels contained the greatest density of carrier, as

Table 2.8 Specific cytochalasin B binding to pig brain, cerebral synaptosomes, brain microvessels and choroid plexus preparations. From Dick and Harik (1986)

Tissue	n	B_{max} (pmol/mg of protein)	K_d (μM)
Cerebral cortex	4	10.6 ± 0.7	0.58 ± 0.16
Cerebral synaptosomes	3	13.6 ± 0.8	0.43 ± 0.11
Cerebellum	4	6.4 ± 0.6	0.51 ± 0.06
Cerebral microvessels	5	64.0 ± 5.8	0.70 ± 0.08
Cerebellar microvessels	5	37.6 ± 3.5	0.52 ± 0.07
Choroid plexus	3	24.3 ± 13.4	0.53 ± 0.27

Data are mean $\pm$ s.e.m. values for the number of observations (n) in each group. Maximal binding (B_{max}) and the dissociation constant of binding (K_d) were calculated according to the method of Scatchard.

One-way analysis of variance of the B_{max} results (excluding those of synaptosomes and choroid plexus) revealed that the particulate fractions of the cerebral cortex and cerebellum were not significantly different from each other. However, cerebral microvessels were significantly different from cerebellar microvessels at $p < 0.01$ (Tukey's procedure). Also, cerebral microvessel and cerebral cortex values and cerebellar microvessel and cerebellum values were significantly different at $p < 0.01$ (Tukey's procedure). There were no significant differences between K_d values.

indicated by the B_{max} for cytochalasin binding. Microvessel binding was compared with that of the particulate fraction of brain tissue, and, more specifically, with that of a synaptosome preparation, and it appeared that the non-microvessel binding was due to these subcellular organs. The lower density of binding by choroid plexus is probably due to the fact that it is only the epithelium that is responsible, the connective tissue reducing the apparent density by comparison with brain microvessels. We have seen that the cerebellum has a similar rate of influx of glucose to that of cerebral cortex in spite of the larger rate of blood flow in the latter; the values of B_{max} for the microvessels of these two tissues were significantly different in the pig, but in the rat this was not true.

cDNA: Rat and Man

Birnbaum *et al.* (1986) cloned and characterized a complementary DNA encoding the rat brain glucose transporter protein; this predicted the synthesis of a 492 amino acid protein that demonstrated 97.6% homology with the human hepatoma hexose carrier identified by Mueckler *et al.* and described in Chapter 1. This extraordinary degree of homology between proteins of such diverse species as rat and man means that all parts of the molecule are essential for its function. According to Boado and Pardridge (1990), it is very likely that the glucose-transporter protein identified in brain belongs exclusively to the brain capillaries, the mRNA encoding it being absent from a brain preparation from which some 98% of the capillaries had been removed by differential centrifugation.

Amino Acids

The amino acids of the blood represent a 'pool' that is constantly changing as the result of absorption in the diet, as occurs exclusively with the so-called essential amino acids, and synthesis of non-essential amino acids. Acting against this is the involvement of the amino acids in protein synthesis; this process can represent the formation of additional protein molecules or it can represent the natural turnover during which the proteins are degraded and resynthesized. This turnover is revealed by adding radioactively labelled amino acids to the blood, and it is found that many proteins become rapidly labelled with radioactivity, although there may be no net change in protein content of a given tissue.

Steady-state Levels

As a result of these several processes, the concentration of a given amino acid in the blood plasma acquires a characteristic value which, however, fluctuates about a mean as a result of the preponderance of one or other process. In general, as Table 2.9 indicates, the concentrations of all amino acids in the CSF are less than those in the plasma; thus, the mean value of R_{CSF} when all amino acids are taken into account is in the region of 0.3. Table 2.10 shows the steady-state condition for some 20 amino acids, and it will be seen that R_{CSF} varies considerably from one

Table 2.9   Concentrations of amino acids (μM) in the CSF of human subjects; included in the table are values for normal human plasma taken from a study of 60 normal human subjects. From Plum (1974)

Amino acid	Gjessing et al. (1972)	Perry et al. (1969)	Dickinson and Hamilton (1966)	Van Sande et al. (1970)	Plasma
Alanine	23.2 ± 5.1	32.7 ± 6.3	23.2 ± 9.4	27.9 ± 9.9	330 ± 78
Arginine	18.3 ± 3.2	21.6 ± 3.9	20.1 ± 5.8	14.2 ± 7.4	80 ± 26
Aspartic acid	0.6 ± 0.3	—	0.9 ± 0.5	2.9 ± 2.7	7 ± 4
Cystine	0.1 ± 0.1	—	0.2 ± 0.3	traces	61 ± 21
Glutamic acid	11.3 ± 6.4	1.79 ± 0.9	7.0 ± 4.9	14.7 ± 13.3	83 ± 34
Glycine	4.7 ± 1.5	5.8 ± 0.9	6.6 ± 1.8	8.5 ± 2.5	249 ± 81
Histidine	11.9 ± 1.7	12.0 ± 1.5	13.0 ± 4.4	11.1 ± 2.9	85 ± 34
Isoleucine	3.9 ± 1.0	5.3 ± 1.5	4.4 ± 1.3	5.0 ± 0.9	61 ± 21
Leucine	10.1 ± 2.1	14.9 ± 3.3	10.9 ± 3.6	11.6 ± 2.4	109 ± 48
Lysine	21.7 ± 3.6	29.1 ± 4.8	18.7 ± 6.6	18.6 ± 6.4	158 ± 28
Methionine	1.9 ± 0.7	2.5 ± 0.6	2.6 ± 1.6	3.2 ± 1.0	41 ± 15
Phenylalanine	6.5 ± 1.2	9.5 ± 2.1	9.2 ± 5.8	7.5 ± 2.2	71 ± 24
Proline	traces	—	0.6 ± 1.6	traces	212 ± 64
Serine	24.5 ± 4.4	23.5 ± 3.6	37.8 ± 22.9	35.7 ± 9.6	149 ± 55
Threonine	27.7 ± 4.7	31.5 ± 4.5	24.8 ± 10.1	26.6 ± 9.3	142 ± 46
Tryptophan	1.3 ± 0.4	—	0.8 ± 1.4	—	62 ± 26
Tyrosine	6.4 ± 1.5	9.0 ± 2.4	9.1 ± 5.0	7.9 ± 2.3	70 ± 32
Valine	15.0 ± 2.8	20.9 ± 5.5	14.6 ± 5.5	14.3 ± 4.0	222 ± 71
Taurine	6.8 ± 1.7	6.4 ± 1.5	6.3 ± 1.8	5.3 ± 1.4	78 ± 25

The numbers of subjects were: 19 (Gjessing *et al.*, 1972); 10 (Perry *et al.*, 1969); 18 (Dickinson and Hamilton, 1966); 13 (Van Sande *et al.*, 1970).

amino acid to another; thus, the value for glycine is in the region of 0.03 compared with 0.25 for serine. An important consideration, from a physiological point of view, is the role of some amino acids, such as glycine and glutamic acid, as transmitters in the central nervous system; thus, on *a priori* grounds, one might expect the concentrations of these amino acids to be held at a low value in the CSF in view of the ease with which they would be able to diffuse from here into adjacent brain tissue. This is certainly true of glycine, but a number of studies agree in showing fairly high values of R_{CSF} for aspartic acid—in the region of 0.1. We shall see that there are active processes tending to remove glycine and some other amino acids from the CSF, and we may presume that the same process occurs across the blood–brain barrier, i.e. across the cerebral microvessels. As with glucose, of course, it could be argued that the low concentrations in CSF are due to metabolic incorporation into proteins of the brain, since these have a definite turnover with a mean half-life of some 4–14 days (Seta *et al.*, 1973). This possibility, as a general explanation, was ruled out by Davson *et al.* (1986), who established concentrations of the non-metabolizable amino acids alpha-aminoisobutyric acid (AIBA) and cycloleucine in the plasma of rats and assayed

Table 2.10 Values of the ratio of concentrations in CSF and plasma derived from five studies in human subjects

Amino acid	Knauff et al. (1961)	Humoller et al. (1966)	Plum (1974)	Perry et al. (1975)	McGale et al. (1977)
Alanine	0.12	0.1	0.08	0.08	0.08
Arginine	0.71	0.5	0.21	0.23	0.31
Aspartic acid	0.33	—	0.24	0.15	—
Glutamic acid	0.91	0.10	0.11	0.08	0.40
Glutamine	0.91	1.11	—	1.00	0.86
Glycine	0.07	0.03	0.03	0.03	0.02
Histidine	0.21	0.15	0.10	0.14	0.16
Isoleucine	0.10	0.10	0.09	0.08	0.09
Leucine	0.11	0.13	0.09	0.11	0.10
Lysine	0.4	0.16	0.12	0.15	0.12
Methionine	0.24	0.16	0.12	0.14	0.10
Ornithine	—	—	—	0.10	0.06
Phenylalanine	0.20	0.19	0.11	0.17	0.17
Proline[a]	—	—	—	—	0.86
Serine	0.32	—	0.15	0.25	0.23
Threonine	0.003	—	0.24	0.22	0.25
Tryptophan	—	—	—	0.03	—
Tyrosine	0.21	0.19	0.11	0.15	0.14
Valine	0.09	0.10	0.08	0.08	0.07
Taurine	0.20	—	—	0.12	0.11

[a] Perry *et al.* (1975) were unable to detect this amino acid in CSF: the plasma concentration was 176 ± 59 μmol/l.

the steady-state distributions. The estimated value of R_{CSF} for AIBA was approximately 0.22 and that for cycloleucine was 0.11.

The Concentrations in Brain

Columns 1 and 2 of Table 2.11 show the concentrations of 18 amino acids in plasma and brain of the rat. The significance of these values is only revealed by estimates of the concentrations of the amino acids in the intracellular compartment. Estimates of these have been made (Column 4) on the assumption that the water content of whole brain is 78%, and that the extracellular space of brain is 15% of its weight. In addition, it has been assumed that the concentrations in the extracellular fluid are equal to those in the CSF; this last is not an improbable, but is nevertheless an unproven, assumption. It will be seen that there is a very considerable accumulation of some amino acids in the intracellular compartment of the brain, whether referred to the blood plasma or CSF. Thus, the estimated concentration of glycine in the CSF of the rat is 20 ± 1.0 μmol/l, while the concentration in the intracellular water is some hundred times this (1.93 mmol/kg H_2O or 1930 μmol/kg H_2O). This tendency of the brain cells to accumulate amino acids was established by studies on brain slices suspended in an artificial medium, and illustrated by Table 2.12 from Tsukada *et al.* (1963).

Table 2.11 Concentrations of amino acids in brain and plasma of the rat. In Column 2 the concentration is in mmol/kg brain; in Column 3 in mmol/kg brain H_2O; in Column 4 estimated intracellular concentration, assuming that 15% of the brain weight is extracellular fluid containing the same concentration as that in the CSF

Amino acid	(1) Plasma (mM)	(2) Brain (mmol/kg)	(3) Brain H_2O (mM)	(4) Brain intracellular H_2O (mM)
Alanine	0.37	0.82	1.14	1.42
Arginine	0.09	0.08	0.11	0.125
Aspartic acid	0.02	2.6	3.61	—
Glutamine	0.66	5.0	6.95	8.54
Glutamic acid	0.10	9.0	12.5	—
Glycine	0.28	1.2	1.53	1.93
Histidine	0.04	0.05	0.07	—
Isoleucine	0.08	0.05	0.07	—
Leucine	0.13	0.10	0.14	—
Lysine	0.28	0.24	0.33	0.39
Methionine	0.05	0.07	0.10	—
Phenylalanine	0.08	0.05	0.07	—
Proline	0.19	0.13	0.18	—
Serine	0.33	0.90	1.25	1.58
Taurine	0.24	4.9	6.8	8.57
Threonine	0.22	0.52	0.73	—
Tyrosine	0.05	0.06	0.08	—
Valine	0.19	0.12	0.17	—

Brain concentrations from Carver (1965): CSF concentrations used to calculate Column 4 from Franklin *et al.* (1975).

Table 2.12 Accumulation of some amino acids by brain slices of the guinea-pig. From Tsukada *et al.* (1963)

Amino acid	Slice/Medium
GABA	3.4
L-Glutamic acid	17.8
D-Glutamic acid	18.1
D-Glutamine	1.6
L-Aspartic acid	5.8
β-Alanine	4.9
L-Valine	1.3

Synthesis by the Brain

The high concentrations of some amino acids in the brain, e.g. glutamic acid, gamma-aminobutyric acid (GABA), glutamine and glycine, undoubtedly reflect their synthesis within this tissue from glucose. Beloff-Chain *et al.* (1955) showed that GABA, glutamic acid and glutamine were produced by brain slices on addition of labelled glucose to the medium. Glutamic acid is the first step in the transformation from glucose. Altogether some 80% of the free amino acids of brain are made up of glutamic and aspartic acids and their derivatives—glutamine, asparagine, acetylaspartic acid and GABA—and this is undoubtedly connected with the role of GABA and others of these compounds as transmitters in the central nervous system. We may note, in passing, that brain contains enzymes that are capable of oxidation, transamination, amidation and decarboxylation of glutamic acid, this tissue being peculiar in the possession of the last two enzymes. The decarboxylation of glutamic acid leads to the formation of GABA.

Concentrations in the Extracellular Fluid

We have seen that estimates of the concentration of glucose in brain extracellular fluid have been made on the basis of an *in vivo* microdialysis technique; the same technique has been applied by Lerma *et al.* (1986) and Tossman and Ungerstedt (1986) to the concentrations of some amino acids in brain tissue. Table 2.13 gives the concentrations of some seven amino acids in blood plasma, CSF and extracellular fluid of the rat's hippocampus. If these figures are correct, it would seem that the concentrations in extracellular fluid are less than in CSF but closer to those in CSF than in blood plasma. Since most amino acids are accumulated by brain cells, this is not surprising, and would be expected, especially of neurotransmitters such as glycine and aspartic acid. In a study of the concentrations of excitatory transmitters in the corticostriate pathway, employing the microdialysis technique, Young and Bradford (1986) found the following concentrations (μM) in the extracellular fluid:

Aspartate	Glutamate	Glutamine	Threonine
0.15	0.37	2.06	0.83

These values differ very considerably from those of Lerma *et al.* (1986). The results on the relative concentrations of glutamine and glutamate tended to confirm the view that glutamine was the precursor of glutamate.

Table 2.13 Amino acid concentrations in plasma, cerebrospinal fluid and hippocampal extracellular fluid and tissue. From Lerma *et al.* (1986)

			Hippocampus	
	Plasma	*CSF*	*EC fluid*	*Tissue* (μmol/g)
Aspartate	33.8 ± 3.26	5.8 ± 0.98	1.7 ± 0.22	3.59 ± 0.13
Glutamate	159.6 ± 7.45	11.4 ± 2.04	2.9 ± 0.38	11.80 ± 0.38
Serine	247.0 ± 15.19	62.3 ± 5.02	24.9 ± 1.42	1.05 ± 0.03
Glutamine	834.6 ± 71.99	523.6 ± 11.35	193.4 ± 10.90	5.08 ± 0.19
Arginine	227.1 ± 10.10	32.5 ± 2.43	6.9 ± 0.52	0.09 ± 0.01
Taurine	324.1 ± 24.60	59.7 ± 5.08	20.6 ± 1.03	8.43 ± 0.57
Alanine	430.0 ± 30.40	85.4 ± 5.68	7.7 ± 0.51	0.71 ± 0.03
GABA	n.d.	n.d.	0.8 ± 0.15	2.08 ± 0.15

Values (means ± s.e.m.) are expressed in μM, except for tissue. Numbers of animals used were 4 for plasma, 5–6 for CSF and 5 for tissue. EC fluid figures correspond to the computer-estimated values.

The Transport of Amino Acids

The Blood–Brain Barrier

Oldendorf (1971), in his original description of the BUI technique, described the penetration of a number of amino acids into the rat's brain. His results are illustrated in Figure 2.11, and it will be noted that the non-essential amino acids, i.e. those that can be synthesized by the organism, penetrated slowly—so slowly, indeed, as to give insignificant values for the BUI. A similar difference between the essential and non-essential amino acids was demonstrated by Baños *et al.* (1973), employing an intravenous infusion technique permitting the measurement of brain uptake over longer periods than the 15 s employed in the BUI technique. Figure 2.11 shows that penetration is inhibited if the labelled amino acid is dissolved in rat plasma rather than saline, presumably owing to competition by amino acids in the plasma.

The Amino Acid Transport Systems

We have seen that classical studies of transport of amino acids by animal cells, mainly carried out by Christensen (see, for example, Christensen, 1969; Christensen and Kilberg, 1987), have led to the classification of the amino acids in accordance with their affinities for three main systems, in the sense that a given class of amino acids, e.g. neutral amino acids, compete with each other for a presumptive carrier molecule, but do not compete with other classes, such as the basic or acidic amino acids, which apparently have their own transporter molecules. This segregation is by no means absolute, however; and this is reasonable, since it would be difficult to envisage carrier molecules that could distinguish precisely between any pair of amino acids. The three main groups were the neutral, acid and basic amino acids. The neutral amino acids were subdivided into an L and an A system. The L system, characterized by leucine, had a reactivity with its carrier proportional to the mass of its hydrocarbon chain, while the A system, which included alanine, AIBA and MeAIBA, had as its main feature a dependence on the presence of Na^+ in the medium, a feature indicating the probability that transport involved movement against a gradient of electrochemical potential. The ASC system was discriminated from the A system by the absence of competition with MeAIBA, but transport was Na^+-dependent; characteristic substrates were 3- and 4-carbon aliphatic and hydroxyaliphatic amino acids such as proline and cysteine.

It will be seen from Oldendorf's study, that the A and ASC amino acids have low blood–brain barrier permeabilities, and this is consistent with their probable involvement in active transport, since movement against a gradient of electrochemical potential requires, in general, a low passive permeability across the actively transporting membrane, in the interests of thermodynamic efficiency.

Stereospecificity

Oldendorf (1973b), employing his BUI technique, showed that penetration of

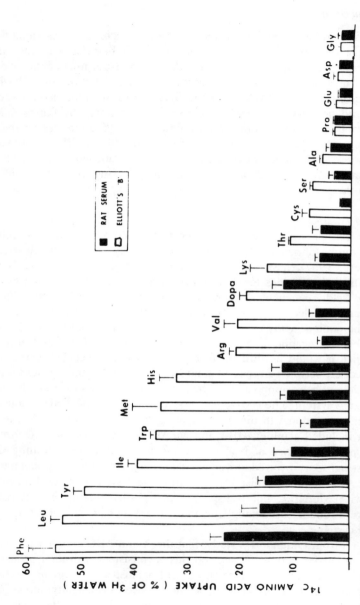

Figure 2.11 Effect of using rat serum as a diluent (dark bars) on brain uptake index for amino acids. All amino acids having a measurable uptake using an inorganic diluent (light bars) show a reduction in presence of rat serum. From Oldendorf (1971)

amino acids into brain was stereospecific, in the sense that the natural laevo-enantiomorph usually penetrated more rapidly than the dextra-compound. When competitive inhibition was studied, the L-enantiomer was always the more effective in depressing penetration of itself (self-inhibition) than was the D-enantiomer in depressing uptake of the L-enantiomer. The D-enantiomer was sometimes effective in inhibiting penetration of the L-enantiomer, but this varied with the amino acid.

Carrier Classes

Oldendorf and Szabo (1976) assigned the amino acids to three groups, namely neutral, acidic and basic; of the 22 amino acids studied, all, except glycine and alanine, could be assigned to one group only, but the BUIs for these two were so small that competitive studies with other amino acids were not feasible. Later work suggests that the A system is absent, so far as transport across the blood–brain barrier is concerned, so that transport of glycine, alanine, serine and proline is small and probably mediated by the L system (Wade and Katzman, 1975; Betz and Goldstein, 1978). This generalization probably applies to transport from blood to brain across the brain microvessels; however, when transport of amino acids out of the CSF is studied, as with ventriculocisternal perfusion (e.g. Lorenzo, 1977; Davson *et al.*, 1982), there is no doubt that glycine and alanine, and probably other amino acids, are transported out of the CSF, and probably brain tissue, by active processes that take place against a gradient of electrochemical potential and thus presumably utilize a Na^+-dependent mechanism comparable with the A system as defined by Christensen.

Michaelis–Menten Parameters

Values of K_m and V_{max} may be determined with the BUI technique by varying the concentration of unlabelled amino acid in the bolus of labelled material; this is practicable with the BUI technique, because the bolus effectively removes the blood plasma from the microvessels during the period of measurement, so that this is not complicated by the presence of the normally present amino acids of plasma. [Note 1.] Some values of K_m and V_{max}, obtained under these or comparable conditions are shown in Table 2.14; the important feature is that K_m is in the

Table 2.14 Michaelis–Menten parameters for amino acids deduced from their penetration from a saline bolus in the BUI technique. After Segal and Zlokovic (1990)

	K_m (mM)	V_{max} (nmol min^{-1} g^{-1})	Concn in plasma (mM)
Leucine	0.03	59 ⎱	0.13
	0.13	86 ⎰	
Phenylalanine	0.011	41	0.08
Tryptophan	0.22	17	–
	0.015	55	–
Tyrosine	0.06	97	0.05
Valine	0.21	49	0.19

neighbourhood of the concentrations in plasma, so that passage across the blood–brain barrier is strongly influenced by changes in concentration of the amino acid and, more important, of other competing amino acids. From a pathological point of view this is of especial importance; thus, in phenylketonuria the high levels of phenylalanine in the blood of the infant prevent normal development of the brain by inhibiting the uptake of other amino acids (Udenfriend, 1961; Oldendorf, 1973b).

The Apparent K_m and V_{max}

Pardridge (1977) deduced 'apparent' values for the Michaelis–Menten parameters that took into account the expected competitive inhibition due to the other amino acids of the plasma. He employed the simple equation of Cleland (1967), which related the apparent K_m to the K_ms of the competing amino acids at their existing concentrations, S:

$$K_{m(app)} = K_m \left(1 + \sum \frac{(S)}{K_m} \right)$$

the summation being taken over the competing amino acids in serum. Having estimated these apparent K_ms, and from the known concentrations in plasma, he was able to predict the actual rates of influx of amino acids into the brain during steady-state conditions, and they agreed reasonably well with those determined directly by Baños *et al.* (1973) and Daniel *et al.* (1976).

Perfused Rat Brain

Smith *et al.* (1987) have applied the Takasato technique to the study of three neutral amino acids of differing lipid-solubility, deducing values of V_{max}, K_m and K_D from studies lasting only 10–15 s. Figure 2.11, shows that the reciprocal of K_m, a measure of affinity for the carrier, increases linearly with lipid-solubility when plotted semi-logarithmically.

In another study (Momma *et al.*, 1987) the kinetics of penetration of the large neutral amino acid phenylalanine into the perfused rat brain were examined in greater detail than was possible with the BUI technique, since they could be sure of the absence of interfering amino acids in the perfusion fluid, whereas it seems that with the BUI technique, although the initial bolus injection is free of other amino acids, intermixture of the entering bolus with the animal's blood does take place. Their estimated value of K_m, namely 0.011 μmol/ml, was some 1/3 to 1/72 of previous estimates, indicating a higher affinity for the transport system than had previously been thought. The only mammalian tissue showing such a high affinity is the rat hepatocyte, a transport system for neutral amino acids named by Weissbach *et al.* (1982) the L1 system to differentiate it from a second, L2, Na^+-independent neutral amino acid system. The affinity and substrate-specificity of the blood–brain barrier system were considered by Momma *et al.* to be different from those of other Na^+-independent neutral amino acid systems, such as L2, T and ASC (Shotwell *et al.*, 1983; Christensen, 1985). Of some interest was the observation that D-phenylalanine was able to inhibit transport of

L-phenylalanine completely, the value of K_i being about ten times that for the K_m of L-phenylalanine.

Tryptophan

This neutral amino acid is closely involved with the serotonin economy of the brain, so that the special features of its transport within the central nervous system are of great pathological interest, since disturbances in the economy may lie at the basis of some neurological diseases. Unlike other amino acids (except cysteine: Rassan, 1990) tryptophan is reversibly bound to plasma albumin, so that its transport requires, as a first step, dissociation from its albumin complex. As with other amino acids, transport across the blood–brain barrier is carried-mediated, so, on the basis of Pardridge's treatment of transport of protein-bound solutes, we may expect the rate of transport to be governed by the plasma level of albumin and the competition between the plasma albumin and the membrane carrier for the tryptophan molecule. In general, because of the binding of tryptophan to albumin, and its pH-dependence, the transport of tryptophan from blood to brain is not easily predictable (Davson *et al.*, 1987). Of interest is the finding of Pardridge and Fierer (1990) that the dissociation constant of the tryptophan–albumin complex is very much higher *in vivo* than *in vitro* (p. 113), namely 1.67 compared with 0.13 mM, indicating an adaptation of the carrier system at the blood–brain barrier that permits a more ready penetration of this important metabolite.

Non-metabolizable Amino Acids

Two of these, AIBA and cycloleucine, have been employed in several valuable studies—valuable because they represent probably the A and L classes of amino acids so far as transport across the blood–brain barrier is concerned, and also because they are not involved in protein metabolism. Schain and Watanabe (1972) showed that penetration of AIBA into the guinea-pig brain was very slow, whereas that of cycloleucine was very rapid; and this is consistent with the view that an A system, capable of transporting glycine and other representatives of the class, is lacking so far as transport from blood to brain is concerned.

As we shall see, however, the brain capillaries exhibit an asymmetry in this respect, so that, whereas AIBA penetrates from blood to brain only very slowly, the transport in the reverse direction, as during ventriculocisternal perfusion, is relatively rapid and exhibits Michaelis–Menten kinetics.

Isolated Brain Microvessels

Betz and Goldstein (1978) showed that isolated brain capillaries accumulated amino acids, and emphasized that uptake of A-system amino acids, typified by methyl-AIBA, was dependent on the presence of Na^+ in the medium, and therefore was probably active, whereas that of leucine, typical of the L system, was not. This indicated an asymmetry of the blood–brain barrier, since, as we have seen, studies involving transport from blood to brain have indicated the absence of an A system. Thus, so far as the A system amino acids are concerned, at any rate, the possibility of an active transport out of the brain into the blood was confirmed.

This would be consistent with the view that transmitter amino acids, such as glycine, are removed from brain tissue by an active process.

Glutamine
Although technically an amide, glutamine is referred to as an amino acid, being the amide of glutamic acid:

$$\underset{\text{Glutamic acid}}{\overset{\displaystyle \text{HOOC}-\underset{\underset{\text{H}}{|}}{\overset{\overset{\text{H}}{|}}{\text{C}}}-\underset{\underset{\text{H}}{|}}{\overset{\overset{\text{H}}{|}}{\text{C}}}-\underset{\underset{\text{H}}{|}}{\overset{\overset{\text{NH}_2}{|}}{\text{C}}}-\text{COOH}}{}}$$

$$\underset{\text{Glutamine}}{\overset{\displaystyle \text{H}_2\text{N}-\underset{\underset{\text{O}}{||}}{\text{C}}-\underset{\underset{\text{H}}{|}}{\overset{\overset{\text{H}}{|}}{\text{C}}}-\underset{\underset{\text{H}}{|}}{\overset{\overset{\text{H}}{|}}{\text{C}}}-\underset{\underset{\text{H}}{|}}{\overset{\overset{\text{NH}_2}{|}}{\text{C}}}-\text{COOH}}{}}$$

Along with alpha-ketoglutaric acid, it is involved in detoxication of ammonia within the brain, and this may account for its high concentration in this tissue and in the CSF. Cangiano *et al.* (1983) have examined its uptake by brain microvessels; it apparently employs both the A and L systems, a portion of the uptake being Na^+-dependent and competing with MeAIBA, and the rest being Na^+-independent and inhibited by BCH, an L-system inhibitor. When brain microvessels are allowed to accumulate glutamine, it is found that the uptake of other neutral amino acids, such as tryptophan, is accelerated. Cangiano *et al.* suggested that the A system of transport, localized to the abluminal side of the capillary membrane, co-operated with the L system, localized at both sides, in transport of neutral amino acids across the brain capillaries.

Isolated Cerebral Capillary Cells
Cancilla and DeBault (1983) prepared a line of cultured endothelial cells (ME-2), which maintained some of the properties of the parent cell through successive passages *in vitro*. The cells exhibited both a Na^+-dependent A system and a Na^+-independent L system so far as transport of neutral amino acids was concerned; transport into the cells by the L system was much more rapid than with the A system.

Gamma-glutamyl Transpeptidase
This enzyme, located in the membranes of epithelial cells involved in transport, such as the intestinal epithelium, catalyses the reaction

$$\text{glutathione} + \text{amino acid} \rightarrow \gamma \text{glutamyl-amino acid} + \text{cysteinylglycine}$$

It was suggested by Orlowski (1963) that this reaction, which makes the degradation of glutathione dependent on amino acids, might function in the transport of these last across cell membranes. Orlowski and Meister (1970) integrated this reaction into the glutamic acid cycle, as illustrated by Figure 2.12. Thus, after the amino acid has been converted to the γ-glutamyl derivative by

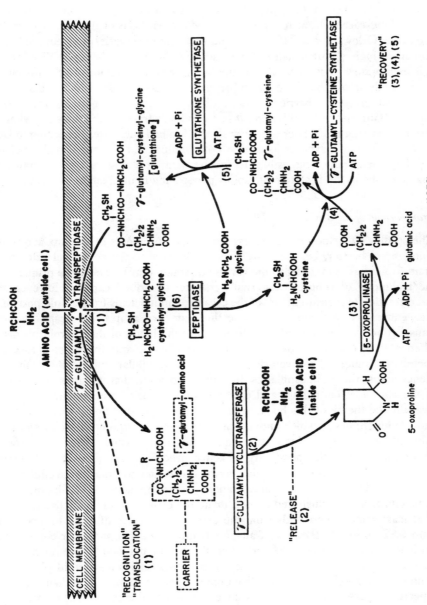

Figure 2.12   The γ-glutamyl cycle. From Meister (1973)

glutathione at or near the cell surface, a translocation step brings it into the cell, and the amino acid is released by the enzyme γ-glutamyl-cyclotransferase with the concurrent formation of L-pyrrolidone-carboxylic acid. The conversion of L-pyrrolidone-carboxylic acid to glutamate and the synthesis of glutathione complete the cycle. Orlowski *et al.* (1974) showed that brain capillaries, but not glial cells, contained high γ-glutamyl-transferase activity, the enzyme being localized to the cell membranes. It is likely that if this is, indeed, a mechanism of transport of amino acids across the blood–brain barrier, it applies mainly, if not exclusively, to those that cross the barrier rapidly. Thus, methionine penetrates the barrier rapidly (Battistin *et al.*, 1971) and it is a good substrate for the enzyme, whereas glycine, crossing the barrier only very slowly, is a bad substrate. According to Betz *et al.* (1980), the enzyme is located in both luminal and abluminal regions of the capillary membrane, suggesting an involvement in a passive type of transport characteristic of the L system of rapidly penetrating neutral amino acids.

Transport out of the Brain

The studies so far described are essentially measurements of the flux across the blood–brain barrier, i.e. transport from the luminal to the abluminal side of the brain capillaries. Transport in the reverse direction may be measured primarily by the technique of ventriculocisternal perfusion described earlier. However, the interpretation of measurements of the escape of amino acids from a fluid perfusing the ventricles is not simple, because there are two routes for escape—namely transport across the choroidal epithelium into the blood of the choroid plexuses, whence it is conveyed to the systemic circulation, and transport across the ependymal linings of the ventricles into the extracellular fluid of the brain and thence across the brain capillaries. It is likely, however, that the transport features of the choroidal epithelium and of the brain capillaries are similar, and this is basically the theme of this book, so that studies on ventriculocisternal perfusion, and cruder studies in which amino acids are injected into the ventricles and their subsequent fate determined (see, e.g. Banks and Kastin, 1990) can provide important clues to the possibility of active processes that tend to restrain the equilibration of certain amino acids between plasma and brain extracellular fluid and CSF. Thus, the low concentrations of amino acids in CSF and brain extracellular space, illustrated earlier, invite the explanation of an active transport of at least some amino acids from the extracellular space of brain to blood and from CSF to blood. By active transport is meant, in this particular context, the tendency for outflux from CSF, or extracellular fluid, to blood to be more favoured than influx. Thus, although there must in both situations—choroid plexus and brain capillaries—be a net influx from blood, this net influx is less than would be expected of passive diffusion under concentration gradients when active transport takes place.

Ventriculocisternal Perfusion

Pioneers in these studies of transport from the perfused ventricles were Lorenzo and Cutler (see Lorenzo, 1977, for a review). In general, they established that transport out of the CSF involved a carrier-mediated process, and they determined Michaelis–Menten parameters for the process. Figure 2.13 illustrates a Lineweaver–Burk plot for transport of ^{14}C-labelled leucine. A K_m of 0.61 mM was deduced from the intercept, comparing with a normal concentration in the CSF in the region of 0.026 mM in the same animal (cat).

Losses to the Blood and Brain
When an amino acid is incorporated into the artificial CSF perfusing the ventricles of the brain, losses may be attributed to escape into the blood—by way of the choroid plexuses and the capillaries of the brain—and losses to the brain through accumulation in the brain cells. By measuring both the total loss from the perfusion fluid and the amount in the brain at the end of the perfusion, the two pathways of loss may be separately evaluated. Davson *et al.* (1982) compared these, and the results are shown in Table 2.15, where the losses under carrier-free conditions, and when transport is suppressed by addition of 5 mM unlabelled acid to the perfusion fluid, are shown. In general, it is the blood into which the amino acids are primarily transported. Aspartic acid is especially interesting; as a putative central nervous system transmitter, we may note that it is removed primarily into the blood. Glycine, another transmitter, is treated rather differently in that the brain cells take up a larger proportion, but still the greater output is into the blood.

Active Transport from CSF to Blood
To demonstrate, in the living animal, an active transport of amino acid from CSF to blood in an unequivocal manner, we must establish a high concentration of the amino acid in the blood and measure the loss of the amino acid from the perfused

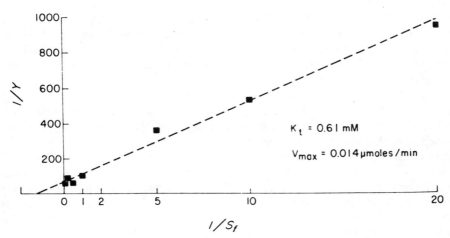

Figure 2.13 Lineweaver–Burk plot for rate of loss of ^{14}C-leucine from ventriculo-cisternal perfusate. From Snodgrass *et al.* (1969)

Table 2.15 The losses of labelled amino acids from the perfusion fluid during 2 h (1) broken down to losses to brain (2) and to blood (1) − (2). The losses are in arbitrary units based on equating the activity in the perfusion fluid to a fixed value; they are strictly comparable both in the rows and in the columns[a] (Davson *et al.*, 1982)

Amino acid	n	Lost (1)	Brain (2)	Blood (1) − (2)
Aspartic acid CF	4	69.0 ± 2	5.6 ± 0.5	63.4 ± 6
Aspartic acid 5 mM	4	24.5 ± 2	2.6 ± 1	21.9 ± 3
Phenylalanine CF	3	65.3 ± 6	12.1 ± 1	53.2 ± 5
Phenylalanine 5 mM	3	26.3 ± 3	6.0 ± 1	20.3 ± 1.8
Glycine CF	6	62.4 ± 5	27.0 ± 2	35.4 ± 5
Glycine 5 mM	5	31.6 ± 4	13.9 ± 1	17.7 ± 5
Arginine CF	3	58.7 ± 4	8.9 ± 1	49.8 ± 3
Arginine 5 mM	3	12.8 ± 4	9.3 ± 2	3.5 ± 2
Leucine CF	3	58.4 ± 6	16.2 ± 3	42.2 ± 9
Leucine 5 mM	3	20.8 ± 3	6.4 ± 1	14.4 ± 5
Tryptophan CF	3	56.0 ± 6	10.8 ± 2.5	45.2 ± 7
Tryptophan 5 mM	3	28.1 ± 7	6.5 ± 0.5	21.6 ± 7
Serine CF	4	53.5 ± 9	18.4 ± 2	35.1 ± 10
Serine 5 mM	3	33.2 ± 7	19.5 ± 2	13.9 ± 8
Alanine CF	3	42.8 ± 4	8.7 ± 2	34.1 ± 2
Alanine 5 mM	3	30.7 ± 5	2.9 ± 0.2	27.8 ± 4
Cycloleucine CF	4	38.4 ± 2	10.7 ± 2	27.7 ± 4
Cycloleucine 5 mM	3	27.1 ± 4	8.6 ± 2	18.5 ± 6
Lysine CF	5	34.5 ± 3	13.2 ± 1	21.3 ± 4
Lysine 5 mM	3	27.7 ± 1	11.7 ± 0.5	16.0 ± 1

[a]Limits are s.e.; n = number of experiments.

ventricle when the concentration is lower than that in the blood. If active transport were impossible, then there would be no loss into the blood. Davson *et al.* (1982) measured the escape of ^{14}C-labelled glycine from the fluid perfusing the ventricles of the rabbit, and, at a given point, raised the concentration of the ^{14}C-labelled glycine in the plasma to a value much higher than that in the perfusion fluid, by means of an intravenous infusion. Figure 2.14 illustrates the experiment. Initially, ventriculocisternal perfusion was established, and the loss of labelled glycine occurred, leading to a steady state with the concentration in the outflowing perfusion fluid some 30% of the inflowing concentration. Thus, glycine was being taken up by the blood and brain tissue at a high rate. At 60 min, a high level of labelled glycine was established in the blood, as indicated by the upper graph; in spite of this, glycine continued to escape from the ventricular perfusion fluid and continued to do so until the end of the perfusion period. There was, indeed, some reduction in the loss from the perfusion fluid, indicated by an upturn in the graph, but there was nothing like a complete suppression, which would have meant a rise in the graph to an ordinate of some 87.5, indicated by the dotted line on the graph, a line indicating the reduction in concentration that would be expected were there no loss at all from the perfusion fluid, the decrease from 100 being due to dilution by newly secreted fluid. Studies with cycloleucine and labelled methionine were

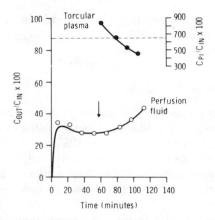

Figure 2.14　The effect of establishing a high activity of [^{3}H]-glycine in the plasma on clearance of [^{3}H]-glycine from the ventricles. At the arrow, the intracarotid infusion was begun. Left-hand ordinates: $C_{out}/C_{in} \times 100$. Right-hand ordinates: radioactivity in plasma as percentage of that in the entering perfusion fluid, C_{in}. Abscissae: time in min. The dashed line represents the value of $C_{out}/C_{in} \times 100$ expected in absence of clearance, determined by Blue Dextran. From Davson *et al.* (1982)

also consistent with an ability of amino acids to move from CSF to blood against a gradient of concentration. It must be emphasized, however, that the mere continuation of loss from the perfusion fluid, when the concentration in blood was raised, is no definite proof of an active transport from the CSF, whether across the choroid plexuses or across the blood–brain barrier, since the amino acid could continue to diffuse into the brain tissue and be accumulated by the brain cells. The analysis of the kinetics, however, tended to confirm the interpretation of an active transport out of the CSF, probably through the choroid plexuses and the brain capillaries.

Patlak–Fenstermacher Model

As indicated in Chapter 1 (p. 96), when the ventricles of the brain are perfused with an artificial CSF containing a solute of interest, such as an amino acid, Patlak and Fenstermacher (1975) showed that it was possible to deduce the permeability of the blood–brain barrier to the solute in question, provided that a steady state had been achieved, the brain being frozen at the end of a long period of perfusion and a block of tissue being removed and cut into thin sections that were analysed for the solute. Fenstermacher and Davson (1982) perfused the rabbit's ventricular system with the non-metabolizable amino acids AIBA and cycloleucine. With cycloleucine a steady state was achieved, and a transfer constant of 0.09 min^{-1} was derived, corresponding to a $t_{1/2}$ of 8 min. With AIBA a steady state was not achieved, so a corresponding value for a transfer constant could not be calculated; nevertheless it was clear that transport of AIBA out of the brain, across the blood–brain barrier, was much slower than that of cycloleucine. This agrees with the results of Watanabe and Schain and others, who were measuring, however, transport from blood to brain, so that if there is an asymmetry in the system, the experiments are not strictly comparable.

The Isolated Perfused Sheep Choroid Plexus

We have seen that this preparation has permitted the characterization of transport processes across the choroidal epithelium uncomplicated by processes taking place across the blood–brain barrier. Preston *et al.* (1989) and Segal *et al.* (1990) adapted the perfused plexus to the study of single-pass transport, establishing a high concentration of the labelled amino acid in the perfusate by means of a single bolus and estimating extraction by the measurement of concentration in the venous outflow in the great vein of Galen. Figure 2.15 illustrates the application of the technique to extraction of [3H]-leucine, the graph showing the recovery of the amino acid compared with that of [14C]-mannitol, a substance that would not cross the blood–CSF barrier appreciably in the short time of measurement. By varying the concentration of unlabelled amino acid, they determined Michaelis–Menten parameters for transport from blood to CSF across the choroid plexus; these are shown in Table 2.16. The value of K_m for phenylalanine is 0.003 mM, compared with 0.011 mM for the blood–brain transport measured in conscious rats by Miller *et al.* (1985).

Sodium Dependence
Segal *et al.* found that the transport across the choroid plexus of the six amino

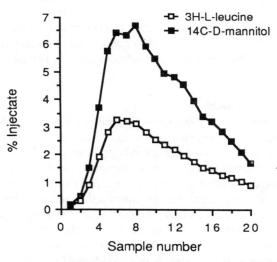

Figure 2.15 Recovery of L-[3H]-leucine and D-[14C]-mannitol in 20 consecutive venous samples plotted as a percentage of total radioactivity injected. Lower recovery of L-[3H]-leucine relative to D-[14C]-mannitol indicated cellular uptake of this amino acid by basolateral face of choroid plexus. From Segal *et al.* (1990)

Table 2.16 Michaelis–Menten parameters for several amino acids derived from measurements of transport from blood to choroidal epithelium of the perfused choroid plexus. From Segal *et al.* (1990)

Amino acid	K_m (μM)	V_{max} (nmol min^{-1} g^{-1})
Serine	24.90 ± 4.21	28.83 ± 1.89
Arginine	25.38 ± 5.10	15.95 ± 1.37
Glycine	12.43 ± 2.20	14.33 ± 1.28
Phenylalanine	3.24 ± 0.19	4.57 ± 0.10
Glutamate	2.59 ± 0.67	8.84 ± 0.82

Values are means $\pm$ s.e.; number of preparations is 5 or 6.

acids studied—namely alanine, glycine, glutamine, leucine, glutamate and lysine—was unaffected by lowering the concentration of Na$^+$ in the perfusing blood to less than 6 mM, a reduction that caused a marked inhibition of CSF secretion (65.6%). This confirms the apparent absence of an A system so far as transport from blood to the CSF is concerned, and emphasizes the asymmetry of the system pointed out by Betz and Goldstein (1978).

Steady-state Fluxes
In the steady state the choroid plexuses are secreting a fluid containing amino acids into the ventricles, so that there will be a net flux of the amino acid from blood to CSF across the choroidal epithelium. If the newly secreted fluid contained the same concentration of an amino acid as that in the parent plasma, then the net flux would be simply determined by the rate of secretion of the CSF. Since, however, the steady-state concentrations of most amino acids in CSF are considerably lower than those in plasma, the net flux in the steady state will be less than expected of the flow of CSF. In general, the net flux is given by the difference in the measured fluxes in the two directions across the choroid plexus under steady-state conditions, the flux from CSF to blood being greater, often by a large factor, when the value of R_{CSF} for the amino acid is low, as with glycine or alanine. Preston and Segal (1990) measured fluxes from both directions in the perfused choroid plexus, and the difference between the two gave a measure of the degree to which transport from blood to CSF was restrained. Some values are shown in Table 2.17. Of great interest was the finding that, when the concentration of unlabelled amino acid was increased in both blood and CSF (in this latter case an artificial CSF flowing over the perfused plexus), the direction of the net flux for aspartate and glycine reversed when the unlabelled concentration was increased to 0.1 mM; this was due to an increase in the flux in the direction from CSF to blood. Only when the concentrations of unlabelled amino acids were increased to 1 mM did all the amino acids show this reversal. As Preston and Segal point out, this reversal of net flux, as the concentration in the CSF increases, serves a homoeostatic mechanism that tends to keep the level constant, and is similar to one described earlier by Bradbury and Stulcova (1970) for potassium. Thus, rises in concentration of this ion in the CSF are counteracted by a facilitated movement

Table 2.17 Fluxes of amino acids from blood to CSF and CSF to blood in perfused isolated choroid plexus of sheep. From Preston and Segal (1990)

Amino acid	*Flux* (nmol min^{-1} g^{-1})		
	$B \rightarrow CSF$	$CSF \rightarrow B$	*Net*
Aspartate	8.7 ± 1.1	6.7 ± 1.1	2.1 ± 0.9
Cycloleucine	2.3 ± 0.3	0.3 ± 0.1	2.0 ± 0.2
Glutamine	4.9 ± 0.6	1.1 ± 0.2	3.9 ± 0.3
Glycine	3.3 ± 0.1	1.4 ± 0.3	1.9 ± 0.1
Lysine	2.7 ± 0.7	2.5 ± 0.2	0.3 ± 0.2
Phenylalanine	3.1 ± 0.3	0.1 ± 0.1	3.0 ± 0.2
Proline	2.6 ± 0.3	0.7 ± 0.1	1.9 ± 0.3
Serine	13.7 ± 0.4	0.6 ± 0.1	13.2 ± 0.3

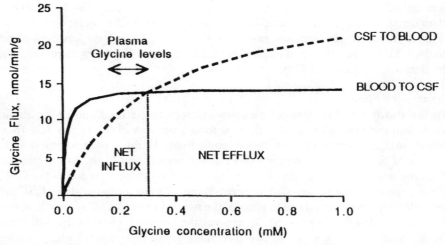

Figure 2.16 Rectangular hyperbolae fitted to data for glycine transport at the basolateral face of the choroid plexus, using the single-pass experiments (blood to CSF) and glycine flux from the CSF (CSF to blood). The intersection point is at close to 0.3 mM, the upper level for normal plasma glycine concentrations. After Preston and Segal (1990)

of the ion from CSF to blood; as a result, the concentration of K$^+$ in CSF is held remarkably constant at some 60% of the plasma level in spite of large fluctuations in plasma level. Figure 2.16 illustrates schematically the mode of operation of the system with respect to glycine; as plasma glycine level rises, the curves for the two fluxes intersect, indicating the point of no net flux; beyond this the flux outwards exceeds that inwards, and the situation is one of net efflux.

Levels in Newly Formed Fluid
As with glucose, it is possible to estimate the level of an amino acid in the newly formed secretion from a measurement of its rate of formation together with the net flux of amino acid into the CSF. The calculated concentrations are shown in

Table 2.18 Concentrations of some amino acids in newly formed CSF, computed from net influx and an average rate of CSF secretion of 133 ± 5.7 µl/min. After Preston and Segal (1990)

Amino acid	Computed concentration (µM)	Bulk concentration (µM)
Aspartate	15.8	
Cycloleucine	15.0	
Glutamine	29.3	
Glycine	14.2	18
Lysine	2.3	58
Phenylalanine	22.5	24
Proline	99.2	26

Table 2.18; actual values for the bulk CSF of the sheep have not been determined. Some figures for the cat, taken from Snodgrass *et al.* (1969), have been included.

References

Ames, A., Higashi, K. and Nesbett, F.B. (1965). A relation of potassium concentration in choroid plexus fluid to that in plasma. *J. Physiol.*, **181**, 506–515

Atkinson, A.J. and Weiss, M.F. (1969). Kinetics of blood–cerebrospinal fluid glucose transfer in the normal dog. *Am. J. Physiol.*, **216**, 1120–1125

Bachelard, H.S. (1971). Specificity and kinetic properties of monosaccharide uptake into guinea pig cerebral cortex *in vitro*. *J. Neurochem.*, **18**, 213–222

Bachelard, H.S., Daniel, P.M., Love, E.R. and Pratt, O.E. (1973). The transport of glucose into the brain of the rat *in vivo*. *Proc. Roy. Soc. B*, **183**, 71–82

Banks, W.A. and Kastin, A.J. (1990). Peptide transport systems for opiates across the blood–brain barrier. *Am. J. Physiol.*, **259**, E1–E10

Baños, G., Daniel, P.M., Moorhouse, S.R. and Pratt, O.E. (1973). The influx of amino acids into the brain of the rat *in vivo*: the essential compared with the non-essential amino acids. *Proc. Roy. Soc. B*, **183**, 59–70

Battistin, L., Grynbaum, A. and Lajtha, A. (1971). The uptake of various amino acids by the mouse brain. *Brain Res.*, **29**, 85–99

Beloff-Chain, A., Chain, E.B., Masi, I. and Pocchiari, F. (1955). Fate of uniformly labelled ^{14}C glucose in brain slices. *Proc. Roy. Soc. B*, **144**, 22–28

Beneviste, H. (1989). Brain microdialysis. *J. Neurochem.*, **52**, 1667–1678

Beneviste, H. and Diemer, W.H. (1987). Cellular reactions to implantation of a microdialysis tube in the rat hippocampus. *Acta Neuropathol.*, **74**, 234–238

Beneviste, H., Hansen, A.J. and Ottosen, N.S. (1989). Determination of brain interstitial concentrations by microdialysis. *J. Neurochem.*, **52**, 1741–1750

Beneviste, H. and Hüttenmeier, P.C. (1990). Microdialysis—theory and application. *Progr. Neurobiol.*, **35**, 195–215

Betz, A.L., Firth, J.A. and Goldstein, G.W. (1980). Polarity of the blood–brain barrier: distribution of enzymes between the luminal and antiluminal membranes of brain capillary endothelial cells. *Brain Res.*, **192**, 17–28

Betz, A.L. and Goldstein, G.W. (1978). Polarity of the blood–brain barrier: neutral amino acid transport into isolated brain capillaries. *Science*, **202**, 225–227

Betz, A.L. and Iannotti, I. (1983). Simultaneous determination of regional cerebral blood flow and blood–brain glucose transport kinetics in the gerbil. *J. Cereb. Blood Flow Metab.*, 3, 193–199

Birnbaum, M.J., Haspel, H.C. and Rosen, O.M. (1986). Cloning and characterization of a cDNA encoding the rat brain glucose-transporter protein. *Proc. Natl Acad. Sci. USA*, 83, 5784–5788

Bito, L.Z. and Davson, H. (1966). Local variations in cerebrospinal fluid composition and its relationship to the composition of the extracellular fluid of the cortex. *Exp. Neurol.*, 14, 264–280

Bito, L.Z., Davson, H., Levin, E., Murray, M. and Snider, N. (1966). The concentrations of amino acids and other electrolytes in cerebrospinal fluid, *in vivo* dialysate of brain and blood plasma of the dog. *J. Neurochem.*, 13, 1057–1067

Boado, R.J. and Pardridge, W.M. (1990). The brain-type glucose transporter mRNA is specifically expressed at the blood–brain barrier. *Biochem. Biophys. Res. Comm.*, 166, 174–179

Bradbury, M.W.B. and Brøndsted, H.E. (1973). Sodium dependent transport of sugars and iodide from cerebral ventricles of the rabbit. *J. Physiol.*, 234, 127–143

Bradbury, M.W.B. and Davson, H. (1964). The transport of urea, creatinine and certain monosaccharides between blood and fluid perfusing the cerebral ventricular system of rabbits. *J. Physiol.*, 170, 195–211

Bradbury, M.W.B. and Stulcova, B. (1970). Efflux mechanism contributing to the stability of the potassium concentration in cerebrospinal fluid. *J. Physiol.*, 208, 415–430

Brøndsted, H.E. (1970a). Cerebrospinal fluid glucose and phlorrhizin. *Acta Neurol. Scand.*, 46, 637–641

Brøndsted, H.E. (1970b). Ouabain-sensitive carrier-mediated transport of glucose from the cerebral ventricles to surrounding tissues in the cat. *J. Physiol.*, 208, 187–201

Bryan, R.M., Hawkins, R.A., Mans, A.M., Davis, D.W. and Page, R.B. (1983). Cerebral glucose utilization in awake unrestrained rats. *Am. J. Physiol.*, 244, C270–C275

Buschiazzo, P.M., Terrell, E.B. and Regen, D.M. (1970). Sugar transport across the blood–brain barrier. *Am. J. Physiol.*, 219, 1505–1513

Cancilla, P.A. and DeBault, L.E. (1983). Neutral amino acid transport properties of cerebral endothelial cells *in vitro*. *J. Neuropathol. Exp. Neurol.*, 42, 191–199

Cangiano, C. *et al.* (1983). Brain microvessels take up large neutral amino acids in exchange for glutamine. Cooperative role of Na^+-dependent and Na^+-independent systems. *J. Biol. Chem.*, 258, 8949–8954

Carver, M.J. (1965). Influence of phenylalanine administration on the free amino acids of brain and liver in the rat. *J. Neurochem.*, 12, 45–50

Christensen, H.N. (1969). Some special kinetic problems of transport. *Adv. Enzymol.*, 32, 1–31

Christensen, H.N. (1985). On the strategy of kinetic discrimination of amino acid transport systems. *J. Membrane Biol.*, 84, 97–103

Christensen, H.N. and Kilberg, M.S. (1987). Amino acid transport across the plasma membrane: role of regulation in interorgan flow. In Yudilevich, D.L. and Boyd, C.A.C. (Eds), *Amino Acid Transport in Animal Cells*. Macmillan, Press, London

Cleland, W.W. (1967). The statistical analysis of enzyme kinetic data. *Adv. Enzymol.*, 29, 1–32

Cremer, J.E., Ray, D.E., Sarna, G.S. and Cunningham, V.J. (1981). A study of the kinetic behaviour of glucose based on simultaneous estimation of influx and phosphorylation in brain regions of rats in different physiological states. *Brain Res.*, 221, 331–342

Crone, C. (1963). The permeability of capillaries of various organs as determined by the use of the 'indicator diffusion' method. *Acta Physiol. Scand.*, 58, 292–305

Crone, C. (1965). Facilitated transfer of glucose from blood into brain tissue. *J. Physiol.*, 181, 103–113

Crowdon, W.A., Bratton, T.S., Houston, M.C., Tarpley, H.L. and Regen, D.M. (1971). Brain glucose metabolism in the intact mouse. *Amer. J. Physiol.*, 221, 1738–1745

Daniel, P.M., Noorhouse, S.R. and Pratt, O.E. (1976). Do changes in blood levels of other aromatic amino acids influence levodopa therapy? *Lancet*, **i**, 95

Davson, H. (1955). A comparative study of the aqueous humour and cerebrospinal fluid in the rabbit. *J. Physiol.*, **129**, 111–133

Davson, H. (1958). Some aspects of the relationship between the cerebrospinal fluid and the central nervous system. In *The Cerebrospinal Fluid*. Ciba Foundation Symposium. Churchill, London, pp. 189–203

Davson, H. (1967). *Physiology of the Cerebrospinal Fluid*. Churchill, London

Davson, H. (1976). The blood–brain barrier. *J. Physiol.*, **255**, 1–28

Davson, H., Begley, D.J., Chain, D.G., Briggs, F.O. and Shepherd, M.T. (1986). Steady-state distribution of cycloleucine and α-aminoisobutyric acid between plasma and cerebrospinal fluid. *Exp. Neurol.*, **91**, 163–173

Davson, H., Hollingsworth, J.G., Carey, M.B. and Fenstermacher, J.D. (1982). Ventriculo-cisternal perfusion of twelve amino acids in the rabbit. *J. Neurobiol.*, **13**, 293–318

Davson, H., Welch, K. and Segal, M.B. (1987). *Physiology and Pathophysiology of the Cerebrospinal Fluid*. Churchill Livingstone, London

Deane, R. and Segal, M.B. (1982). The transport of sugars by the choroid plexus of the sheep. *J. Physiol.*, **326**, 19P–20P

Deane, R. and Segal, M.B. (1985). The transport of sugars across the perfused choroid plexus of the sheep. *J. Physiol.*, **362**, 245–260

Des Rosier, M.H., Kennedy, C., Patlak, C.S., Pettigrew, K.D. and Sokoloff, L. (1974). Relationship between local cerebral blood flow and glucose utilization in the rat. *Neurology*, **24**, 389

Dick, A.P.K. and Harik, S.I. (1986). Distribution of the glucose transporter in the mammalian brain. *J. Neurochem.*, **46**, 1406–1411

Dick, A.P.K., Harik, S.I., Klip, A. and Walker, D.M. (1984). Identification and characterization of the glucose transporter of the blood–brain barrier by cytochalasin B binding and immunological reactivity. *Proc. Natl Acad. Sci. USA*, **81**, 7233–7237

Dickinson, J.C. and Hamilton, P.B. (1966). The free amino acids of human cerebrospinal fluid determined by ion exchange chromatography. *J. Neurochem.*, **13**, 1179–1187

Drewes, L.R., Horton, R.W., Betz, A.L. and Gilboe, D.D. (1977). Cytochalasin B inhibition of brain glucose transport and the influence of blood composition on inhibitor concentration. *Biochim. Biophys. Acta*, **471**, 477–486

Feise, G.K., Kogure, K., Busto, R., Scheinberg, P. and Rehmuth, O.M. (1976). Effect of insulin hypoglycaemia upon cerebral energy metabolism and EEG activity in the rat. *Brain Res.*, **126**, 263–280

Fenstermacher, J.D. and Davson, H. (1982). Distribution of two model amino acids from cerebrospinal fluid to brain and blood. *Am. J. Physiol.*, **242**, F171–F180

Fishman, R.A. (1964). Carrier transport of glucose between blood and cerebrospinal fluid. *Am. J. Physiol.*, **206**, 836–844

Franklin, G.M., Dudzinski, D.S. and Cutler, R.W.P. (1975). Amino acid transport into the cerebrospinal fluid of the rat. *J. Neurochem.*, **25**, 367–372

Gjedde, A. (1980). Rapid steady-state analysis of blood–brain glucose transfer in the rat. *Acta Physiol. Scand.*, **108**, 331–339

Gjedde, A., Hansen, A.J. and Siemkowicz, E. (1980). Rapid simultaneous determination of regional blood flow and blood–brain glucose transfer in brain of rat. *Acta Physiol. Scand.*, **108**, 321–330

Gjedde, A. and Rasmussen, M. (1980). Pentobarbital anesthesia reduces blood–brain glucose transfer in the rat. *J. Neurochem.*, **35**, 1382–1387

Gjessing, L.R., Gjesdahl, P. and Sjaastad, O. (1972). The free amino acids in human cerebrospinal fluid. *J. Neurochem.*, **19**, 1807–1808

Hawkins, R., Hass, W.K. and Ransohoff, J. (1979). Measurement of regional brain glucose utilization *in vivo* using 2.^{14}C-glucose. *Stroke*, **10**, 690–703

Hawkins, R.A., Mans, A.M., Davis, D.W., Hibbard, L.S. and Lu, D.M. (1983). Glucose availability to individual cerebral structures is correlated to glucose metabolism. *J. Neurochem.*, **40**, 1013–1018

Humoller, F.L., Mahler, D.J. and Parker, M.M. (1966). *Int. J. Neuropsychiat.*, **2**, 293–297 (quoted by McGale, 1977)

Kety, S.S. (1951). The theory and application of the exchange of inert gas at the lungs and tissues. *Pharmacol. Rev.*, **3**, 1–41

Knauff, H.G., Schabert, P. and Zickergraf, H. (1961). Die Konzentration der freien Aminosäuren in Liquor cerebrospinalis und ihre Beziehungen zur Konzentration der freien Plasmaaminosäuren. *Klin. Wschr.*, **39**, 778–784

LaManna, J.C. and Harik, S.I. (1985). Regional comparison of brain glucose influx. *Brain Res.*, **326**, 299–305

Lassen, H.N. (1978). *Scientific American*, **239**, 62

Lerma, J., Herranz, A.S., Herreras, O., Abraira, V. and Del Rio, R.M. (1986). *In vivo* determination of extracellular concentration of amino acids in the rat hippocampus. A method based on brain dialysis and computerized analysis. *Brain Res.*, **384**, 145–155

Lewis, L.D., Ljunggren, B., Norberg, K. and Siesjo, B.K. (1974). Changes in carbohydrate substances, amino acids and ammonia in the brain during insulin-induced hypoglycaemia. *J. Neurochem.*, **23**, 659–671

Lönnroth, P., Jansson, P.-A. and Smith, U. (1987). A microdialysis method allowing characterization of intercellular water space in humans. *Am. J. Physiol.*, **253**, E228–E231

Lorenzo, A.V. (1977). Factors governing the composition of the cerebrospinal fluid. *Exp. Eye Res.*, **25**, (Suppl.), 205–228

Lund-Andersen, H. (1979). Transport of glucose from blood to brain. *Physiol. Rev.*, **59**, 305–352

Lund-Andersen, H. and Kjeldsen, C.S. (1976). Uptake of glucose analogues by rat brain cortex: a kinetic analysis based upon a model. *J. Neurochem.*, **27**, 361–368

McGale, E.H.F., Pye, I.F., Stonier, C., Hutchinson, E.C. and Aber, G.M. (1977). Studies on the inter-relationship between cerebrospinal fluid and plasma amino acid concentrations in normal individuals. *J. Neurochem.*, **29**, 291–297

Meister, A. (1973). On the enzymology of amino acid transport. *Science*, **180**, 33–39

Miller, L.P., Pardridge, W.M., Braun, L.D. and Oldendorf, W.H. (1985). Kinetic constants for blood–brain barrier amino acid transport in conscious rats. *J. Neurochem.*, **45**, 1427–1432

Momma, S., Aoyagi, M., Rapoport, S.I. and Smith, Q.R. (1987). Phenylalanine transport across the blood–brain barrier as studied with the *in situ* brain perfusion technique. *J. Neurochem.*, **48**, 1291–1300

Oldendorf, W.H. (1971). Brain uptake of radiolabeled amino acids, amines and hexoses after arterial injection. *Am. J. Physiol.*, **221**, 1629–1639

Oldendorf, W.H. (1973a). Stereo-specificity of blood–brain barrier permeability to amino acids. *Am. J. Physiol.*, **224**, 967–969

Oldendorf, W.H. (1973b). Saturation of blood–brain barrier transport of amino acids in phenylketonuria. *Arch. Neurol.*, **28**, 45–48

Oldendorf, W.H. and Szabo, J. (1976). Amino acid assignment to one of three blood–brain barrier amino acid carriers. *Am. J. Physiol.*, **230**, 94–98

Orlowski, M. (1963). *Arch. Immunol. Exp. Ther.*, **11**, 1 (quoted by Orlowski *et al.*, 1974)

Orlowski, M. and Meister, A. (1970). The γ-glutamyl cycle: a possible transport system for amino acids. *Proc. Natl Acad. Sci.*, **67**, 1248–1255

Orlowski, M., Sessa, G. and Green, J.P. (1974). γ-Glutamyl transpeptidase in brain capillaries: possible site of a blood–brain barrier for amino acids. *Science*, **184**, 66–68

Pappenheimer, J.R. and Setchell, B.P. (1973). Cerebral glucose transport and oxygen consumption in sheep and rabbits. *J. Physiol.*, **233**, 529–551

Pardridge, W.M. (1977). Kinetics of competitive inhibition of neutral amino acid transport across the blood–brain barrier. *J. Neurochem.*, **28**, 103–108

Pardridge, W.M., Crane, P.D., Mietus, L.J. and Oldendorf, W.H. (1982). Kinetics of regional blood–brain barrier transport and brain phosphorylation of glucose and 2-deoxyglucose in the barbiturate-anesthetized rat. *J. Neurochem.*, **38**, 560–568

Pardridge, W.M. and Fierer, G. (1990). Transport of tryptophan into brain from the circulating albumin bound pool in rats and rabbits. *J. Neurochem.*, **54**, 971–976

Pardridge, W.M. and Oldendorf, W.H. (1975). Kinetics of blood–brain barrier transport of hexoses. *Biochim. Biophys. Acta*, **382**, 377–392

Patlak, C.S. and Fenstermacher, J.D. (1975). Measurements of blood–brain transfer constants by ventriculocisternal perfusion. *Am. J. Physiol.*, **229**, 877–884

Perry, T.L., Hansen, S., Diamond, S. and Stedman, D. (1969). Plasma-aminoacid levels in Huntington's chorea. *Lancet*, **i**, 806–808

Perry, T.L., Hansen, S. and Kennedy, J. (1975). CSF amino acids and plasma-CSF amino acid ratios in adults. *J. Neurochem.*, **24**, 587–589

Plum, C.M. (1974). Free amino acid levels in the cerebrospinal fluid of normal humans and their variations in cases of epilepsy and Spielmeyer–Vogt disease. *J. Neurochem.*, **23**, 595–600

Pollay, M. and Stevens, A. (1979). Simultaneous measurement of regional blood flow and glucose extraction in rat brain. *Neurochem. Res.*, **4**, 109–123

Pollay, M., Stevens, A., Estrada, E. and Kaplan, R. (1972). Extracorporeal perfusion of choroid plexus. *J. Appl. Physiol.*, **32**, 612–617

Preston, J.E. and Segal, M.B. (1990). The steady-state amino acid fluxes across the perfused choroid plexus of the sheep. *Brain Res.*, **525**, 275–279

Preston, J.E., Segal, M.B., Walley, G.J. and Zloković, B.V. (1989). Neutral amino acid uptake by the isolated perfused sheep choroid plexus. *J. Physiol.*, **408**, 31–43

Rassan, D.K. (1990). Transport into brain of albumin-bound amino acids. *J. Neurophysiol.*, **55**, 722

Reivick, M., Jehle, J., Sokoloff, L. and Kety, S.S. (1969). Measurement of regional cerebral blood flow with antipyrine-^{14}C in awake cats. *J. Appl. Physiol.*, **27**, 296–300

Reivick, M., Sokoloff, L., Kennedy, C. and Des Rosier, M. (1975). An autoradiographic method for the measurement of local glucose metabolism in the brain. In Ingvar, D.H. and Lassen, N.A. (Eds), *Brain Work: The Coupling of Function Metabolism and Blood Flow in the Brain.* Munksgaard, Copenhagen, pp. 377–384

Sage, J.I., Van Uitert, R.L. and Duffy, T.E. (1981). Simultaneous measurement of cerebral blood flow and unidirectional movement of substances across the blood–brain barrier: theory, method, and application to leucine. *J. Neurochem.*, **36**, 1731–1738

Sandberg, M., Butcher, S.P. and Hagberg, H. (1986). Extracellular overflow of neuroactive amino acids during severe insulin-induced hypoglycaemia: *in vivo* dialysis of the rat hippocampus. *J. Neurochem.*, **47**, 178–184

Schain, R.J. and Watanabe, K.S. (1972). Distinct patterns of entry of two non-metabolizable amino acids into brain and other organs of guinea pigs. *J. Neurochem.*, **19**, 2279–2288

Segal, M.B., Preston, J.E., Collis, C.S. and Zloković, B.V. (1990). Kinetics and Na independence of amino acid uptake by blood side of perfused sheep choroid plexus. *Am. J. Physiol.*, **258**, F1288–F1294

Segal, M.B. and Zloković, B.V. (1990). *The Blood–Brain Barrier, Amino Acids and Peptides.* Kluwer Academic Publishers, Dordrecht, London

Seta, K., Sansur, M. and Lajtha, A. (1973). The rate of incorporation of amino acids into brain proteins during infusion in the rat. *Biochim. Biophys. Acta*, **294**, 472

Shotwell, M.A., Kilberg, M.S. and Oxender, D.L. (1983). The regulation of neutral amino acid transport in mammalian cells. *Biochim. Biophys. Acta*, **737**, 267–284

Smith, Q.R., Mommo, S., Aoyagi, M. and Rapoport, S.I. (1987). Kinetics of neutral amino acid transport across the blood–brain barrier. *J. Neurochem.*, **49**, 1651–1658

Snodgrass, S.R., Cutler, R.W.P., Kang, E.S. and Lorenzo, A.V. (1969). Transport of neutral amino acids from feline cerebrospinal fluid. *Am. J. Physiol.*, **217**, 974–980

Sokoloff, L. *et al.* (1977). The [^{14}C]-deoxyglucose method for the measurement of local cerebral glucose utilization: theory, procedure, and normal values in the conscious and anesthetized rat. *J. Neurochem.*, **28**, 897–916

Spector, R. (1986). Nucleoside and vitamin homeostasis in the mammalian central nervous system. *Ann. N.Y. Acad. Sci.*, **481**, 221–230

Tossman, U. and Ungerstedt, U. (1986). Microdialysis in the study of extracellular levels of amino acids in the rat brain. *Acta Physiol. Scand.*, **128**, 9–14

Tsukada, Y., Nagata, Y., Hirano, S. and Matsutani, T. (1963). Active transport of amino acids into cerebral cortex slices. *J. Neurochem.*, **10**, 241–256

Udenfriend, S. (1961). Phenylketonuria. *Am. J. Clin. Nutr.*, **9**, 691–694

Van Sande, M., Mardens, Y., Adriassene, K. and Lowenthal, A. (1970). The free amino acids in human cerebrospinal fluid. *J. Neurochem.*, **17**, 125–135

Wade, I.A. and Katzman, R. (1975). Synthetic amino acids and the nature of the L-DOPA transport at the blood–brain barrier. *J. Neurochem.*, **25**, 837–842

Weissbach, L., Handlogten, M.E., Christensen, H.N. and Kilberg, M.S. (1982). Evidence for two Na^+-dependent neutral amino acid transport systems in primary cultures of rat hepatocytes. *J. Biol. Chem.*, **257**, 12006–12011

Welch, K., Sadler, K. and Hendee, R. (1970). Cooperative phenomena in the permeation of sugars through the lining epithelium of the choroid plexus. *Brain Res.*, **19**, 465–482

Young, M.J. and Bradford, H.F. (1986). Excitatory amino acid neurotransmitters in the corticostriate pathway: studies using intracerebral microdialysis *in vivo*. *J. Neurochem.*, **47**, 1399–1404

Yudilevich, D.L. and De Rose, N. (1971). Blood–brain transfer of glucose and other molecules measured by rapid indicator dilution. *Am. J. Physiol.*, **220**, 841–846

Note

[1] This is not strictly true, and there is now evidence that there is some intermixing of the bolus with the animal's blood during the 15 s transit.

Chapter 3

Peptides and Proteins

Peptides in the Central Nervous System

Peptides are short chains of amino acids containing, usually, less than 50–100 residues linked by peptide bonds. A number of peptides have been shown to exist in the cell bodies, as well as in the axons and nerve terminals, of the central nervous system and, by definition, these are called *brain peptides* or *neuropeptides*. Neuropeptides have been identified in different brain regions, and neuronal peptidergic pathways have been visualized and characterized in the central nervous system by means of different immunocytochemical, immunofluorescence and radioreceptor assay techniques. For most brain peptides, the localization of their neuronal pathways has been one of the most powerful tools in the understanding of their functions.

Basic Techniques

Most neuropeptides have been isolated from the brain, and their chemical structures identified. Highly specific and sensitive radioimmunoassay (RIA) procedures are frequently used to determine peptide concentration in brain homogenates, microdissected brain nuclei and cerebrospinal fluid (CSF), while quantitative autoradiography, with computer assisted digital image analysis is employed to yield the concentration of bound peptide in discrete, anatomically defined regions of the brain. To avoid the problem of cross-reactivity in radioimmunoassay and immunocytochemical studies, extracts from different brain areas may be subjected to high-performance liquid chromatography (HPLC) following purification by affinity chromatography, to determine whether the material that interacts with the antibody exhibits the same physical characteristics as the authentic peptide. The detailed regional, quantitative analysis of neuropeptide distribution in the central nervous system with the appropriate chemical analysis may be compared with localization of positive immunohisto-chemical or immunofluorescent material to decide whether most, if not all, of the immunohistochemical and/or immunofluorescent staining represents the original and intact molecule.

Brief Historical Perspective

During the early 1950s the regulation of the hypothalamo–hypophysiotropic axis for some neuropeptides was suggested. But it was not until 1969 that the Harris portal-vessel chemotransmitter hypothesis gained firm experimental support from the isolation of thyrotropin releasing hormone (TRH) from ovine and porcine hypothalamic tissue, and identification of its chemical structure as a tripeptide amide (Table 3.1). The availability of TRH in a pure form permitted the development of specific peptide radioimmunoassays, which led a few years later, in 1974, to the discovery of the extrahypothalamic brain localization of TRH (see for review, Jackson and Lechan, 1983). Shortly after that, in 1974, two other hypophysiotropic hormones, luteinizing hormone releasing hormone (LHRH) and somatostatin (SRIF), were isolated and demonstrated in extrahypothalamic brain areas (for review, see Reichlin, 1983a, b; Krieger, 1986).

Extrahypothalamic Location

Although it was proposed that the primary physiological role of the hypothalamic–hypophysiotropic hormones was related to their transport to the anterior pituitary by way of the portal circulation, to cause the release of thyroid stimulating hormone (TSH), luteinizing hormone (LH) and adrenocorticotrophin (ACTH), and inhibition or release of growth hormone (GH), the existence of these peptides in extrahypothalamic brain loci also suggested a role in neurotransmission and/or neuromodulation in the central nervous system. In 1981 and 1982 the locations of corticotrophin releasing factor (CRF) and gonadotrophin releasing hormone (GNRH) in the extrahypothalamic regions were also described, supporting the hypothesis of multiple peptide functions in the brain (de Souza and Kuhar, 1986; Kreiger, 1986).

Enkephalins

In 1975 two naturally occurring brain opioid peptides, methionine- and leucine-enkephalin, were isolated from brain tissue and their chemical structures were determined by Hughes *et al.*; a year later their findings were confirmed by Simantov and Snyder (1976) by means of different assays, by isolation procedure and in different species. The discovery of opioid brain peptides was closely related to the identification of opiate brain receptors by molecular binding techniques; and it was suggested that these pentapeptides were involved in the normal opiate functions of the brain (Goodman *et al.*, 1983; Kreiger, 1986).

Posterior Pituitary Hormones

Vasopressin (VP) was among the first mammalian hormonal peptides to be identified, in 1919 by Dudley; to have its structure determined in 1953; and to be synthesized in 1954 by Du Vigneaud. For a long period, the only undisputed physiological role of this nonapeptide was as a circulating neurohypophysial hormone with antidiuretic activity, i.e. as the *antidiuretic hormone (ADH)*. However, in 1978, in addition to hypothalamo–hypophysiotropic hormones, the neurohypophysial hormones VP (arginine) and oxytocin, as well as the structurally related pineal gland hormone, vasotocin-arginine, VT (arginine), were found to be

Table 3.1 Classification of mammalian peptides found in the central nervous system: representative members of each family, and their commonly used abbreviated nomenclature. Modified from Kreiger (1986)

Hypothalamo–Hypophysiotropic Hormones

Thyrotrophin-releasing Hormone (TRH)
pGlu–His–Pro–NH$_2$

Gonadotrophin-releasing Hormone (GnRH)
pGlu–His–Trp–Ser–Tyr–Gly–Leu–Arg–Pro–Gly–NH$_2$

Somatostatin (SRIF)
Ala–Gly–Cys–Lys–Asn–Phe–Phe–Trp–Lys–Thr–Phe–Thr–Ser–Cys
‖————————————S————S————————————‖

Corticotrophin-releasing Hormone (CRF)
Ser–Gln–Glu–Pro–Pro–Ile–Ser–Leu–Asp–Leu–Thr–Phe–His–Leu–Leu–Arg–Glu–Val–
Leu–Glu–Met–Thr–Lys–Ala–Asp–Gln–Leu–Ala–Gln–Gln–Ala–His–Ser–Asn–Arg–
Lys–Leu–Leu–Asp–Ile–Ala–NH$_2$

Growth Hormone-releasing Hormone (GHRH)
Tyr–Ala–Asp–Ala–Ile–Phe–Thr–Asn–Ser–Tyr–Arg–Lys–Val–Leu–Gly–Gln–Leu–Ser–
Ala–Arg–Lys–Leu–Leu–Gln–Asp–Ile–Met–Ser–Arg–Gln–Gln–Gly–Glu–Ser–Asn–Gln–
Glu–Arg–Gly–Ala–Arg–Ala–Arg–Leu–NH$_2$

Anterior Pituitary Hormones

Adrenocorticotropic Hormone (ACTH)
(see Table 3.11)

β-Endorphin (β-E)
(see Table 3.11)

α-Melanocyte-stimulating Hormone (MSH)
(see Table 3.11)

Luteinizing Hormone (LH)
Ala–Pro–Asp–Val–Gln–Asp–Cys–Pro–Glu–Cys–Thr–Leu–Gln–Glu–Asp–Pro–Phe–Phe–
Ser–Gln–Pro–Gly–Ala–Pro–Ile–Leu–Gln–Cys–Met–Gly–Cys–Cys–Phe–Ser–Arg–Ala–
Tyr–Pro–Thr–Pro–Leu–Arg–Ser–Lys–Lys–Thr–Met–Leu–Val–Gln–Lys–Asn*–Val–
Thr–Ser–Glx–Ser–Thr–Cys–Cys–Val–Ala–Lys–Ser–Tyr–Asn–Arg–Val–Thr–Val–Met–
Gly–Gly–Phe–Lys–Val–Glx–Asn*–His–Thr–Ala–Cys–His–Cys–Ser–Thr–Cys–Tyr–Tyr–
His–Lys–Ser–COOH

Thyrotrophin (TSH)
Phe–Cys–Ile–Pro–Thr–Glx–Tyr (Met,Thr,His,Val,) Glu–Arg–Arg–Glx–Cys–Ala–Tyr–
Cys–Leu–Thr–Ile–Asn*–Thr–Thr–Ile–Cys–Ala–Gly–Tyr–Cys (Met,Thr,) Arg–Asx–Ile–
Asx–Gly–Lys–Leu–Phe–Leu–Pro–Lys–Tyr–Ala–Leu–Ser–Gln–Asx–Val–Cys–Thr–Tyr–
Arg–Asp–Phe–Ile–Tyr–Arg–Thr–Val–Glx–Ile–Pro–Gly–Cys–Pro–Leu–His–Val
(Ala,Pro,Tyr) Phe–Ser–Tyr–Pro–Val–Ala–Leu–Ser–Cys–Lys–Cys–Gly–Lys–Cys–Asx–
Thr–Asx–Tyr–Ser–Asp–Cys–Ile–His (Glu,Ala,Ile) Lys–Thr–Asx–Tyr–Cys–Thr–Lys–
Pro–Glx–Lys–Ser–Tyr–COOH

*Show the points of attachment of carbohydrate. Parentheses indicate regions where the sequence is based only on composition.

Table 3.1 (*continued*)

Posterior Pituitary Hormones
Vasopressin (VP)
Cys–Tyr–Phe–Gln–Asn–Cys–Pro–Arg–Gly–NH$_2$

    └──── S — S ────┘

Oxytocin (OT)
Cys–Tyr–Ile–Gln–Asn–Cys–Pro–Leu–Gly–NH$_2$

    └──── S — S ────┘

Pineal Gland Hormones
Vasotocin (VT)
Cys–Tyr–Ile–Gln–Asn–Cys–Pro–Arg–Gly–NH$_2$

    └──── S — S ────┘

Opioid Peptides
Enkephalin-Leucine (Enk-Leu)
(see Table 3.11)

Enkephalin-Methionine (Enk-Met)
(see Table 3.11)

Gastrointestinal Hormones
Vasoactive Intestinal Polypeptide (VIP)
His–Ser–Asp–Ala–Val–Phe–Thr–Asp–Asn–Tyr–Thr–Arg–Leu–Arg–Lys–Gln–Met–Ala–
Val–Lys–Lys–Tyr–Leu–Asn–Ser–Ile–Leu–Asn–NH$_2$

Cholecystokinin (CCK)
Lys–Ala–Pro–Ser–Gly–Arg–Val–Ser–Met–Ile–Lys–
Asn–Leu–Gln–Ser–Leu–Asp–Pro–Ser–His–Arg–Ile–
SO$_3$H
|
Ser–Asp–Arg–Asp–Tyr–Met–Gly–Trp–Met–Asp–Phe–NH$_2$

Gastrin
pGlu–Gly–Pro–Trp–Leu–Glu–Glu–Glu–Glu–
SO$_3$H
|
Glu–Ala–Tyr–Gly–Trp–Met–Asp–Phe–NH$_2$

Substance P
Arg–Pro–Lys–Pro–Gln–Gln–Phe–Phe–Gly–Leu–Met–NH$_2$

Neurotensin (NT)
pGlu–Leu–Tyr–Glu–Asn–Lys–Pro–Arg–Arg–Pro–Tyr–Ile–Leu

Others
Angiotensin II
(see Table 3.11)

Bradykinin
(see Table 3.11)

Delta Sleep-inducing Peptide (DSIP)
Tyr–Ala–Gly–Gly–Asp–Ala–Ser–Gly–Glu

Table 3.1 (*continued*)

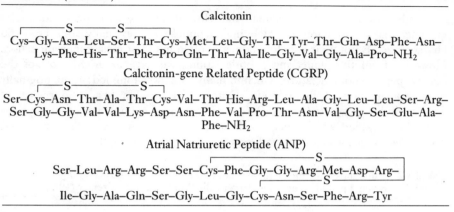

Calcitonin

┌──────S────────S────────┐
Cys–Gly–Asn–Leu–Ser–Thr–Cys–Met–Leu–Gly–Thr–Tyr–Thr–Gln–Asp–Phe–Asn–
Lys–Phe–His–Thr–Phe–Pro–Gln–Thr–Ala–Ile–Gly–Val–Gly–Ala–Pro–NH$_2$

Calcitonin-gene Related Peptide (CGRP)

┌──S──────────S─┐
Ser–Cys–Asn–Thr–Ala–Thr–Cys–Val–Thr–His–Arg–Leu–Ala–Gly–Leu–Leu–Ser–Arg–
Ser–Gly–Gly–Val–Val–Lys–Asp–Asn–Phe–Val–Pro–Thr–Asn–Val–Gly–Ser–Glu–Ala–
Phe–NH$_2$

Atrial Natriuretic Peptide (ANP)

Ser–Leu–Arg–Arg–Ser–Ser–Cys–Phe–Gly–Gly–Arg–Met–Asp–Arg–
Ile–Gly–Ala–Gln–Ser–Gly–Leu–Gly–Cys–Asn–Ser–Phe–Arg–Tyr

distributed within the central nervous system and released at extrahypothalamic, extrapituitary and extrapineal nerve terminals. Although the endocrine functions of oxytocin are to promote uterine contraction and lactation, and those of VP (arginine) are concerned with water balance and vasopressor effects, these nonapeptides, when released at other sites in the central nervous system, have different functions (de Wied *et al.*, 1984).

Gastrointestinal Hormones

In 1902 Bayliss and Starling described secretin as the first gastrointestinal hormone and later other hormones of this group, such as gastrin and cholecystokinin (CCK), were found. For a long period, it was considered that these gastrointestinal peptides were exclusively concerned with the regulation of digestion, although this was in contrast to the situation in neuroendocrinology, where it has been accepted that the actions of the anterior pituitary hormones are regulated by the secondary control of hypothalamo–hypophysiotropic peptides. However, in 1979 the concept of the APUD (*amine precursor uptake and decarboxylation*) system, and the discovery of the same embryological origin of gastrointestinal hormone-secreting cells and brain neurotransmitter cells, proposed by Pearse, linked gastrointestinal peptide physiology to more general mechanisms. Even more striking was a demonstration of gastrin-like immunoreactivity in the brain in 1976, followed shortly by similar findings for other gastrointestinal peptides, such as vasoactive intestinal peptide (VIP) and CCK, and insulin and glucagon in 1978 and 1979, respectively. Some of the neuropeptides within the so-called gut–brain peptide family were subsequently discovered also in the skin, lung and other tissues (for review, see Figlewicz *et al.*, 1987).

Multiple Functions

A number of recent experimental and clinical studies have provided strong evidence that the function by which most peptides were originally discovered and characterized is not their only function, and often not their most important action. However, from the pioneering peptide studies we have inherited most of the current peptide nomenclature, which in many cases was founded on the originally proposed function of the peptide. Dorothy Kreiger, in her 1986 review of neuropeptides, suggested that different categories of mammalian brain peptides might be classified with respect to the original tissues in which they were first discovered, or according to some functional aspects (Table 3.2).

Table 3.2   Functions of mammalian peptides in the brain classified according to the route by which a secreted peptide reaches its target cells. Modified from Kreiger (1986)

Peptide function	Mode of cell-to-cell communcation	Secreting tissue	Peptide action
Endocrine	At a distance	Gastrointestinal tract Hypophysis Pineal gland	Hormonal regulation of distant tissue functions
Paracrine	Local	Gastrointestinal tract Hypophysis	Regulation of the functions of other cells in the same tissue from which peptide is secreted
Autocrine	Local	Tissue cell Unicellular organism	Autoregulation of the tissue cell and unicellular organism functions
Neurocrine	Local	Central nervous system Ganglia	Neurotransmitter and/or neuromodulator synaptic actions on nerve cells
		Sympathoadrenal tissue	Neuroendocrine regulation of hormonal secretion from the adrenal medulla

Structural Variations

It has been shown that the primary structure of a given peptide is often the same among its various tissues: for instance, neurotensin (NT), somatostatin (SRIF) and substance P are identical in the gut and brain. On the other hand, in others, the predominant form may vary, as, for instance, CCK 8 in the brain and CCK 33 in the gut. The primary structures of some brain peptides are given in Table 3.1. However, the nature of receptors in various tissues for the same peptide may often be different: for example, there is evidence that insulin receptors present in the brain may differ from those in the gastrointestinal tract (Heidenreich *et al.*, 1983).

Functions of Peptides in the Brain

The functions of peptides in the central nervous system are complex and multiple, underlying the basic physiological phenomena of the brain such as: (1) neurotransmission and/or neuromodulation, (2) regulation of the behaviour, and higher integrative and vegetative central nervous functions generally, (3) regulation of the neuroendocrine axis, (4) regulation of cerebral blood flow, (5) regulation of cerebrospinal fluid secretion, (6) possible modulation of blood–brain barrier permeability and (7) possible role in the maturation of the blood–brain barrier. Peptide functions in the brain may be also classified with respect to the mode by which a secreting neuropeptide may reach its target cells (Table 3.2) as (a) endocrine, (b) paracrine, (c) autocrine and (d) neurocrine (Kreiger, 1986).

Pharmacological Experiments

In the last 15 years there has been an expansion of research on the effects of peptides on the central nervous system, including their behavioural effects, as well as the effects on the higher integrative and vegetative functions of the central nervous system. However, certain peptide effects in some pharmacological experiments can be obtained only by using a certain route of administration, and, moreover, the opposite effects on the same function may be obtained, depending on the route of administration. For instance, oxytocin, applied by iontophoresis into the dorsal vagal nucleus, produced a decrease in the heart rate (Rogers and Hermann, 1985), while intracerebro-ventricular (ICV) injection of the same peptide had the opposite effect (Zerbe *et al.*, 1983), presumably because in the latter situation it had access to the brain region.

An important characteristic for most peptides is that they can exert central actions after systemic administration, provided that they are given in a sufficiently high pharmacological dose (see, for review, Kastin *et al.*, 1979; Zadina *et al.*, 1986). As relatively large doses of peptides are used in most pharmacological studies, one has to be cautious of drawing the conclusion that peptide-induced central effects in such circumstances provide experimental proof that a given peptide is involved in normal physiological regulation of certain central nervous functions. However, the fact that most peripherally administered peptides may induce multiple actions implies that they can reach the brain by way of the general circulation, assuming, of course, that the primary site of action is not located in the periphery. Therefore, transport, enzymic, receptor and metabolic events during an interaction of the circulating peptide with the blood–brain and blood–CSF barriers or with circumventricular organs (CVO) must be intimately involved in the mechanism by which peptides influence the central nervous system.

Neurotransmitter and Neuromodulator Functions: Experimental Requirements

The list of neuronal circuits in the central nervous system that contain and may receive peptidergic signals is extending rapidly, with novel names of peptides that are recognized as candidates for neurotransmitters and neurotransmission modulating factors, i.e. neuromodulators. However, if one examines the growing list of peptides proposed as neurotransmitters in the central nervous system, one may find that for nearly all the potential peptide transmitters there is not as yet rigorous experimental proof of the synaptic transmitter status described for the classical amino acid and monoamine transmitters such as: γ-aminobutyrate, dopamine, glutamate, aspartate, glycine and taurine (see, for review, Siggins and Groul, 1986). In addition, we may also point out that the long history of central nervous transmitter research has suggested that the substance must satisfy many requirements in order to be considered as a neurotransmitter, such as: (1) to be contained in the nerve terminals at the given synapse, (2) to be released upon presynaptic depolarization into the synaptic cleft, (3) to exert electrophysiological effects upon the postsynaptic neuron which must be identical with the action of firing of the postsynaptic neuron, (4) the existence of the specific enzyme to inactivate each neurotransmitter or (5) inactivation of neurotransmitter by re-uptake into the nerve endings and (6) proof of the synthesis of neurotransmitter *in situ* in the brain.

The first three of these criteria are based on the pioneering work with classical neurotransmitters such as acetylcholine, biogenic amines and amino acids, while the last three criteria impose more rigorous requirements that are based on modern genetic experimental strategies for discovery of transmitter function (Bloom, 1987). However, it has been estimated that the 'classical' neurotransmitters account for only about 40% of the known synapses of the brain.

Synaptic Localization

Most of the brain peptides have in common at least one criterion essential to classify them as neurotransmitters: the compound has to be localized in nerve endings. The peptidergic pathways were recognized in the brain by means of specific immunocytochemical methods, using which, neuropeptides such as the endogenous opioid peptides, TRH, CRF, SRIF, LHRH, VP (arginine), delta-wave sleep-inducing peptide (DSIP), oxytocin, angiotensin II, insulin, cholecystokinin (CCK), bombesin-like peptides (BBS), vasoactive intestinal polypeptide (VIP), natriuretic factor (NF), etc., were identified in nerve terminals (Kreiger, 1986).

Depolarization-induced release of the compound is an important transmitter criterion and it has been demonstrated for many peptides: for example, the calcium-dependent release of enkephalins from the rat brain synaptosomes (Iversen *et al.*, 1980), calcium-dependent VP release by depolarizing stimuli from VP-containing vesicles in the lateral septum (Buijs and Van Heerikhuize, 1982) and TRH release from hypothalamic synaptosomal preparations (Lackoff and Jackson, 1981); and these examples are by no means exhaustive.

Synaptic Mimicry

In addition, the so-called 'synaptic mimicry' has been demonstrated for many neuropeptides, i.e. the peptide attachment to the specific postsynaptic receptors and induction of biological effect almost identical with those achieved by direct nerve stimulation. For instance, depolarization of the neurons in the lateral septum by superfusion of slices with a physiological concentration of VP (arginine) (Urban, 1981); excitatory depolarization in the CA1 region of hippocampal slices following application of BBS into the cell body layer of the pyramidal cells of the hippocampus (Dodd and Kelly, 1981), late slow EPSP following application of LHRH to frog sympathetic ganglion cells, and opening of potassium channels by enkephalins (via μ and δ receptors) and SRIF, and closing of potassium channels by SP, VIP, SRIF (concentration-dependent effect), BBS, and NT (reviewed in North, 1986).

Enzymatic Inactivation

A variety of enzymes capable of degrading peptides, once they are released from postsynaptic neurons, have been demonstrated in the brain, and often their function has been interpreted as one of inactivation, i.e. of terminating, the action of the peptide on postsynaptic neurons.

Peptide Synthesis

De Wied (1987) has formulated a current concept of neuropeptide synthesis in the brain as follows: 'Neuropeptides are endogenous substances present in nerve cells which are involved in nervous system function. Neuropeptides are synthesized in large precursor proteins, and several are dervied from the same precursor such as ACTH and β-endorphin in pro-opiomelanocortin (POMC). A cascade of processes evolves in peptidergic neurons to express the genetic information into biologically active neuropeptides. These processes control the quantities of neuropeptides synthesized as well as the nature of their biological activity, true size, form, and derivatization of the end-product. In this way sets of neuropeptides with different, opposite, and more selective properties are formed from the same precursor'. A schematic representation of biosynthesis of some neuropeptides from a large precursor molecule is illustrated in Figure 3.1.

Modern Molecular Biological Approach

It has been accepted that every peptide expressed in the brain depends for its synthesis on the transcription of the specific piece of genetic information into the messenger RNA which governs the synthesis of the gene product. By using the powerful methods of recombinant DNA technology, Bloom and his colleagues (1987) were able to study distinct molecular systems involved in brain peptide synthesis, storage, release and recognition by the target cells. The development of

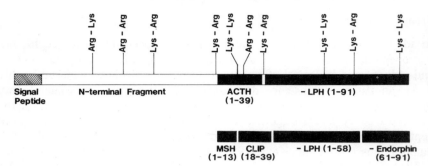

Figure 3.1 Processing of POMC-derived neuropeptides from pro-opiomelanocortin (POMC) is a cell-specific phenomenon, and POMC peptides undergo several proteolytic, non-proteolytic, co- and post-translational modifications such as acetylation, sulphation, glycosylation and phosphorylation, which may affect their biological activity. For instance, anterior pituitary corticotrophs convert POMC into β-LPH, ACTH and 16 K N-terminal fragment, and β-LPH is further processed to α-MSH and corticotropin-like intermediate lobe peptide (CLIP). α-MSH and β-endorphin are predominant in brain tissue, and β-endorphin is further processed to gamma- and α-endorphins. One of the early precursor fragments for enkephalins in the brain is α-neoendorphin, 15 amino acid peptide, with a group of three basic amino acids at the carboxyl terminal group of enkephalin leucine. Modified from de Wied (1987)

these new molecular genetic techniques has now imposed new cellular, subcellular and biochemical criteria for the proof of neurotransmitter peptide prohormones.

The Final Criterion

However, it seems that deciding whether a given peptide is a neurotransmitter or a neuromodulator is probably more a question of semantics rather than the lack of experimental evidence for a complete set of criteria. In other words, whatever classification is used, it does not rule out important functions of peptides in the regulation of various neuronal circuits in the central nervous system.

Behavioural Responses

Most peptides can cause pronounced changes in behavioural and higher integrative and vegetative central nervous functions in both man and lower animals, which can be demonstrated either by peripheral administration of a given peptide or following administration by a local route. Different behavioural patterns such as drinking, feeding, alcohol intake, satiety, aggression, locomotor activity, mating, sleep and stereotypy can be influenced by peptides.

Higher Integrative Responses

It is more than 20 years since de Wied and his collaborators suggested that vasopressin-modulated processes might underlie the mechanism of memory consolidation. This hypothesis was derived from the observations that rats that had the posterior pituitary removed, as well as Brattleboro rats, which are naturally deficient in vasopressin, may restore the rate of extinction of the avoidance response to normal, if they are given vasopressin. Subsequently it has been shown that a number of peptides may also affect various higher integrative functions of the brain: for instance, systemic administration of VP (arginine) (Hoffman *et al.*, 1988), VT (arginine) (Davis and Pico, 1984), methionine-enkephalin (Stickrod *et al.*, 1982), melanocyte stimulating hormone (MSH) and MSH/ACTH analogues (Sandman *et al.*, 1980) may enhance the process of learning in both the adult and developing animal. Also, MSH/ACTH analogues as well as some synthetic analogues of VP (arginine), DDAVP (Beckwith *et al.*, 1983) may increase attention when administered peripherally, whereas β-endorphin decreases attention (Hoehler and Sandman, 1981). Memory processing may be influenced by systemic administration of VP (arginine), VP (lysine) and DDAVP (Hoffman *et al.*, 1988), DSIP (Susić *et al.*, 1987), MSH, and methionine-enkephalin (Stickrod *et al.*, 1982). An avoidance response is affected by many peptides, including VP (arginine), CCK 8 (Cohen *et al.*, 1983), MSH, DDAVP and MSH/ACTH analogues.

Vegetative Responses

A number of vegetative central nervous functions are altered by either peripheral or local administration of peptides, including regulation of heart rate and blood pressure, gastric secretion, respiration and body temperature. For example, intra-arterial and intravenous injection of both naturally occurring enkephalins increases the blood pressure and heart rate (Varagic *et al.*, 1988), and the same effects can be obtained by local application of the synthetic enkephalin analogues DADLE and DAGO (Hassen *et al.*, 1983). Intracerebro-ventricular or local iontophoretic application of VP (arginine) causes an increase in blood pressure and heart rate (Zerbe *et al.*, 1983). Systemic administration of angiotensin II (Gross *et al.*, 1985), leucine-enkephalin (Giles and Sander, 1983) and TRH (Tenner *et al.*, 1980) increases the blood pressure, while peripheral administration of bradykinin, CRF, eledoisin, SP and VIP (Kalin *et al.*, 1983) induces a drop in the arterial blood pressure. Gastric secretion is reduced after intracerebro-ventricular administration of bombesin-like substance (BBS), calcitonin, gastrin-related peptide and litorin (Tache *et al.*, 1981; Guglietta *et al.*, 1985), as well as after intracisternal administration of BBS, β-endorphin and gastrin-related peptides. A stimulatory effect on ventilation may be obtained after local application of BBS, calcitonin and TRH (Niewoehner *et al.*, 1983), whereas local application of synthetic enkephalin analogues may have either stimulatory or depressive effects on respiration, depending on the region of administration. It has been shown that body temperature may be affected by various peptides, including angiotensin II and III (Wilson and Fregly, 1985), substance P, TRH, neurotensin, NT, MSH, β-endorphin, gastrin-related peptides and BBS (Morley *et al.*, 1982), VP (arginine)

(Lee and Lomax, 1983), ACTH and litorin-like peptides (Lipton and Glyn, 1980) and CCK (Denbow and Myers, 1982).

According to the concept of multiple peptide actions introduced by Kastin and colleagues in 1979, most central nervous effects of peptides may occur in parallel.

Primary Peripheral Action

Bradbury (1989) has discussed the possibility that some of the central effects of systemically administered peptides could be attributed to their peripheral actions, which might, in turn, influence brain functions. These might include, for instance, peptide-induced changes in blood pressure or composition of blood in the cerebral vasculature which could represent the primary and/or contributory mechanism for some peptide actions on the central nervous system. On the other hand, there is a possibility that peptides might specifically or generally stimulate afferent peripheral somatic or visceral nerves, and thus secondarily affect the central nervous system. This sequence of events may be of either primary or contributory importance for communication between the peripheral peptidergic gut nervous system and the central nervous system. Although it is reasonable to assume that some of the central peptide actions may involve mechanisms outside the central nervous system, for most of the behavioural, higher integrative and vegetative peptide effects on the central nervous system, obtained after peripheral administration, transport, receptor, enzymic and metabolic events at the blood–brain and blood–CSF barriers and in the circumventricular organs probably play a major role.

Identification of Peptidergic Pathways

Although pharmacological experiments unequivocally show that peripherally or locally administered peptides may elicit different central actions, the identification of peptidergic neuronal pathways within the CNS provides the best clue for an understanding of the physiology of the higher functions in which neuropeptides take part. We will illustrate this type of study with a few examples.

Opioid Pathways

Enkephalin-containing pathways have been visualized by combining lesion experiments and employing compounds which block axonal flow. This approach has permitted identification of both the nerve cell bodies containing enkephalins and the enkephalinergic axons with their terminal endings (see, for review, Goodman *et al.*, 1983; Kreiger, 1986). As far as the anatomical distribution of opioid peptides is concerned, it has been found that enkephalinergic neurons are widely spread within the central nervous system; and the most prominent and longest pathway is located within the limbic system, having cell bodies in the central nucleus and amygdala, and terminals in the bed nucleus of the stria terminalis (thalamus) and possibly in some zones of the hypothalamus. Another important enkephalinergic pathway in the brain starts with enkephalin-containing neurons in the caudate nucleus, which then provide a diffuse input into the globus pallidus. The neuroendocrine central enkephalinergic pathway starts in the supraoptic and paraventricular nuclei of the hypothalamus providing terminals to the posterior pituitary. In the spinal cord, enkephalinergic neurons are localized in layers I and II of the substantia gelatinosa as interneurons. It has been established further that the distribution of methionine-enkephalin neurons coincides with the distribution of CNS μu-opioid receptors, while the distribution of leucine-enkephalin neurons parallels that of δ-opioid receptors. Since μu-receptors appear to be more concentrated in areas associated with integration of pain information, it has been suggested that they might serve as the physiological receptor sites for synaptic action of methionine-enkephalin, maintaining normal opiate functions of the brain. δ-receptors are distributed predominantly in the limbic system and may act as receptor sites for leucine-enkephalin participating in different behavioural and autonomic functions of the brain.

TRH Neurons

In the medulla oblongata TRH has been localized in the nucleus of the tractus solitarius, the nucleus ambiguus, the dorsal motor nucleus of the vagus and the neurons of the phrenic motor nucleus (Holtman et al., 1986). Such localization has indicated that the tripeptide may participate, as a neurotransmitter and/or neuromodulator, in the central nervous regulation of respiratory function.

LHRH Neurons

By means of an *in situ* hybridization using radiolabelled DNA which through complementary base-pairing hybridizes to specific mRNA or LHRH-forming DNA:RNA hybrids, cells in the rat forebrain which contain LHRH mRNA have been identified (Schivers et al., 1986). It has been demonstrated that mRNA and LHRH is localized in the same regions as those previously reported to contain immunoreactive LHRH, thus confirming its physiological neuroendocrine role in cyclic secretion of pituitary gonadotrophins (Wenger, 1987).

Delta Sleep-inducing Peptide (DSIP)

Immunoreactive DSIP neurons were shown to be widespread in the rat brain (Feldman and Kastin, 1984) extending as a continuous rostrocaudal band in the ventral third of the forebrain, from the primary olfactory cortex to the lateral hypothalamus. This peptide is also present in neuronal perikarya in the basal ganglia, amygdala, septum, thalamus, brain stem (including the reticular formation), raphe-nuclei, inferior colliculus, cerebellum, locus caeruleus, periventricular grey matter, and vagal and hypoglossal nuclei. The immunocytochemical distribution suggests that DSIP may act as a neurotransmitter or neuromodulator in various central nervous pathways, such as visual, auditory and vestibular, as well as taking part in the arousal system and locomotor pathways.

Corticotropin Releasing Factor (CRF)

The identification and localization of CRF receptors in the brain (de Souza and Kuhar, 1986) have provided the basis for elucidating the role of this peptide in co-ordination of a variety of endocrine, autonomic and behavioural functions. Thus, the localization of these receptors in post-mortem human brain tissue suggested their possible involvement in some neurological and psychiatric disorders, such as depression, alcoholism, anorexia nervosa, bulimia, obsessive compulsive neurosis and dementia (Gold *et al.*, 1984).

Somatostatin (SRIF)

By comparing the density of the receptor-specific SRIF binding sites and distribution of endogenous SRIF, it has been postulated that SRIF participates in the regulation of feeding behaviour, extrapyramidal motor activity, turnover of brain acetylcholine and the release of brain serotonin (Reichlin, 1983a, b).

Vasopressin (VP)

The best-known VP (arginine) immunoreactive brain cells are found in the hypothalamo–neurohypophysial system, which releases the peptide into the systemic circulation to exert its well-known hormonal effects on the target tissues which include antidiuresis, a pressor effect by stimulating vascular smooth muscle and glycogenolysis in the liver. On the other hand, VP (arginine) is also synthesized at other sites in the brain within neurons that provide a vasopressinergic input to various brain regions. These findings implicate VP (arginine) in processes such as consolidation of memory and learning, temperature regulation, sexual behaviour and central blood pressure regulation (de Wied *et al.*, 1984).

Oxytocin

Radioimmunoassay (RIA) and immunocytochemical studies have shown that another neurohypophysial hormone, oxytocin, is widely distributed within the brain in extrahypothalamic areas, including the motor cortex, medulla oblongata, hippocampus, striatum/septum, septal nuclei, bed nucleus of the stria terminalis, caudate nucleus, putamen and pallidum (Ermisch *et al.*, 1986). On the basis of the foot-shock brightness discrimination test in rats, a group of animals with a high behavioural performance was selected and oxytocin and VP (arginine) concentrations were determined in different brain areas. It has been suggested that high endogenous levels of both neuropeptides in septum/striatum and the low level of oxytocin in the hippocampus are intimately related to the performance of this conditioned reaction.

Insulin

Localization of insulin receptors in brain slices by quantitative autoradiography (QAR) has provided an estimate of the number of insulin receptor binding sites in morphologically discrete loci such as the external plexiform layer of the olfactory bulb and cortical layers (see, for review, Baskin *et al.*, 1988). It has been tempting to suggest that insulin may modulate synaptic transmission in the external plexiform layer, influencing the integration of olfactory stimuli, which then can modify food-intake behaviour. The distribution of insulin receptors in the arcuate, dorsomedial and paraventricular hypothalamic nuclei (Corp *et al.*, 1986) suggests that insulin may influence the synthesis and release of hypothalamic neuropeptides, with their subsequent consequences for neuroendocrine functions.

Bombesin

The demonstration of bombesin receptors in rat brain membranes has revealed a high concentration in the limbic forebrain, hippocampus, amygdala, hypothalamus, periaqueductal grey matter, caudate putamen and forebrain (Moody *et al.*, 1981). Apart from direct peripheral regulation of gastrointestinal motility, secretion and the release of gastrointestinal hormones, it has been suggested that at least part of the effects of bombesin is mediated centrally, including regulation of body temperature, blood glucose, sleep, feeding behaviour, locomotor activity and generalized arousal effects (Koslo *et al.*, 1986; Figlewicz *et al.*, 1987).

Cholecystokinin (CCK)

Ligand-binding and *in vitro* quantitative autoradiography have demonstrated that the cerebral cortex, olfactory bulb, caudate nucleus, hypothalamus and hippocampus are regions with high specific binding of CCK (Gaudreau *et al.*, 1983; Van Dijk *et al.*, 1984). It has been postulated that the central role of the CCK brain system is to modulate feeding behaviour, as well as to play a role in satiety, while its peripheral role, as a local hormone, is to regulate gastrointestinal activities.

Vasoactive Intestinal Peptide (VIP)

VIP is also widely distributed within the brain, and the highest concentrations are found in the hypothalamus, hippocampus and frontal cortex (Fahzenkrug, 1979). Particularly high densities of VIP receptors have been demonstrated in the dentate gyrus, pineal gland, supraoptic and suprachiasmatic nuclei, superficial layer of the superior colliculus and area postrema. Moderate grain densities were found in the olfactory bulb and tubercle, cerebral cortex, oculomotor nucleus, caudate putamen, interstitial nucleus of the stria terminalis, paraventricular thalamic nucleus, amygdaloid nucleus, subiculum and medial geniculate nucleus (Schaffer and Moody, 1986). It has been suggested that VIP may take a part in integrating sensory information in the visual and olfactory systems.

Regulation of a Neuroendocrine Axis

The morphological and functional basis of the regulation of pituitary hormone secretion depends primarily on the multifactorial organization of communications between the median eminence and hypothalamic signalling system, on the one hand, and the anterior pituitary, on the other. It has been recognized that several neural peptides may interact presynaptically with each other in the median eminence and other regions of the hypothalamus, modulating their efficacy of action at the level of membrane transduction mechanisms. According to the concept of the coding system of hypothalamic information for the regulation of pituitary hormone secretion (Kordon *et al.*, 1987), the neuroendocrine controlling structures are organized in a complex network in which neurosecretory neurons containing peptidergic and classical neurotransmitters are interconnected by numerous collateral axons. For example, pulsatile control systems for luteinizing hormone (LH) and growth hormone (GH) (Figure 3.2) can operate in the absence of any intrinsic input to the medial basal hypothalamus, but also the dopaminergic and LHRH inputs may exhibit redundant interactions for LH control, whereas endorphinergic, SRIF and GRF inputs show a comparable organization pattern for GH control. Mechanisms underlying this reverberating loop involve inhibition of LH pulsatility by dopamine or its agonists, while opioid peptides may block the presynaptic release of dopamine, LHRH and SRIF, and stimulate GRF release. In addition to that, an extrinsic noradrenergic component is also involved in modulation of both systems, with GABA tuning for LHRH. The tubero-infundibular endorphinergic neurons possess oestrogen receptors and therefore may act as target cells for oestrogens, which may account for the modulation of episodic frequencies by steroids.

Stress

Opioid peptides are also involved in mediating stressful stimuli to neuroendocrine control systems, and it appears that an increased opiate tone may induce temporary disturbances of the normal regulatory circuits in the brain. Although in a stress response, the hypothalamo–hypophyseo–adrenal axis is activated in different ways, depending on the stress, a number of neuropeptides, including corticotrophin releasing factor (CRF), VP (arginine), oxytocin, angiotensin II, VIP and PHI-27, as well as biogenic amines, may induce ACTH secretion from the anterior pituitary (Rivier and Vale, 1985), participating in the mechanisms of the response to stress. Based on the feedback mechanism, stress may also influence directly the CRF neurons, as well as the vasopressinergic, oxytocinergic and angiotensin II-containing neurons, inducing the release of neuropeptides, which can either potentiate the action of CRF at the pituitary level or act synergistically with CRF on the target cells (Makara, 1985). These examples are by no means exhaustive.

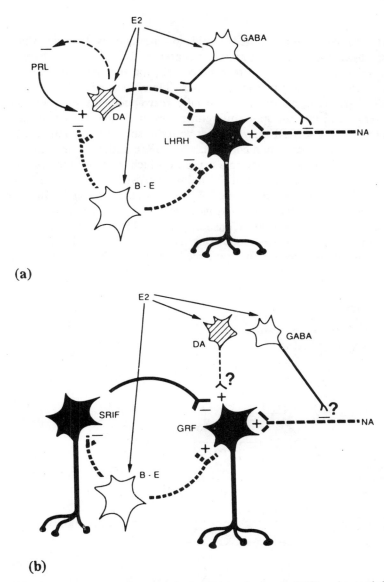

(a)

(b)

Figure 3.2 Pulsatile control systems for luteinizing hormone (LH) and growth hormone (GH) in hypothalamus. Neuronal circuits organized as reverberating loops involve dopa-minergic (DA) and endorphinergic (β) redundant interactions with LH-releasing hormone neurons for LH control; while endorphinergic (β), and somatostatin- and GH-releasing factor neurons show comparable pattern of neuronal circuits for GH control. Norad-renergic (NA) signals may modulate both control systems, and neurons from both loops are target for oestrogen hormones (E). Regulation of LH secretion involves also an indirect GABA input, and prolactin signal. Modified from Kordon *et al.* (1987)

Coupling

Many studies have demonstrated significant interactions between the major coupling intracellular chains of pituitary receptors and their different transduction modes (Figure 3.3). It has been recognized that, for any given receptor, cellular receptor coupling is the same in all tissues. Thus, the major difference in cell responses depends upon the cell's specific rearrangements between coupling chains themselves, but not upon different modes of elementary signal reception. For instance, VIP and CRF may interact with the stimulatory component of the GTP-binding–coupling protein complex, while SRIF and dopamine interact with the inhibitory component of the same complex, which regulates the activity of the catalytic adenylate cyclase unit and formation of cAMP. Other peptides, such as LHRH and TRH, may activate phospholipase A_2 in the same cell, which triggers the formation of arachidonic acid and its metabolites, prostaglandins and leukotrienes. Prostaglandins may act synergistically with GTP-binding–coupling protein complex on adenylate cyclase, modulating its stimulation, which may amplify an initial phospholipid-dependent message mediated by diacyl-glycerol (DAG). The

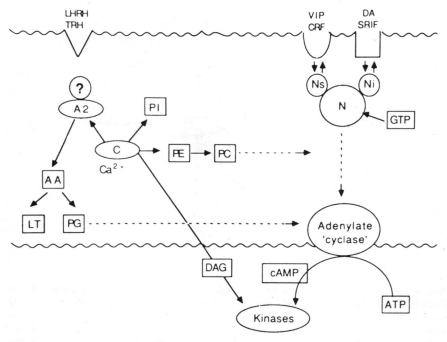

Figure 3.3 Interactions between two major coupling intracellular chains of the pituitary cell receptors. Ni, Ns, inhibitory and stimulatory components of GTP binding coupling protein complex (N); A2, C, phospholipase A_2 and C; AA, LT, PG, arachidonic acid and its metabolites leukotrienes and prostaglandins; DAG, diacylglycerol; PI, phosphoinositol; PE, PC, phosphatidylethanolamine and -choline. Modified from Kordon *et al.* (1987)

feedback mechanism between cAMP and DAG dependent-protein kinases and phosphorylation of receptors or coupling proteins is also described in pituitocytes. Thus, a peptidergic signal may induce phosphorylation of receptors in either a homologous or a heterologous manner, modulating either its own sensitivity and coupling, or the sensitivity and coupling of another receptor.

Regulation of Cerebral Blood Flow

The association of many neuropeptides, including SRIF, BBS, VIP, neurotensin, substance P, substance Y, etc., with cerebral vessels has provided morphological evidence for peptide regulation of cerebral blood flow (CBF) (Uddman *et al.*, 1981, 1983; Kapadia and DeLanerolle, 1984; Pardridge, 1986a,b). Vasomotor effects of peptides were studied mostly on isolated cerebral vessel preparations with the aim of elucidating their vasomotor actions by studying the effects on the vascular smooth muscles of the brain *in vitro* (Hanko *et al.*, 1981). For instance, it has been found that angiotensin II, VP (arginine), bradykinin and VP (lysine) may cause vasoconstriction in feline pial arteries with half maximal concentration (ED_{50} value) varying between 3.7 and 7.5 nanomolar, while oxytocin and SRIF were somewhat less potent with ED_{50} values between 16 and 30 micromolar. Other peptides, such as calcitonin, enkephalins, neurotensin, pentagastrin and substance P, did not exert any vasoconstrictive effect. In the presence of calcium-uptake inhibitors nifedipine and nimodipine, vasoconstriction induced by VP (lysine), bradykinin and oxytocin was greatly reduced, suggesting the importance of extracellular calcium entry for the vascular effect. When the same peptides were tested in the extracranial arteries, no significant difference in potency was observed, apart from the lack of VP (arginine)-induced constriction. Vasodilatation of cerebral vessels (pial arteries) by enkephalins in a dose-dependent manner with ED_{50} between 39 and 31 micromolar was observed, as well as inhibition of enkephalin-induced vasodilatation by the opiate-receptor blocking agent naloxone.

Some peptides such as VIP did not have an effect on isolated cerebral blood vessels during resting conditions, but when an active tone was induced by either prostaglandin $F_{2\alpha}$ or serotonin, the cumulative application of VIP resulted in a dose-dependent relaxation of both pial and extracranial vessels (Edvinsson *et al.*, 1981). Intracarotid infusion of VIP did not influence cerebral blood flow, oxygen consumption or EEG pattern in the baboon, but if an intracarotid bolus of hypertonic urea was given in advance to open the BBB, VIP induced a significant increase in both CBF and oxygen consumption, which was accompanied by changes in EEG activity.

On the other hand, studies in the cat and rat demonstrated that intracarotid infusion of large doses of VP (arginine) can increase cerebral blood flow (Rap *et al.*, 1980, 1981) and subsequently it was shown that the endothelial-dependent relaxation of canine basilar arteries is mediated via V_1 vasopressinergic receptors (Katusic *et al.*, 1984, 1986). It has been demonstrated that VP (lysine) elicits dilatation of the pial arterioles in the newborn pig under controlled conditions, but also constricts pial arterioles previously dilated by physiological and pharmacological intervention. VP (lysine)-induced dilatation is accompanied by increased periarachnoid CSF levels of 6-keto-prostaglandin $PGF_{1\alpha}$, PGE_2, thromboxane B_2 and $PGF_{2\alpha}$. These studies may indicate that peptide regulation of cerebral blood flow may vary from one species to another as well as from adult to newborn animals.

Influence on CSF Secretion

It has been demonstrated that vasopressin inhibits CSF secretion when presented to the choroid plexus from the CSF side during ventriculocisternal perfusion in the rabbit (Davson and Segal, 1970). Inhibition of CSF formation was accompanied by a significant reduction of sodium entry from blood into CSF. Similar effects were obtained following an intracarotid injection of peptide (Rap *et al.*, 1980), as well as during vasogenic brain oedema induced by a cold lesion in rabbits (Rap, 1981).

Peptidergic-VIP nerve terminals were found in the mammalian choroid plexus and a dose-dependent relaxation of the choroidal blood vessels which had an active tone was observed after the administration of VIP (Hanko *et al.*, 1981). Moderate dose-dependent inhibition of CSF secretion rate by DSIP in an isolated perfused choroid plexus of the sheep was also demonstrated (Zlokovic *et al.*, 1988b). It is proposed that vasomotor effects of peptides on the choroid plexus blood vessels may influence the perfusion of these organs and consequently the rate of CSF secretion, which may be important in the regulation of water and electrolyte content in the brain.

Control of the Water and Electrolyte Content of the Brain

Considerable evidence indicates that the regulation of the ionic environment of the brain is co-ordinated by a central neuroendocrine peptidergic system that is capable of influencing: (1) the cerebral microvessels, (2) the choroid plexus secretion rate and (3) the astroglia. It has been shown that neuropeptide-mediated regulations at all three sites may be responsible for precise control of brain volume by adjusting the cell water and electrolyte content.

Vasopressin

For instance, vasopressin-positive vascular connections demonstrated by immunoelectron histochemistry were found in close or direct contact with the capillary endothelium. It is suggested that centrally released VP (arginine) leads to brain water accumulation by increasing the permeability of cerebral microvessels to water, which may account for facilitating the development of brain oedema under various pathological circumstances (Doczi *et al.*, 1988). Also, it has been proposed that a central atrial natriuretic factor (NF) system may exert the opposite effect, preventing water accumulation through a significant sodium loss from the brain tissue. The effects of NF on water and electrolyte central nervous system homoeostasis are thought to be mediated, in large part, by an alteration of blood–brain barrier permeability to sodium, and this might represent a balance to VP (arginine) actions.

Angiotensin

The central angiotensin II system is supposed to play an important part in the homoeostatic responses to hypertonicity and dehydration. The major neural connections of the median eminence and angiotensin-binding sites in the brain were investigated by tracing the anterograde and retrograde transport of wheat-germ agglutinin conjugated with horseradish peroxidase (WGA–HRP) in the sheep and rat brain (Figure 3.4) (McKinley *et al.*, 1987). When WGA–HRP was microinjected into the median preoptic nucleus, retrograde transport was observed into the subfornical organ, organum vasculosum of the lamina terminalis, parabrachial nucleus, nucleus of the tractus solitarius and ventrolateral medulla, indicating that these regions may send monosynaptic inputs to the median preoptic nucleus.

Anterograde transport of the WGA–HRP was observed in the supraoptic nucleus and paraventricular nuclei along with a number of hypothalamic and

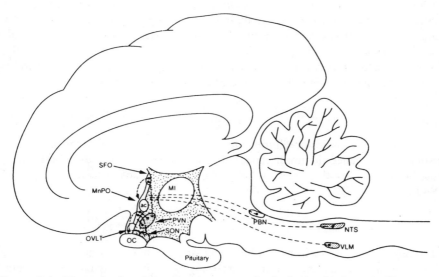

Figure 3.4 Network of angiotensinergic neurons in the brain. Angiotensin II receptors located at the circumventricular organs (CVOs) may respond to blood-borne angiotensin II, while those in the median preoptic nucleus (MnPO) and paraventricular nucleus (PVN) may mediate effects of centrally released peptide. SFO, OVLT, subfornical organ and organum vasculosum of the lamina terminalis; SON, supraoptic nucleus; PBN, NTS, VLM, parabrachial nucleus, nucleus tractus solitaris, ventrolateral medulla; MI, OC, massa intermedia, optic chiasma. Modified from McKinley *et al.* (1987)

septal sites, suggesting that the neurons from the median preoptic nucleus project to these areas. These findings suggest the possible existence of a network of angiotensinergic neurons within a number of brain regions exhibiting a high density of angiotensin II receptors. In order to elucidate the physiological role of angiotensin II receptor brain zones, in water and electrolyte brain homoeostasis, some lesion experiments were performed with ablation of the lamina terminalis, the richest angiotensin II receptor area in the sheep brain (Congiu *et al.*, 1984). This kind of lesion destroys the midline region of the median preoptic nucleus and organum vasculosum of the lamina terminalis, which causes the animal to be hyperdipsic or adipsic. The responses to thirst and VP (arginine) release are also disrupted and the animal exhibits impaired excretion of sodium in response to dehydration (Coghlan *et al.*, 1986). On the basis of these experiments, it may be suggested that the receptors at the circumventricular organs (CVOs) are sensitive to blood-borne angiotensin II, while those in the median preoptic nucleus and paraventricular nucleus may respond to centrally released peptide.

Regulation of Blood–Brain Barrier Permeability

It has been demonstrated that both blood-borne and centrally released peptides play an important part in continuous regulation of the blood–brain barrier permeability to different blood-borne or brain-derived substrates. It has been suggested that so-called short-term regulation of the permeability by neuropeptides may involve one, or all, of the following mechanisms: (a) temporary change of the affinity and capacity of various carrier-transport systems at the barrier, (b) alterations of pinocytotic activity across the barrier and (c) control of the tight junctions between adjacent endothelial cells in the barrier (Pardridge, 1986b). We shall illustrate these possibilities with a few examples.

Insulin

By means of the indicator-dilution method it has been shown that intravenous insulin may enhance the unidirectional influx of D-glucose blood-to-brain transport by modulating the transport properties of the hexose carrier (Barry *et al.*, 1980).

Vasopressin and Oxytocin

VP (arginine) and oxytocin may enhance transport of blood-borne orotic acid, the RNA precursor, when injected intra-arterially in the brain circulation (Landgraff *et al.*, 1977) but does not affect D-glucose transport (Landgraff *et al.*, 1978). Recently it has been shown that VP (arginine) may change the transport of large neutral blood-borne amino acids, such as L-leucine, by decreasing both the K_m and V_{max} of the transport process, and this is unrelated to changes in the cerebral blood flow (Reith *et al.*, 1987). The following hypothetical mechanism for VP (arginine)-induced changes in transport properties of the large amino acid carrier

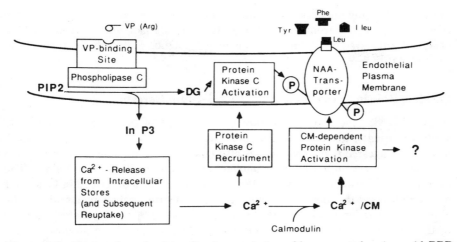

Figure 3.5 Proposed mechanisms for the regulation of large neutral amino acid BBB carrier by vasopressin. PIP2, InP3, DG, phosphoinositol 4,5-biphosphate, inositol 1,4,5-triphosphate and diacylglycerol; VP, vasopressinergic receptor; NAA, large neutral amino acids; CM, calmodulin. Modified from Ermisch *et al.* (1988)

is proposed by Ermisch *et al.* (1988) (Figure 3.5): (a) binding of a blood-borne VP (arginine) to the V_1 receptors located at the luminal side of the brain capillaries, (b) induction of a specific transduction signal by V_1 receptor to the large neutral transport system amino acid carrier, (c) conformational changes of the amino acid carrier leading to changes in affinity and transfer capacity of blood-to-brain large neutral amino acid transfer. [Note 1]

Second Messengers

It has been proposed that the 'second messengers', cAMP and cGMP, may influence transendothelial molecular transport and pinocytosis across the blood–brain barrier (Joó, 1986, 1988). For instance, increased activity of cerebral adenylate cyclase was found to correlate with an increased pinocytic activity and transport of albumin into the brain microvessels (Adam *et al.*, 1988).

The role of hormonally sensitive adenylate cyclase, calcium-sensitive guanylate cyclase and magnesium-activated phosphodiesterase in regulating macromolecular transfer across the barrier is indicated by changes in the intracellular level of second messengers, and this may well represent a mechanism by which neuropeptides affect phosphorylation of certain protein kinases activating transendothelial transport. It seems that the calcium–calmodulin system is also involved in the regulation of macromolecular transfer by slowing down the cyclic nucleotide-stimulated transport.

It is noteworthy that all vasoactive peptides that change either cerebral blood flow or transport across water-filled pores may influence the blood-to-brain transport of highly lipophilic compounds. This may account, for instance, for the effect of reduced permeability to antipyrine (Goldman and Murphy, 1981), observed after systemic administration of ORG2766, the synthetic analogue of ACTH/MSH 4–9.

Possible Role in Maturation of the Blood–Brain Barrier

In parallel with the short-term induced neuropeptide permeability changes to various nutrients, macromolecules, and hydrophilic and lipophilic substances, it has been suggested that peptides may also take a part in the long-term regulation of genetic expression in the brain capillary endothelium (Pardridge, 1986b). The experiments of Stewart and Wiley (1981) and later studies described in Chapter 1 have emphasized that the specific biochemical and structural characteristics of the blood–brain barrier may be induced during maturation by trophic factors secreted by the brain tissue itself. Neuropeptides of glial origin have been proposed as the most serious candidates for these trophic factors (Pardridge, 1986b), and this is consistent with the original suggestion of Davson and Oldendorf (1967) that the glial sheaths of brain capillaries served to induce the barrier characteristics of the brain capillaries. The identification of brain capillary-specific proteins, such as gamma-glutamyl transpeptidase, the 50 kD and 55 kD triplets, or phosphoproteins and/or low-molecular weight proteins in the region of 14–18 kD, and a 46 kD protein (Pardridge, 1986b), which are not found in brain cells or in synaptosomal plasma membranes, but exclusively in capillary preparations, seems to offer better opportunities of studying the influences of neuropeptides on maturation of the blood–brain barrier.

Peptide and Protein Interactions at the Blood–Brain Barrier

History of the Concept

Circulating peptides and proteins may come into contact with the brain and cerebrospinal fluid via interfaces located in the luminal side of the blood–brain barrier, basolateral side of the choroidal epithelium and blood side of the circumventricular organs that are situated outside the barrier (for review, see Segal and Zloković, 1990). The hypothesis that the polarity and size of peptide and protein molecules would preclude their rapid transport across the blood–brain barrier has been confirmed by short-term kinetic brain-uptake studies (Cornford *et al.*, 1978; Zloković *et al.*, 1985a, b). It has also been suggested that the peptide bond may prevent peptides from utilizing the L-amino acid transporter at the barrier, and therefore be responsible for restricting their significant blood-to-brain transfer (Zloković *et al.*, 1983). However, recent investigations, conducted with the long-term brain perfusion technique, have suggested that the extremely low initial brain extractions of small neuropeptides, measured in short-term extraction experiments (BUI) could have resulted from relatively slow, but specific, uptake mechanisms for these molecules at the luminal side of the blood–brain barrier (Zloković, 1990).

Proteins

The concept of barrier impermeability to proteins has been supported by electron-microscopical studies with horseradish peroxidase (HRP), entry of which into the brain across cerebral capillaries was restricted, owing to the presence of tight junctions and a limited capacity for vesicular transport (Chapter 1). On the other hand, it has been demonstrated that HRP may penetrate into the brain across the segments of some cerebral arterioles (Westergaard and Brightman, 1973).

Transcytosis

While the transport of some proteins across the blood–brain barrier undoubtedly occurs, the transcytotic mechanism postulated for the process, whereby the protein is engulfed into the cytoplasm of the brain capillary endothelial cells as a vesicle and ejected at the opposite face of the endothelial cell by exocytosis, has yet to be fully demonstrated (Chapter 1). Thus, as indicated earlier, the mere engulfment of a protein by the capillary endothelium may represent a stage in its incorporation into a secondary lysosome for final degradation.

Pathophysiological Interest

The importance of exchanges of peptides and proteins across the blood–brain barrier for normal brain function and in diseased states has been emphasized and will be discussed in this and the final chapter.

Transport of Peptides

Receptor or Transporter

The distinction between peptide blood–brain barrier transporters, receptors and enzymes seems to be more difficult than for some other substrates, since peptides are present both in the body fluids and in the brain in very low concentrations. It has been generally proposed that membrane endothelial protein may qualify predominantly as a transporter if the rate of internalization process is orders of magnitude faster than the dissociation rate; and vice versa, if the rate of dissociation is greater than the internalization rate, the protein is better defined as a receptor. Mathematically this relationship may be illustrated as suggested by Gjedde and Bodsh (1987):

$$K_m = \frac{k_{to} + k_{off}}{k_{on}}$$

where K_m is the half-saturation concentration (i.e. Michaelis constant), k_{to} is the turnover rate constant of the internalization process, k_{off} is the rate constant of ligand dissocation and k_{on} is the rate-constant of ligand association with the membrane protein.

According to this formula, K_m of the peptide transporter represents more the internalization turnover rate, while K_m of peptide receptors reflects mainly the dissociation rate. However, the distinction between transporters, receptors and enzymes for some peptides seems to disappear at the blood–brain barrier, since certain endothelial receptors may also function as transporters, i.e. to internalize their ligands into the cytoplasm of the endothelial cells (Pardridge, 1988), as well as function as enzymes (Zloković *et al.*, 1988a).

Blood-to-brain Transport

Effects on the Central Nervous System

The hypothesis that peptides might cross the blood–brain barrier was proposed in the mid-1970s by Kastin and his colleagues (1976) to explain how peptides, given parenterally, or even orally, could affect the central nervous system (see, for reviews, Kastin *et al.*, 1979, 1981). As pointed out before, in the late-1970s it was recognized that most peptides occurred in both peripheral organs and brain, and it was of considerable interest to answer the question as to whether exchanges between two peptide pools, separated by the blood–brain barrier, could play a role in the normal physiological functions of the brain, as well as in diseased states. In the early 1980s most laboratories that addressed this question assumed that the polarity and size of peptide molecules would preclude significant transport across the blood–brain barrier, and, if some passage occurred, it could still be negligible and therefore irrelevant to cause significant central effects (Oldendorf, 1981).

Methodological Considerations

Conflicting results regarding peptide transport across the blood–brain barrier in the mid-1970s and early-1980s may be explained in part on the ground of some methodological considerations such as relatively short exposure time of the peptides to the BBB, the rapid degradation of peptides in the blood and central nervous system, overestimation of passage due to the contamination of brain tissue by residual blood, underestimation because of the use of relatively insensitive methods of assay, and inappropriate sampling sites for CSF (Banks *et al.*, 1988; Zloković *et al.*, 1988a). Several attempts have been made to measure the extraction of small peptides by the brain during a single passage through the cerebral circulation by means of the Oldendorf (1971) intracarotid injection method, with calculation of the brain-uptake index (BUI), or by estimating only the extraction fraction after an intracarotid injection without correction for the residual vascular radioactivity. However, as Davson suggested, the single-pass techniques, although most valuable to study rapid uptake of substrate by the brain, are usually not sensitive enough to distinguish between an absolute impermeability and slow penetration. His view has been confirmed by several experimental findings: for example, the extraction of electrolytes, such as sodium and chloride, is negligible during a single pass, yet these ions still have measurable uptake by the brain when exposed over a period of several minutes (Davson, 1955; Sarna *et al.* 1978; Smith *et al.*, 1984; Abbott *et al.*, 1988).

Short-term Studies
Apart from an early study with enkephalins (Kastin *et al.*, 1976), most of the rapid-uptake kinetic studies conducted over a period of only 5–15 s failed to demonstrate a significant passage of peptides from blood to brain. The results of these studies are summarized in Table 3.3. It can be seen that short-term studies have produced BUI values or extraction values for a number of peptides containing 2–31 amino acids which were all in the range of the inert polar molecules, such as mannitol, sucrose, inulin and dextran. Although some pitfalls in the measurement of barrier permeability to the neuropeptides have been enumer-

Table 3.3 Brain extraction of peptides obtained by rapid uptake kinetic studies (5–15 s) by means of intracarotid injection technique. Modified from Zloković (1990)

Peptide	Numbers of residues	Extraction (%)
Carnosine	2	1.1
Gly–Phe	2	0.9
Gly–Leu	2	0.5
Glutathione	3	0.6
Thyrotropin-releasing hormone	3	1.0
		0.15
Leucine-enkephalin	5	2.4
		None
DADLE	5	2.0
Methionine-enkephalin	5	15
		2.4
β-Casomorphin-5	5	1.9
DGAVP	8	1.2
Cholecystokinin 8	8	None
Arginine-vasopressin	9	2.4
Lysine-vasopressin	9	1.3
Oxytocin	9	1.3
Delta sleep-inducing peptide	9	Measurable
Gonadotropin-releasing hormone	10	1.1
		1.3
Substance P	11	0.5
Somatostatin	14	0.01
β-Endorphin	31	1.9

Inert polar molecules	Molecular weight	BUI (%)
D-Mannitol	167	1.8
		2.12
Sucrose	342	2.31
Inulin	5 000	1.4
Dextran	70 000	0.9

ated by Oldendorf (1981) and Begley and Zloković (1986), the absence of a significant rapid blood-to-brain transport of enkephalins, their synthetic analogues, VP, DSIP, beta-carnosine, TRH, SRIF, BBS, CCK and NF has been experimentally confirmed. Taken at their face value, therefore, these rapid-uptake studies would exclude the possibility that peptides would cross the blood–brain barrier in amounts sufficient to exert the observed central nervous effects of their parenteral administration. In consequence, alternative hypotheses have been put forward to account for these central effects.

Longer-term Studies

To understand the transport of very slowly penetrating substances, however, it is clearly necessary, as indicated above, to measure penetration from the blood over periods of minutes, rather than a few seconds. The first longer-term study of a peptide along these lines was made by Rapoport *et al.* (1980), the solutes being administered as a single intravenous bolus according to the technique of Ohno *et al.* (1978), and uptake being measured over periods of 3–11 min. ^{14}C-analogues of naturally occurring opioids, D-(Ala^2)-methionine enkephalin-amide. β-(D-Ala^{62}-Homarg^{69})-lipoprotein 61–69, α-(D-Ala^2-Homarg^9)-endorphin and β-(D-Ala^2-Homarg)-endorphin were employed, the stable analogues being used to avoid significant systemic degradation.

The permeability coefficients derived from this study were comparable with those for glycerol and thiourea, suggesting a moderate permeability of the barrier to peptides. To extend this type of study to metabolically unstable peptides, however, is not practicable, owing to the exposure of the peptide to such organs as the liver, lung and kidney. In this case the labelled amino acid might be split off and the measurement of radioactivity in the brain would give a false impression of crossing of the intact peptide across the barrier.

Vascular Brain Perfusion

To avoid this difficulty the perfused *in situ* brain preparation described in Chapter 1 have been employed, and applied to a number of small peptides including [^{3}H]-leucine-enkephalin, [^{3}H]-TRH, [^{3}H]-VP (arginine), [^{121}I]-DSIP and [^{3}H]-cyclosporin. Figure 3.6 shows the brain uptake of leucine-enkephalin and TRH as a function of perfusion time. The slopes of the lines, which are a measure of K_{in}, are significantly greater than those for inert polar molecules such as D-mannitol and polyethylene glycol (PEG) it becomes evident that, during short periods of time, up to 1 or even 2 min, it is practically impossible to distinguish the uptake of peptides from that of inert polar molecules. As illustrated in Table 3.4, the long-term vascular brain perfusion method provides an accurate quantitative estimate of the rate of peptide interaction at the lumina side of the central nervous capillary. When permeability coefficients of neuropeptides and inert polar molecules, derived from the brain perfusion results, were compared with their olive oil/water partition coefficients, and/or reciprocal values of the square root of their molecular weight, no correlation was found. This analysis unequivocally indicates that physicochemical factors, such as diffusion through the water-filled pores, or

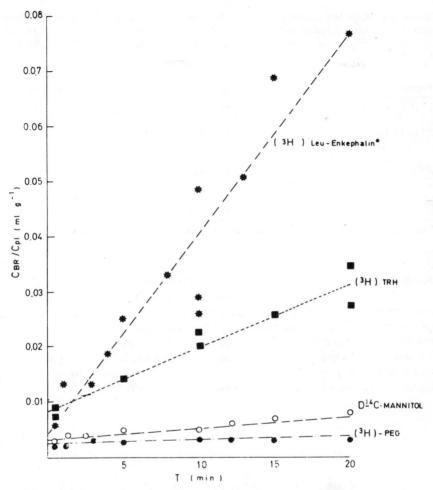

Figure 3.6 Kinetics of [³H]-labelled enkephalin-leucine and thyrotropin-releasing hormone uptake by the parietal cortex of the guinea-pig perfused brain; uptake of inert polar molecules, D-mannitol and polyethylene glycol is given for comparison. From Zloković *et al.* (1987, 1988a, 1989a)

across the endothelial cells, owing to different degrees of lipophilicity, do not play a major role in peptide interactions with the blood–central nervous system barrier.

Leucine-enkephalin
Further characterization of enkephalin (leucine) interactions with the blood–brain barrier was focused on defining whether the estimated cerebrovascular permeability coefficient represented the permeability of the intact molecule or penetration of its labelled hydrolysed peptide fragments, either alone or together with the intact peptide. In order to test this hypothesis, one approach is to add various unlabelled

Table 3.4 Capillary unidirectional transfer constant (K_{in}) and initial volume of distribution (V_i), for various radiolabelled peptides, Immunoglobulin G and D-mannitol graphically estimated during vascular perfusion of the guinea-pig brain. Modified from Zloković *et al.* (1990b)

Peptide	K_{in} (μl min^{-1} g^{-1})	V_i (ml 100 g^{-1})
[^{3}H]-Leu-Enk	3.62 ± 0.11	0.40 ± 0.07
[^{3}H]-AVP	2.78 ± 0.04	0.27 ± 0.04
[^{3}H]-TRH	1.22 ± 0.08	0.78 ± 0.09
[^{125}I]-DSIP	0.93 ± 0.14	0.94 ± 0.13
[^{125}I]-IgG	0.58 ± 0.05	0.29 ± 0.03
[^{3}H]-D-mannitol	0.24 ± 0.04	0.35 ± 0.07
[^{3}H]-Dextran	0.05 ± 0.01	0.31 ± 0.02

Values are means $\pm$ s.e. of 7–12 perfused brains. K_{in} values are significantly different by ANOVA.

potential competitors, or peptide-enzyme inhibitors, to the brain perfusate at relatively high concentrations. The kinetics of entry of [^{3}H]-enkephalin (leucine) as measured in the presence of (a) a saturating concentration of a large neutral L-system amino acid, (b) inhibitors of amino-peptidase blood–brain barrier activity, (c) saturated potential δ and μu BBB opioid receptors are shown if Figure 3.7, which shows that neither hydrolysis of peptides nor utilization of the L-amino acid transporter plays a significant role during interaction of blood-borne enkephalin (leucine) with the barrier (Zloković *et al.*, 1987).

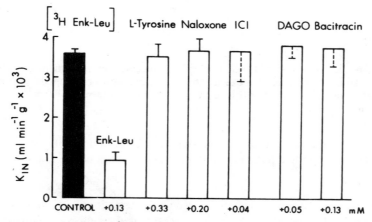

Figure 3.7 Cerebrovascular permeability, *P*, for [^{3}H]-enkephalin-leucine estimated in the presence of unlabelled peptide, L-tyrosine, naloxone, allyl^2–Tyr–AIB–Phe–OH (ICI), Tyr–D-Ala–Gly–Me–Phe–NH(CH$_2$)$_2$OH (DAGO) and bacitracin (aminopeptidase inhibitor). Modified from Zloković *et al.* (1987, 1989a)

Similar findings were obtained in the presence of naloxone, a specific delta-opioid receptor antagonist allyl[2]–Tyr–AIB–Phe–OH, and the μu-opioid receptor agonist Tyr–D-Ala–Gly–Me–Phe–NH(CH$_2$)$_2$OH (Zloković *et al.*, 1989a); neither of these compounds was able to influence the kinetics of enkephalin (leucine) entry into the brain. On the other hand, it was possible to observe a marked self-inhibitory effect, which suggested the presence of a specific saturable mechanism at the barrier. Subsequent studies have revealed a dose-dependent self-inhibition of the unidirectional transfer constant (Figure 3.8) and Michaelis–Menten parameters were estimated by fitting the brain vascular perfusion data with weighted non-linear least squares (Table 3.5). The estimated K_m value for enkephalin (leucine) was 3–4 times lower than the K_m for large neutral amino acids, measured by the BUI method (Pardridge and Oldendorf, 1975), but similar

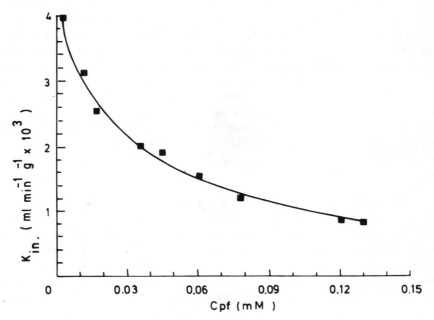

Figure 3.8 Dose-dependent self-inhibition of the unidirectional transfer constant, K_{in}, for [^{3}H]-enkephalin-leucine in the parietal cortex of perfused guinea-pig brain. From Zloković *et al.* (1989a)

Table 3.5 Kinetic parameters for leucine-enkephalin and vasopressin-arginine uptake at the luminal side of the blood–brain barrier. Modified from Zloković *et al.* (1989a, 1990a)

Peptide	K_m (μM)	V_{max} (pmol min^{-1} g^{-1})
Leu-Enk	39 ± 3.2	160 ± 22
AVP	2 ± 0.3	5.49 ± 0.74

Values are means ± s.e. for 5–9 K_{in} observations in the parietal cortex.

to the K_m determined for neutral amino acids by the vascular brain perfusion method in the rat (Smith *et al.*, 1984; Takasato *et al.*, 1985; Smith *et al.*, 1987). However, the V_{max} for the enkephalin transfer system seems to be three orders of magnitude less than for amino acids, and compares best with the capacity of the transport system for thyroid hormones. If both Michaelis–Menten parameters are taken into consideration, the blood–brain barrier enkephalin saturable mechanism compares best with similar mechanisms for purine bases and nucleotides (Pardridge, 1988). The non-saturable component, K_d, was negligible and not significantly different from zero in all studied brain regions.

Specific Transporter

The values of the cerebrovascular permeability constant, P, for enkephalins, and the relatively high half-saturation constant, K_m, would argue strongly for the existence of a specific peptide transporter at the luminal site of the brain capillary. However, the fact that peptide is taken up intact at the luminal side of the capillary does not rule out the possibility that it may be metabolized during the next step in one of the compartments in parallel. This may involve: the cytosolic endothelial space, the abluminal surface of the capillary, the glial end-foot layer in apposition to the abluminal side of the capillary endothelium, and/or enkephalinergic synaptic regions juxtaposed to the brain microvessels. The function of enzymes at the above-mentioned possible loci may well be to prevent intrabrain accumulation of both endogenously released and blood-borne enkephalins by inactivating peptides (Schwartz, 1983), and/or facilitating the diffusion away from receptors (Hersh *et al.*, 1987).

Tetrapeptides

The effects on unidirectional enkephalin transfer rate of tetrapeptides derived from the enkephalin molecule without either the N-terminal or C-terminal amino acid residue were also studied. Moderate inhibition was obtained only with the peptide without the C-terminal leucine, namely Tyr–Gly–Gly–Phe (Zloković *et al.*, 1987). This finding may be consistent with the view that the C-terminal carboxyl group of enkephalin (leucine) is important for the activity at the opioid receptor site, while the N-terminal part of the molecule is more important for its transport.

Thyroid Releasing Hormone (TRH)

Studies with [^{3}H]-TRH have indicated that the tripeptide may penetrate the blood–brain barrier slowly, at a rate significantly greater than that of the smaller inert molecule, D-mannitol (Table 3.4). The finding that this uptake could be strongly inhibited by an amino peptidase and amidase activity inhibitor, bacitracin, indicated the contribution of an enzymatic component during tripeptide interaction with the barrier (Zloković *et al.*, 1988a). This process may involve liberation of the N-terminal amino acid residue, L-proline-amide and/or formation of the free acid (TRH-OH). The failure of unlabelled TRH to inhibit the kinetics of entry of [^{3}H]-TRH in the presence of inhibitory concentrations of bacitracin most likely indicates the absence of a specific internalization mechanism for TRH at the barrier, unless there is a saturable component, with the affinity constant significantly below the K_d value. It may well be that the enzymic transformation of TRH at the barrier is important for the tripeptide to exert its biological activity; this is consistent with the hypothesis that cyclic diketopiperazines, formed after enzymic cleavage of TRH, can mediate the central nervous actions of this tripeptide. However, without definite experimental proof, one may not rule out the possibility that an enzyme is involved in the transfer of TRH across the blood–brain barrier.

Delta Sleep-inducing Peptide (DSIP)

Several uptake studies of ^{125}I-labelled DSIP at the luminal interface of the central nervous capillary have shown the presence of a high-affinity saturable mechanism for transport of DSIP across the blood–brain barrier, with subsequent uptake at brain sites that are highly sensitive to L-tryptophan, and may be modulated by VP (arginine) (Zloković *et al.*, 1989b). We must emphasize here the extremely low concentrations, in the region of 7 μM, of peptide that are effective in inhibiting transport of labelled DSIP during vascular perfusion of the guinea-pig brain; these compare with 1–5 mM required to inhibit amino acid transport systems at the blood–CSF and blood–brain barriers. Thus, the DSIP transport system is comparable with the high-affinity uptake systems described for synaptosomes, and it is most likely that the process revealed by the penetration curves consists in uptake by high-affinity sites, first on the capillaries of the brain and subsequently after translocation through the capillary membrane on other high-affinity sites distributed throughout the brain tissue. The fact that the measured permeability coefficients varied with brain regions, which is an unusual feature of blood–brain barrier studies, would support this view.

The highest uptake occurred in the hippocampus and the same has been found during ventriculocisternal perfusion studies, while immunocytochemical studies have revealed high concentrations of immunoreactive DSIP (Feldman and Kastin, 1984). Whether these findings can be related to the role of DSIP in sleep, with respect to the importance of hippocampal function for the sleep–wake cycle (Susić and Masirević, 1988), has yet to be ascertained. However, TLC analysis of radioactivity in the brain following perfusion with the labelled peptide suggested transfer in the form of the intact molecule (Zloković *et al.*, 1989b).

Vasopressin (AVP)

Saturable retention of ^{3}H-labelled VP (arginine) *in vivo* has been demonstrated in hippocampal vessels in the rat, as well as in non-blood–brain barrier regions, such as the pituitary and pineal glands, by means of an integral technique in which amounts of tracers accumulated in brain during circulation were compared with the time integral of plasma concentration in the same period up to 2 min (Reith *et al.*, 1987). In a recent study using the vascular brain perfusion method and a longer time scale than in the previous study, Zloković *et al.* (1990a) have demonstrated a saturable mechanism for VP (arginine) in other brain regions as well, such as for example, the parietal cortex (Table 3.5) and caudate nucleus.

The AVP system has a similar K_m to that of the carrier-mediated transport system for thyroid hormones, but its capacity is about 35 times less (Pardridge, 1988). AVP peptide fragments, AVP-(1–8), pressinoic acid and [pGlu⁴,Cyt⁶]AVP-(4–9) (Zloković *et al.*, 1990a) did not influence uptake of their parent peptides. These results indicate saturable luminal BBB uptake of intact peptide, as well as the absence of significant saturable metabolism of the peptide fragments.

On the other hand, the V_1 vasopressinergic receptor antagonist, TMeAVP, but not the V_2 agonist, dDAVP, significantly inhibited AVP uptake. The affinity of TMeAVP was less by a factor of about 2 than for the peptide itself (Zloković *et al.*, 1991). The AVP barrier receptors may either represent a part of the peptide transport system, as demonstrated for insulin, IGFI and II and transferrin (Pardridge, 1986a), or may mediate hormone effects on the barrier. In the latter case the cellular uptake of circulating peptide would be limited primarily to its binding at the blood–brain interface, similar to that observed for *in situ* steroid hormone binding (Pardridge, 1987).

As we have mentioned in the case of leucine enkephalin, the fact that small neuropeptides may be taken up intact at the luminal side of the barrier does not rule out the possibility that they may be subsequently metabolized in adjacent compartments. This matter was investigated in more detail with AVP. HPLC analysis of ipsilateral forebrain homogenates indicated that about 70% of the AVP remained in its intact form between 1 and 3 min, while the percentage of the intact peptide progressively fell with time, and, after 10 and 15 min, the radioactivity was eluted primarily in the fraction corresponding to L-[³H]-phenylalanine (Zloković *et al.*, unpublished). This suggests that there is normally a time-dependent, progressive aminopeptidase degradation of circulating AVP once it has been transferred across the luminal side of the blood–brain barrier, and the possibility that AVP is a precursor of more potent centrally active fragments, such as [pGlu⁴,Cyt⁶]-AVP-(4–9) has been suggested (Burbach *et al.*, 1983). On the other hand, TLC analysis of forebrain homogenates has shown that DSIP remained in its intact form in the brain during the 10 min period of perfusion, which is consistent with the previously demonstrated resistance of this peptide to hydrolysis after crossing biological barriers (Banks *et al.*, 1983).

Cyclosporin
One strategy for delivering peptides to brain interstitial fluid following peripheral administration is chemical conversion of the water-soluble peptide into a lipid-soluble derivative. Cyclosporin (Figure 3.9) is a cyclic undecapeptide of fungal origin that is a highly lipid-soluble compound, which one would expect to cross the blood–brain barrier rapidly. However, by means of the BUI method, it has been shown that the transport of cyclosporin is markedly restricted. This is due to its attachment to the plasma proteins, so that the partition coefficient for distribution between plasma and oil is very much less than the distribution coefficient for distribution between water and oil, and it is likely that the rate of penetration is governed by the rate of dissociation from the cyclosporin–plasma protein complex (Begley *et al.*, 1990).

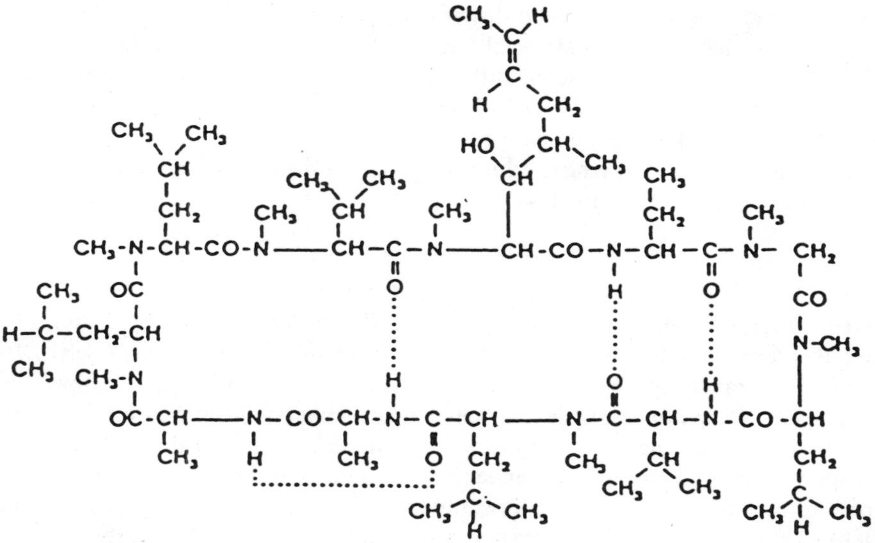

Figure 3.9 Cyclic structure of undecapeptide of fungal origin, cyclosporin, endows molecule with extremely high lipophilicity (octanol–water partition coefficient about 1000)

Conclusions

On the basis of longer-term vascular perfusion of the brain, the following conclusions are suggested so far as transport of small neuropeptides across the blood–brain barrier is concerned.

(1) Cerebrovascular permeability to slowly penetrating neuropeptides (Leu-Enk, AVP, DSIP, TRH) is about 5–70 times higher than for metabolically inert polar molecules.
(2) Olive oil/water partition coefficients and molecular weights are not good predictors of BBB permeability to small peptides.
(3) Neuropeptides do not use blood–brain barrier amino acid transporters, and enzymatic hydrolysis may not necessarily be the primary event at the barrier.
(4) Specific uptake systems for Leu-Enk, AVP and DSIP have been demonstrated at the luminal side of the barrier.
(5) There is no saturable brain uptake of peptide metabolites.
(6) Specific peptidergic receptors can mediate slow brain uptake (binding) of circulating peptide.
(7) The post-luminal step in transport into the brain may result in transformation of a peptide to its more potent neuroactive fragments.

Brain-to-blood Transport

The basic principles of the ventriculocisternal perfusion technique for the study of the blood–brain barrier have been described in Chapter 1. Essentially, the solute of interest is included in an artificial CSF perfusing the ventricles; losses of the solute are due to an unrestricted diffusion across the ependymal linings of the ventricles to the extracellular space of the tissue and a restricted diffusion across capillaries of the brain together with restricted diffusion into the cells of the brain. Additionally, a direct and restricted transport across the epithelium of the choroid plexuses will contribute to the loss.

Opioid Peptides

Figure 3.10 illustrates representative results of ventriculocisternal perfusion of [³H]-sucrose, [³H]-enkephalin-leucine and [³H]-tyrosine in the rabbit during 140 min; the dextran ratio (R_d) is shown to indicate dilution by nascent CSF. In addition, clearances of [³H]-tyrosine, obtained in different animals, are shown for comparison. It has been suggested that leucine-enkephalin is cleared from the CSF by more than one transport mechanism, namely (a) use of the L-amino acid transport system, (b) use of the carrier common for both leucine-enkephalin and tyrosine, and (c) a non-specific uncompetitive mechanism (Begley and Chain, 1988). Although a saturable component was suggested from these experiments, self-inhibition experiments were not performed in this study, which has left open to question the specificity of the hypothetical carrier, as well as the main site of interaction for peptide.

Banks *et al.* (1986) have described carrier-mediated transport of enkephalins and Tyr–MIF1 peptide across the blood–brain barrier by means of a single

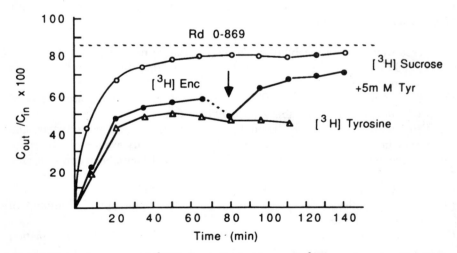

Figure 3.10 Transport of [³H]-enkephalin-leucine and [³H]-tyrosine out of cerebro-spinal fluid during ventriculocisternal perfusion in the rabbit. Arrow shows effect of unlabelled L-tyrosine (N-terminal labelled amino acid residue of [³H]-enkephalin-leucine) clearance. Interrupted line denotes steady level with no clearance and only dilution by the newly secreted cerebrospinal fluid. From Begley and Chain (1982)

intraventricular injection method in mice. It is suggested that this transport system is capable of transferring N-Tyr–MIF1, both enkephalin-methionine and en-kephalin-leucine and β-casomorphin, but not kyotorphins, porcine dynorphin-A, β-endorphin and dermorphin. It has been emphasized that the intact N-terminal tyrosine residue in the peptide molecule is required for the transport, since substitution with phenylalanine and D-tyrosine renders the compound ineffective as an inhibitor. Thus the high degree of specificity for the N-terminal end of the molecule is similar to that required for its opiate activity.

The transfer rate determined for N-Tyr–MIF1 when the amount of radioactive peptide was kept constant while the specific radioactivity varied, or, vice versa, when the specific activity was held constant and the amount of unlabelled peptide increased, yielded similar conclusions indicating a saturable mechanism. It has been demonstrated that the entire molecule is needed for transport of N-Tyr–MIF1, since tyrosine, and peptide fragments, such as tyrosyl-proline, tyrosyl-prolyl-leucine, and prolyl-leucyl-glycine, failed to inhibit transport of radiolabelled Tyr–MIF1. The transfer system appears to be insensitive to ouabain and theophylline but may be inhibited by furosemide as well as stimulated by acetazolamide. Table 3.6 shows the primary structures of compounds causing significant inhibition. Later it was shown that 21 hormones, including LH, FSH, TSH, ACTH, LHRH, TRH, angiotensins I and II, GH, prolactin, and thyroxin, as well as several steroid hormones, fail to inhibit the brain-to-blood transfer system for Tyr–MIF1 and enkephalins in mice (Banks *et al.*, 1988b). Although these authors ascribed the enkephalin-saturable mechanism exclusively to the brain-to-blood transport system, one cannot rule out the possibility that to some extent interactions may occur at the choroidal epithelium which may then rather represent CSF-to-blood transport. Also, the possibility that injected radiolabelled peptide may be cleared in part by CSF bulk flow through the drainage mechanism has to be taken into consideration, although this would not be saturated.

Vasopressin

A separate system capable of transferring vasopressin-like peptides from brain to blood has also been described, using the same intraventricular injection method and measurement of the half-time of disappearance of labelled peptide (Banks *et al.*, 1987). The saturable mechanism is capable of transferring some structurally

Table 3.6   Primary structure of compounds causing significant inhibition of N-Tyr-MIF1 transport (after Banks *et al.*, 1986)

Compound	Structure
N-Tyr–MIF1	Tyr–Pro–Leu–Gly–NH$_2$
Methionine enkephalin	Tyr–Gly–Gly–Phe–Met
Leucine enkephalin	Tyr–Gly–Gly–Phe–Leu
β-Casomorphin	Tyr–Pro–Phe–Pro–Gly–Pro–Ile
D-Met^5-enkephalin	Tyr–Gly–Gly–Phe–D-Met
D-Ala^2-Met-enkephalin amide	Tyr–D-Ala–Gly–Phe–Met–NH$_2$
Dynorphin-(1–8)	Tyr–Gly–Gly–Phe–Leu–Arg–Arg–Ile

similar peptides, such as mezatocin, VP (arginine), pressionic amide, pressionic acid, tocionic acid, and VP (lysine), but does not transport oxytocin, VP (lysine), VP (arginine) free acid, tocionic amide, Tyr-MIF1 or cyclo-leucyl glycine. HPLC analysis of the radioactivity in the blood two minutes after intraventricular injection of VP (arginine) indicated that the intact peptide was transported from CSF to blood, and most degradation of peptide occurred as a result of enzymic activity in the blood, and not during the passage across different CNS compartments.

Synthetic Peptide
Carrier-mediated transport from CSF has been demonstrated also for the synthetic artificial dipeptide, glycyl-leucine during ventriculocisternal perfusion in the rabbit (Begley *et al.*, 1980).

Delta Sleep-inducing Peptide (DSIP)
However, it was not possible to show that the same mechanism is applicable for all peptides when cleared from the CSF. Thus, for example, DSIP exhibits a clearance during ventriculocisternal perfusion in the rabbit which is only slightly greater than that of dextran, a marker of the extracellular space (Zloković *et al.*, 1988b). The value for the clearance of DSIP is found to be at the limit of sensitivity of the ventriculocisternal perfusion technique, even though sleep peptide with high specific activity was employed. However, in contrast, this study has revealed a specific accumulation of DSIP in the hippocampus, expressed as a threefold increase of sucrose: DSIP R_{br} ratio.

TRH
A very low clearance from CSF was also found for TRH (Begley and Chain, 1982).

Neurophysin
A comparable study with ^{125}I-labelled neurophysin, VP (arginine), and oxytocin has revealed that both nonapeptides were cleared more rapidly than their carrier, neurophysin, which has a rate similar to that for inulin (Jones and Robinson, 1982).

Conclusion
Thus, in conclusion, one may say that mechanisms responsible for brain-to-blood or, more precisely, CSF-to-blood peptide transport are similar to those responsible for blood-to-brain transfer, in the sense that both saturable transport and non-saturable diffusion have been demonstrated. However, with respect to the major site of interaction during peptide transfer, it seems that this has been defined to a lesser extent in the case of CSF-to-blood mechanisms, since peptide is exposed to a more complex multicellular system when cleared from CSF than when cleared from the blood.

Receptors in Cerebral Microvessels

Receptor-mediated Effect of Peptides
It has been demonstrated that isolated cerebral microvessels contain various peptide receptors that are linked to second messenger systems in endothelial cells, including (a) a cAMP system and its catalytic unit adenylate cyclase and (b) an inositol triphosphate (IP_3) and phospholipase C system linked with the release of intracellular calcium.

cAMP
A number of peptides, including VIP (Huang and Rorstad, 1983) and PTH (Huang *et al.*, 1983) may stimulate adenylate cyclase and produce an increase in intracellular cAMP level, which then can trigger a cascade of metabolic signals leading to the phosphorylation of endothelial cell proteins which bring about a physiological effect of the peptide. For instance, a physiological concentration of bovine parathyroid hormone (PTH (1–34)) increases capillary adenylate cyclase activity in a manner similar to the actions of β-adrenergic agents (isoproterenol) or forskolin (Table 3.7). This may explain the possible neurotoxic effect of PTH, particularly in some clinical conditions such as renal failure, when plasma levels of PTH are significantly elevated.

Inositol Triphosphate
Other peptides, such as vasopressin (Hess *et al.*, 1987), exert their effect on cerebral microvessels via bradykinin-B_2 and vasopressin-V_1 receptors, by increasing inositol triphosphate and the level of cytosolic calcium. Thus, it may be suggested that peptide-induced activation of the various transduction signals involves a change in intracellular levels of second messengers such as cAMP, cGMP and phosphoinositides, and may take place irrespective of the peptide origin. In other words, peptide may derive either from the brain or from the blood, and it may not be necessary for the receptor-mediated peptide endothelial effect

Table 3.7 Increase of adenylate cyclase activity in the isolated cerebral bovine microvessels by homologous parathyroid hormone. A comparison with β-adrenergic agents and forskolin. Adapted from Pardridge (1986a)

	Additive	Adenylate cyclase activity (% of basal)
PTH1-34	5 nmol/l	115
	10 nmol/l	142
	100 nmol/l	175
Isoproterenol	100 μmol/l	170
Forskolin	100 μmol/l	256

Basal activity was linear for up to 20 min and averaged 14.2 ± 0.7 pmol min^{-1} mg^{-1}. Peptide and β-adrenergic agents were incubated with microvessels into [^{32}P]-ATP-containing medium for 10 min at 30 °C.

that peptide cross the blood–brain barrier in any of the above directions. However, this does not exclude the possibility that a given peptide may be internalized into the endothelial cell following reaction with its endothelial receptor, either for transport or inactivation purposes.

Isolated Microvessels
Radioligand-binding studies on isolated microvessels have been carried out with both ^{125}I or ^{3}H-labelled VP (Arg) (Kretzschmar *et al.*, 1986), which revealed saturable kinetics. Scatchard analysis indicated only high-affinity binding sites with an apparent dissociation constant, K_d, of 2.7 nmol/l and a maximum binding capacity of 390 fmol/mg protein. The number of binding sites was calculated to be within a range from 4000 to 20 000 per hippocampal endothelial cell (Ermisch, 1987). The method used in this study did not allow distinction with respect to the anatomical location of the binding sites, i.e. whether they are at the luminal or abluminal side (Ermisch *et al.*, 1988).

Immunocytochemistry
Immunocytochemical studies have demonstrated vasopressinergic fibres in close vicinity to the brain capillaries; thus, it may be suggested that abluminal binding of VP (Arg) to the brain microvessels is a sign of its major activity. On the other hand, when VP (Arg) was injected intracarotidally, together with a rapidly penetrating amino acid, an alteration in amino acid transport across the barrier was observed, which led to the conclusion that the effect was mediated by receptors located on the *luminal* side of the capillary wall (Hess *et al.*, 1987). Thus, it may be suggested that VP (Arg) receptors are localized on both sides of the blood–brain barrier.

The single transduction in the hippocampal endothelium after an intracardial perfusion of a physiological solution containing 10^{-8} mol/l VP (Arg) consisted of an increase in intracellular Ca^{2+} storage, which was made visible as electron-dense deposits (Hess *et al.*, 1987). X-ray microanalysis confirmed that these deposits contain more calcium than the deposit-free cytoplasm, which suggests also the VP induction of calcium re-uptake. The findings support the hypothesis that VP binding sites on the brain capillaries may represent V_1 receptors.

Specific binding to the isolated microvessels has been also shown for some other small peptides such as oxytocin (Ermisch *et al.*, 1986) and angiotensin II (Speth and Harik, 1985).

Receptor-mediated Transcytosis of Proteins
Studies on isolated brain capillaries have proved to be a useful *in vitro* model system for the characterization of many different endothelial large peptide and protein receptors (Pardridge, 1986a). Their kinetic constants, half-saturation binding (K_d) and maximal binding capacity (B_{max}) may be determined, as illustrated in Table 3.8.

Insulin
Receptor studies with isolated human brain capillaries have shown that insulin

Table 3.8 Half-saturation binding (K_d) and maximal binding capacity (B_{max}) determined for large peptides and proteins in isolated cerebral capillaries. From Pardridge (1988)

Species	Peptide	K_d (nM)	B_{max} (pmol/mg protein)
Human	Insulin	1.2 ± 0.5	0.17 ± 0.08
	IGFI	2.1 ± 0.4	0.17 ± 0.02
	IGFII	1.1 ± 0.1	0.21 ± 0.01
	Transferrin	5.6 ± 1.4	0.10 ± 0.02
Bovine	Insulin	0.44	0.18
	IGFI	2.0	1.7
	IGFII	1.8	1.0
	ANF	0.11	0.058
Canine	Angiotensin II	1.1	0.022

receptors may readily be identified on microvessels, and that the saturation of insulin-binding parallels that found in isolated bovine capillaries (Pardridge *et al.*, 1985b). Some cross-binding could be demonstrated by pro-insulin, while other peptides, such as glucagon and SRIF, were without effect. In addition to binding at the cell surface, insulin was also found in the endothelial cytoplasm. A non-saturable cellular binding of insulin was also demonstrated, and its resistance to an acid-wash indicated the internalization of the protein, and suggested a possible mechanism of insulin transport across the blood–brain barrier by an initial *receptor-mediated endocytosis* (Figure 3.11).

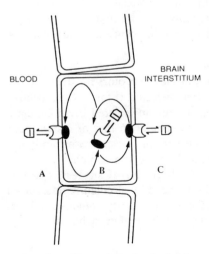

Figure 3.11 Receptor-mediated transport hypothesis for large peptides and proteins across the blood–brain barrier. Proposed transcytosis process involves three subsequent steps: receptor-mediated endocytosis, traffic through the endothelial cytosol and receptor-mediated exocytosis. According to Pardridge (1986a)

Subsequent studies have shown that isolated human brain capillaries may also release unmetabolized [^{125}I]-insulin at 0 °C; and this has been confirmed by HPLC analysis of the medium at different times of exocytosis. These studies strongly suggest that both endocytosis and exocytosis occurred *in vitro* in the isolated capillaries.

Perfusion of [^{125}I]-insulin *in vivo* through the carotid artery of anaesthetized suckling rabbits confirmed these *in vitro* observations, and subsequent HPLC analysis of acid–ethanol extracts of the brain showed that the majority of the brain radioactivity co-migrated with the insulin standard and that this part was immunoprecipitable with insulin antibodies. Thaw–mount autoradiography has also identified radioactive grains in the brain parenchyma after an inatracarotid infusion of [^{125}I]-insulin, and, taken together with HPLC analysis, the findings have provided *in vivo* evidence for the transport of circulating insulin into the brain via a receptor-mediated mechanism.

It has been demonstrated that there is a functional difference between insulin receptors on the neurons and glia compared with those on the endothelial cells, which has been supported by some structural studies. For instance, structural analysis of the insulin receptor in the brain pellet P2 fraction has demonstrated a protein with a molecular weight of 116 kD and lacking the necessary carbohydrate moiety that causes binding of the receptor to a wheat-germ agglutinin (WGA) affinity column (Heidenreich *et al.*, 1983). In contrast, brain capillary insulin receptors, obtained from the pellet P1 fraction, exhibit a molecular weight of 127 kD and both the human and bovine brain microvessel receptors bind to a WGA affinity column (Figure 3.12) (Pardridge *et al.*, 1985b). This structural difference most likely represents a post-translational modification in the carbohydrate moiety, which may be responsible for important differences in subcellular functions of protein receptors in the brain microvessels versus neurons and glia, which may account also for a difference in functional significance.

Insulin-like Growth Factors

In the isolated brain capillaries, receptors for the insulin-like growth factors IGFI and IGFII were also demonstrated (Frank *et al.*, 1986). Like insulin, IGFI and IGFII are internalized by human isolated brain capillaries. The affinity of IGF receptors was found to be similar to that of insulin receptors for the respective ligands (Table 3.8), but the maximal capacity or binding of the IGF receptors was shown to be approximately 5–10 times higher in bovine capillaries. Receptor-mediated transport of IGFI and IGFII suggests that brain growth and development can be strongly influenced by circulating mitogens and that the transport of blood-borne growth factors across the blood–brain barrier may represent an important regulatory step in neuronal growth and development.

Transferrin

The presence of receptors for transferrin in human and rat brain capillaries has been demonstrated by means of monoclonal antibodies to the transferrin receptor and the immunoperoxidase reaction (Jeffries *et al.*, 1984). Again, Pardridge *et al.*

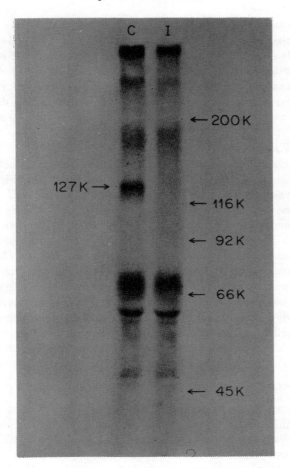

Figure 3.12 Autoradiogram of human BBB plasma membranes after separation with sodium dodecyl sulphate polyacrylamide gel electrophoresis; the major specific binding of insulin is found at 127 K. From Pardridge *et al.* (1985b)

(1987) showed that transferrin bound, in a rapid and saturable manner, to isolated human brain capillaries. In the capillary endothelial cells of extracranial tissues, transferrin receptors were not identified, and this absence has been attributed to the fact that this protein, which is the major iron-transport protein in the blood, does not need a specific endothelial transport system in non-brain areas because of the large non-specific leakage pathways of non-cerebral capillaries that permit molecules to pass into the interstitial fluid of these organs. However, it has also been shown that mRNA, encoding the transferrin molecule, is present in the brain (Levin *et al.*, 1984; Aldred *et al.*, 1987), which suggests that this peptide may be directly neurosecreted by the nerve cells in addition to its receptor-mediated transfer from blood into the brain. Similar findings have recently been reported in the choroid plexus (Dickson *et al.*, 1985).

Cationized Albumin

As indicated in Chapter 1 (p. 118), the negative charge on the cell surface tends to repel negatively charged proteins, so that converting the protein into a positively charged molecule—cationization—would be expected to improve its chances of penetrating into a cell. In general, the cationized form of a protein might represent the mechanisms of transport of some macromolecules across the blood–brain barrier.

Homologous IgG Transport

Recently a measurable transport of an immune protein, namely homologous immunoglobulin G (MW 150 kD) across the blood–brain barrier of the vascularly perfused guinea-pig brain has been demonstrated (Zloković *et al.*, 1989b). It has been shown that there is a specific transport mechanism for native IgG across the blood–brain barrier in the guinea-pig which is saturated at physiological plasma levels of IgG. The unidirectional transfer constant, estimated from vascular perfusion measurements, indicated transport rates some ten times higher than that for the inert polar molecule dextran (MW 70 kD). Immunohistochemical analysis of the brain tissue by means of the avidin–biotin peroxidase reaction revealed a distribution of blood-borne IgG in the endothelial cells of microvessels as well as in the surrounding perivascular tissues. Recent work on microvessels (Triguero *et al.*, 1989), as well as studies on vascular brain perfusion in the rat, have shown that uptake of IgG occurs in the cationized form of this macromolecule.

Structural Aspects of Protein Entry into the Brain

Early experiments at the beginning of the century, notably those of Goldmann (1909, 1913), showed that certain acidic dyes, given systemically, did not stain the brain and CSF, an observation giving rise, as we have seen in Chapter 1, to the concept of a blood–brain barrier. It was later demonstrated that these dyes were largely bound to plasma proteins, so that the early authors were probably demonstrating an impermeability of the blood–brain barrier to proteins rather than crystalloid solutes. Studies with horseradish peroxidase (Reese and Karnovsky, 1967; Brightman and Reese, 1969) confirmed the impermeability of the cerebral capillary to a protein of relatively small size, although some transendothelial transfer from blood to brain in some segments of the fine arterioles (Westergaard and Brightman, 1973), as well as across cerebral capillaries (van Deurs, 1977), has been reported. The possible mechanisms of transport of large molecules have been discussed in Chapter 1, where it was concluded that some transfer certainly occurs, as with insulin and transferrin, most probably by a transcytotic pathway, i.e. by the engulfment of the protein into the capillary endothelial cell and its sequent ejection on the abluminal side of the cell.

Some objections to early experiments have been voiced by Dziegilewska and Saunders (1988b); thus, little attention was paid in these studies to the volume of solution used, the concentration of protein present or the physiological state of the animal in which the experiments were carried out. Also, the absence of pinocytotic vesicles and other possible transcellular routes in most regions of the brain for HRP were based on experiments involving the injection of high concentrations of HRP, and little account had been taken of the special properties of this molecule. In addition, it has been pointed out that restricted movement of this plant enzyme across the blood–brain barrier may not be extrapolated to all naturally occurring mammalian proteins and peptides (Dziegielewska and Saunders, 1988a).

By means of modern, more sensitive techniques, based on immunoelectron-microscopic and ultrathin cryosections with the immunoglobulin–gold technique, Møllgard *et al.* (1988) have demonstrated that both albumin and transferrin in the mature rat brain, as well as fetuin in the fetal sheep brain, could cross from blood into the central nervous perivascular space. Furthermore, gold particles were not seen within the endothelial intercellular tight junctions, but they were found in vesicular and tubular profiles within the endothelial cells, suggesting some form of transcellular transport. Similar studies to these on the blood–CSF barrier of the choroid plexus of the adult rat have suggested that both cellular protein synthesis and protein uptake, followed by transcytosis, take place (Møllgard *et al.*, 1988). Thus, in the epithelial cells of the choroid plexus the transcytotic pathway for transferrin seems to be supplemented by the local synthesis of this protein, a supposition that has been confirmed by the labelling of the endosomal/lysosomal apparatus, and the protein synthetic machinery, following transferrin labelling by the immunogold technique (van Deurs *et al.*, 1981). These studies suggest that transport of naturally occurring proteins across the blood–brain barrier is a highly specific process, most likely involving receptor-mediated endo-exocytosis, but which is very different from the non-specific fluid-phase endocytosis by which HRP is probably taken up by the endothelial cell (Broadwell *et al.*, 1983).

Plasma Protein-mediated Transport

According to the free-hormone drug hypothesis, only the unbound portion of the molecule is available for exchanges across biological membranes such as the brain capillary, and therefore only the free fraction may enter the brain to elicit its physiological or pharmacological response. Many systemically administered therapeutic agents, as well as naturally occurring compounds, are bound to a varying degree to plasma proteins, and, in particular, to serum albumin, which represents more than 50% of the total plasma protein content. Binding of different compounds to proteins may alter significantly their distribution in different organs, including the brain, as well as changing the half-life of the molecule, owing to changes in elimination rate.

Serum Albumin

The surface structure of plasma proteins at physiological pH is very suitable for interactions with a variety of compounds with diverse chemical structure and physiological or pharmacological action. For instance, the tertiary surface structure of serum albumin is stabilized by internal disulphide and hydrogen bonds, and the molecule has a globular shape. At physiological pH its surface is covered by a number of charged groups, including carboxylate anions from glutamic and aspartic acids; hydroxyl groups from tyrosine, threonine and serine; protonated nitrogen atoms from histidine, arginine and lysine; and sulphydryl groups from cysteine. These numerous charged groups account for the water-solubility of albumin in spite of its high proportion of hydrophobic residues such as aromatic or aliphatic side-chains from phenylalanine, tyrosine, isoleucine, proline, valine and methionine (Kragh-Hansen, 1981).

Binding

The degree of binding of a given compound is related to its concentration, the concentration of the binding protein and the affinity of the compound to the protein. Affinity is usually expressed as an association constant, K_a, which depends on: (a) the presence of ionizing groups that usually increase the binding affinity, (b) the presence of polar substituents such as hydroxyl groups that also increase binding and (c) the addition of alkyl chains and aromatic rings that may greatly increase the binding affinity to proteins (Greig, 1989). Thus, it can be seen that protein-binding affects both the hydrophilic and lipophilic compounds, so it is not surprising that lipophilicity cannot be taken as an absolute criterion or parameter that correlates with barrier permeability. Affinities of different homologous long-chain anions for serum albumin, of either human or bovine origin, are illustrated in Table 3.9.

Lipid-soluble Compounds
A number of lipophilic compounds are restricted from penetration from blood to brain, owing to their high-affinity binding to plasma proteins. For instance,

Table 3.9 Apparent association constant, K_a', for the interaction of different homologous long-chain anions with either human or bovine serum albumin. From Greig (1989)

Ligand	No. of carbons	High-energy association constant, K_a' (M^{-1})
Saturated		
Laurate	12	1.6×10^6
Myristate	14	4.0×10^6
Palmitate	16	6.0×10^7
Stearate	18	8.0×10^7
Oleate	18	1.1×10^8
Unsaturated		
Octanol	8	3.0×10^3
Decanol	10	7.0×10^4
Dodecanol	12	1.5×10^5
Octylsulphonate	8	6.0×10^5
Decylsulphonate	10	1.4×10^6
Dodecylsulphonate	12	1.2×10^6

bilirubin (Levine *et al.*, 1982), erythrocin (Levitan *et al.*, 1984) and Evans Blue (Freedman and Johnson, 1969) are bound to a great extent by serum albumin, and this prevents significant uptake of these molecules by the brain. However, if the plasma concentration of these compounds exceeds the binding capacity of the plasma proteins, thus saturating the binding sites, the consequent increase in concentration of the free solute will lead to significant penetration. Thus, in kernicterus the concentration of bilirubin in the blood exceeds the binding capacity of the plasma proteins, the high concentration being due to a failure of the liver to conjugate bilirubin to a water-soluble form.

Delivery System

However, uptake of a given protein-bound compound may be independent of its free unbound portion, if the organ possesses a biological mechanism for extraction of the compound. In other words, binding of the compound to protein does not always act as a system that restricts the organ's uptake but, on the contrary, the protein–compound complex can be viewed as a delivery system, since the drug may be stripped from the plasma protein as it passes through the organ. For instance, palmitate and cholesterol extensively bind to plasma proteins but they exhibit a moderate clearance by the brain even during a single passage through the cerebral circulation (Pardridge, 1981).

Conformational Change in Ligand Binding Site

The efficiency with which a protein-bound substance may be transported to its destined cell could be increased greatly if its dissociation constant were increased when the blood came in contact with the cell. Such an increase has been described in Chapter 1, dissociation constants measured *in vitro* being found to be different from those deduced from *in vivo* studies (Pardridge, 1979). Thus, steroid hormones, tryptophan, and tri-iodothyronine, bound to albumin, as well as amines bound to orosomucoid, have a several-fold greater dissociation constant *in vivo* than *in vitro* (Table 3.10).

Table 3.10 Dissociation constant, K_d, for various plasma protein–ligand complexes determined either *in vivo* or *in vitro*. According to Pardridge (1988)

Plasma protein	Ligand	K_d (µM)	
		in vitro	*in vivo*
Albumin	Testosterone	53 ± 1	2520 ± 710
	Tryptophan	130 ± 30	1670 ± 110
	Corticosterone	260 ± 10	1330 ± 90
	Dihydrotestosterone	53 ± 6	830 ± 140
	Oestradiol	23 ± 1	710 ± 100
	Propranolol	290 ± 30	220 ± 40
	Bupivacaine	141 ± 10	211 ± 107
	Triiodothyronine	4.7 ± 0.1	46 ± 4
Orosmomucoid	Propranolol	3.3 ± 0.1	19 ± 4
	Bupivacaine	6.5 ± 0.5	17 ± 4

Transport of Binding Proteins

Transport of binding proteins across the BBB was also studied and developmental changes in the brain uptake for circulating testosterone and testosterone-binding proteins, such as testosterone-binding globulin (TeBG) or albumin, have been demonstrated (Pardridge, 1987). It has been suggested that sexually dimorphic changes in brain structure may be mediated by circulating testosterone. It has been shown that the binding system for testosterone in serum is modulated in a parallel fashion with its system in the brain and that the uptake mechanisms for both TeBG and albumin exist in the capillaries of the brain.

Conclusion

In general, for a given protein-bound compound, a restricted or non-restricted clearance during passage through the cerebral circulation depends on a number of factors, such as: (a) transit time through the brain, (b) concentration of the free compound, (c) affinity to form reversible protein complexes, (d) affinity to endothelial and other brain receptors and (e) dissociation time from the plasma protein *in vivo*.

Regulation of Protein Transport

Cyclic AMP System

It has been established that the level of cyclic nucleotides plays a major role in regulating most of the metabolic processes in the cerebral endothelial cells, including regulation of macromolecular transport and pinocytosis across the BBB (Joó, 1986). For instance, histamine, in a similar way to cAMP, may enhance pinocytosis and macromolecular transport in isolated brain microvessels (Joó, 1972). The histamine effect was found to be mediated via endothelial adenylcyclase (Karnushina *et al.*, 1980), which is coupled to the endothelial histamine H_2 receptors. An increased protein transfer rate was observed after intracarotid perfusion of histamine (Dux and Joó, 1982). On the other hand, during an ischaemic injury associated with an increase of monoamine neurotransmitter content in the brain, increased activity of adenylate cyclase has been shown in the microvessels, which correlated with the formation of brain oedema accompanied by the extravasation of Evans Blue–albumin complex during the recirculatory period (Adam *et al.*, 1988).

Catecholamines, histamine and some other substances, such as adenosine, some metabolites of arachidonic acid (Schwartz *et al.*, 1981) and VIP (Huang and Rorstad, 1983), may stimulate microvascular adenylate cyclase activity. In addition, it has been suggested that some vasodilators, including epinephrine (Kowarski *et al.*, 1985), arachidonic acid (Wolf *et al.*, 1986) and histamine (Matsumoto *et al.*, 1986) may influence protein transport by altering the level of cytoplasmic ionized calcium via stimulation of calcium-sensitive guanylate cyclase.

Stimulation of pinocytosis and macromolecular transport was also obtained in isolated cerebral capillaries in the presence of cAMP (Joó *et al.*, 1983). The role of hormonally sensitive adenylate cyclase, calcium-sensitive guanylate cyclase and magnesium-activated cyclic phosphodiesterase in the regulation of protein transport across the blood–brain barrier by way of changes of intracellular concentration of different second messengers has been extensively studied (Joó, 1986).

In order to elucidate the cellular components involved in the regulation of macromolecular transport across the cerebral microvasculature, an attempt was made to identify the proteins in the cerebral microvessels that may be subject to phosphorylation induced by an elevated level of the second messengers (Joó, 1988). It has been observed that many vasoactive substances, acting on the endothelial cells, do initiate the generation of cyclic nucleotides, which, after phosphorylation of certain protein kinases, may activate transendothelial protein transport. There is also evidence that the calcium–calmodulin system is involved in the regulation of protein transfer by slowing down the transport stimulated by the cyclic nucleotides. This, in fact, may prevent the phosphorylation of proteins in the microvessels; and it has been suggested that such an event has to occur simultaneously with an increase of cyclic nucleotide concentration in order to achieve macromolecular transport homoeostasis across the blood–brain barrier.

Modulation of Peptide Transport

Banks and Kastin (1988a) have reviewed the possibilities that both saturable and non-saturable transport of peptides across the barrier may be modulated by a number of factors. These include changes in lighting conditions: for example, constant darkness and a reversed lighting cycle may increase blood-to-brain transport of DSIP (Banks *et al.*, 1985), while constant lighting decreases CSF-to-blood transfer of Tyr-MIF1 (Kastin and Dickson, 1987). Aluminium increases blood to brain transport of DSIP (Banks *et al.*, 1985) and peptide T (Barrera *et al.*, 1987) as well as CSF-to-blood transport of Tyr-MIF1 (Banks *et al.*, 1988). The exact mechanism of this aluminium effect is still not understood, although it has been suggested that it may be mediated by a direct action on endothelial cell membranes that may be more sensitive to aluminium than other cells. Age-related differences in transfer rate have been demonstrated for enkephalin and Tyr-MIF1 CSF-to-blood transport (Banks and Kastin, 1986a), while an increased availability of circulating insulin to the newborn rat brain has been suggested (Frank *et al.*, 1985). Other factors, such as stress (Banks *et al.*, 1988) and water loading (Banks *et al.*, 1987), have been associated with a decreased rate of CSF-to-blood transport of VP (arginine) and Tyr-MIF1. Also, inhibition of brain-to-blood transport of some peptides, such as enkephalins, and Tyr-MIF1 may be observed under analgesic conditions (Banks *et al.*, 1988). Some amino acids may affect saturable systems for other peptides acting in an allosteric manner (Banks and Kastin, 1986b), as demonstrated for brain-to-blood transport. Amino acids and peptides may also alter the blood-to-brain transport of other peptides; for instance, L-tryptophan and VP (arginine) may influence transport of DSIP across the blood–brain barrier (Zloković *et al.*, 1989b).

Enzymatic Degradation of Peptides

Peptidases

It is generally accepted that the physiological actions of endogenously released peptides may, in part, be terminated by enzymatic degradation (Schwartz *et al.*, 1981; Hersch, 1982; Hersch *et al.*, 1987). For instance, several peptidases have been characterized as participating in the brain's 'enkephalinase' activity, including membrane-bound neutral metalo-endopeptidase, endopeptidase 24.11, also termed enkephalinase (Schwartz, 1983), an extrinsic membrane-associated aminopeptidase termed aminopeptidase MII, aminoenkephalinase, aminopeptidase and a true integral membrane aminopeptidase called aminopeptidase M (Gros *et al.*, 1985). It has been suggested that, *in vivo*, neutral endopeptidase 24.11 and aminopeptidase M are responsible for the enkephalinase activity. Although these peptidases play an important role in regulating the concentration of free enkephalins in the brain, it has been demonstrated that none is specific for the enkephalins. For example, neutral endopeptidase 24.11 can act on different neuropeptides, including substance P (Matsas *et al.*, 1985), NT, angiotensins I and II (Gafford *et al.*, 1983), ANF (Stephenson and Kenny, 1987), chemotactic peptide (Connelly *et al.*, 1985) and bradykinin (Gafford *et al.*, 1983). By means of synthetic substrates, the broad specificity of the aminopeptidases has also been shown and it is noteworthy that both aminopeptidases are not brain-specific proteins and could be found in different tissues—in particular, in the kidney (Hersch *et al.*, 1987).

Localization

Immunohistochemical localization of aminopeptidase M in the central nervous system has demonstrated that this enzyme is localized only in cerebral microvessels (Hersch *et al.*, 1987). It has been suggested that such localization requires that the synaptically released enkephalins diffuse away from the site of release prior to degradation. Thus, the diffusion away from enkephalinergic synapses probably plays a key role in terminating enkephalin action.

Enzyme-like Transfer

Another interesting hypothesis has been proposed, based on the mechanisms of TRH transport from blood to brain, where the possibility of an enzyme-like transfer system has been suggested (Zloković *et al.*, 1988a). However, some peptides appear to be more stable, such as DSIP, which penetrates the blood–brain barrier in the intact form in sufficient amounts during vascular brain perfusion (Zloković *et al.*, 1988b) and even if given orally in newborn animals (Banks and Kastin, 1983).

Control of Action

Enzymatic degradation of peptides plays an important role in controlling peptide actions in the central nervous system by affecting (a) the amount of peptide available for neurosecretion at its site of production, (b) the amount of peptide reaching the receptor site of action and (c) the amount of peptide reaching the central nervous system from body fluids. In addition, enzymes are involved in inactivation of peptides at the receptor sites in target brain areas and in their removal from the bloodstream. For instance, rapid degradation of circulating enkephalins occurred in the blood even during a single capillary passage to the brain (Zloković *et al.*, 1985a). The same was true for TRH (Zloković *et al.*, 1985b), LHRH and SRIF. Enkephalin is also degraded in the CSF by a soluble aminopeptidase (Begley and Chain, 1988), while TRH, VP (arginine), oxytocin, insulin and NY appear to be more stable in the CSF (see, for review, Davson *et al.*, 1987).

Peptide Analogues

Over the past few years significant research has been made in the pharmaceutical industry with respect to producing analogues of naturally occurring peptides that are resistant to enzymic degradation and yet retain their biological activities. This approach has produced a number of synthetic peptides which not only have an extended half-life in body fluids, but often have a greatly enhanced physiological activity, which is of special value when the peptides are given systemically (as illustrated in Table 3.11). As it can be seen, for example, that the replacement of the amino acid L-alanine or D-alanine in the 2nd position or L-leucine by D-leucine in the 5th position of the enkephalin molecule significantly increases the resistance of the peptide to enzymatic degradation, nevertheless at the same time it may potentiate its analgesic properties. A similar effect may be obtained by replacement of methionine by methionine amide in the 5th position in the Enk (methionine) molecule.

Peptide Receptors in Non-barrier Regions

Peptide interactions with non-barrier regions are by no means restricted to the choroid plexus, but also include other circumventricular organs (CVO) in close vicinity to the ventricular surface of the third and fourth ventricles. As indicated in Chapter 1, these areas, like the choroid plexuses, are vascularized by permeable fenestrated capillaries, thus lacking a blood–brain barrier, and may offer a potential route for the movement of peptides and proteins into adjacent brain

Table 3.11 Synthetic analogues of naturally occurring peptides. Modified from Segal and Zloković (1990)

Peptides and analogues	Amino acid sequences	Action
ACTH (human)	Ser–Tyr–Ser–Met–Glu–His–Phe–Arg–Trp– Gly–Lys–Pro–Val–Gly–Lys–Lys–Arg–Arg– Pro–Val–Lys–Val–Tyr–Pro–Asn–Gly–Ala– Glu–Asp–Glu–Ser–Ala–Glu–Ala–Phe–Pro–Leu– Glu–Phe	
[Met(O)^4-D-Lys^8-Phe^9] ACTH(4–9) ORG 2766	Met[O]–Glu–His–Phe–D–Lys–Phe	Potent ACTH/MSH analogue
Angiotensin II	Asp–Arg–Val–Tyr–Ile–His–Pro–Phe	
[Val^5]-angiotensin II	Asp–Arg–Val–Tyr–Val–His–Pro–Phe	Hypertensive
[Sar^1]-angiotensin II	Sar–Arg–Val–Tyr–Ile–His–Pro–Phe	Hypertensive
[Sar^1,Ala^8]-angiotensin II	Sar–Arg–Val–Tyr–Ile–His–Pro–Ala	Inhibition to angiotensin II
[Sar^1,Ile^8]-angiotensin II	Sar–Arg–Val–Tyr–Ile–His–Pro–Ile	Specific inhibitor for angiotensin I
[Sar^1,Val^5,Ala^8]-angiotensin II (Saralasin)	Sar–Arg–Val–Tyr–Val–His–Pro–Ala	Specific inhibitor for angiotensin II
Bradykinin	Arg–Pro–Pro–Gly–Phe–Ser–Pro–Phe–Arg	
[D-Phe^7]-bradykinin	Arg–Pro–Pro–Gly–Phe–Ser–D–Phe–Phe–Arg	Competetive antagonist of bradykinin
Des–Arg^9–bradykinin	Arg–Pro–Pro–Gly–Phe–Ser–Pro–Phe	Biologically active bradykinin analogue
Des–Arg^9,[Leu^8]-bradykinin	Arg–Pro–Pro–Gly–Phe–Ser–Pro–Leu	Bradykinin inhibitor
Dynorphin A	Tyr–Gly–Gly–Phe–Leu–Arg–Arg–Ile–Arg– Pro–Lys–Leu–Lys–Trp–Asp–Asn–Gln	
Dynorphin A 1–13	Tyr–Gly–Gly–Phe–Leu–Arg–Arg–Ile–Arg– Pro–Lys–Leu–Lys	Extraordinarily potent opioid action
β-E (β-LPH 61–91)	Tyr–Gly–Gly–Phe–Met–Thr–Ser–Glu–Lys– Ser–Gln–Thr–Pro–Leu–Val–Thr–Leu–Phe– Lys–Asn–Ala–Ile–Ile–Lys–Asn–Ala–His– Lys–Lys–Gly–Gln	
Enk(Leu)	Tyr–Gly–Gly–Phe–Leu	
D-Ala^2–D-Leu^5–Enk(DADLE)	Tyr–D–Ala–Gly–Phe–Leu	Potent opioid action
Des–Tyr^1–Enk(Leu)	Gly–Gly–Phe–Leu	Tetrapeptide important for study of enkephalinase inhibition

Peptide	Sequence	Properties
ACTH (human)	Ser–Tyr–Ser–Met–Glu–His–Phe–Arg–Trp–	
[D-Ser^5]Enk(Leu)–Thr(DSLET)	Tyr–D-Ser–Gly–Phe–Leu–Thr	Specific δ opioid receptor agonist
Enk(Met)	Tyr–Gly–Gly–Phe–Met	
D-Ala^2-Enk(Met)(DAME)	Tyr–D-Ala–Gly–Phe–Met	Potent Enk(Met) analogue
D-Ala^2-Enk(Met)amide(DAMA)	Tyr–D-Ala–Gly–Phe–Met–NH	Potent Enk(Met) analogue
[D-Ala^2,N-MePhe^4,Gly^5-ol]-Enk(DAGO)	Tyr–D-Ala–Gly–N-Me–Phe–Gly–ol	Selectively binds to μ opioid receptors
α-MSH	N-acetyl–Ser–Tyr–Ser–Met–Glu–His–Phe–Arg–Trp–Gly–Lys–Pro–Val–NH$_2$	
[Nle4–D-Phe7]–α-MSH	N-acetyl–Ser–Tyr–Ser–Nle–Glu–Hist–D-Phe–Arg–Trp–Gly–Lys–Pro–Val–NH$_2$	Potent in adenylate cyclase assay
VP(Arg)	Cys–Tyr–Phe–Gln–Asn–Cys–Pro–Arg–Gly–NH$_2$	
[deamino–Cys^1–D-Arg^{8}VP (desmopressin)	3–Mercaptopropionyl–Tyr–Phe–Gln–Asn–Cys–Pro–D-Arg–Gly–NH$_2$	Specific antidiuretic and memory enhancement activity
[β–mercapto–β,β,cyclopenta-methylene-propionyl]',O-Me-Tyr^2,Arg^8-VP	[1–Mercaptocyclohexyl]–acetyl–Tyr [Me]–Phe–Gln–Asn–Cys–Pro–Arg–Gly–NH$_2$	Antagonist of VP(Arg)
[pGlu^4,Cyt^8]-VP–(Arg)4–9	pGlu–Asn–Cys(Cys)–Pro–Arg–Gly–NH$_2$	Potent analogue of VP(Arg) with selective effects on memory
des–Gly–NH$_2$^{9}–VP(Arg)^8 (DGAVP)	Cys–Tyr–Phe–Gln–Asn–Cys–Pro–Arg	Potent analogue of VP(Arg)

tissue or CSF. A number of studies have provided evidence for the presence of peptide receptors in the CVO areas, suggesting that they can mediate a direct peptide hormone action on the brain, thus serving as a rapid signalling system between blood and the central nervous system (van Houten and Posner, 1983). Receptors for insulin, prolactin, antiogensin II, calcitonin and ACTH have been characterized by autoradiography in CVO regions, and it has been proposed that, after binding of these peptides to the nerve endings at a CVO and/or distribution in the interstitial space of the CVO, circulating peptides may either (a) reach other brain regions, by diffusion, and exert their effects or (b) elicit peptide-mediated effects in the target CVO region.

Insulin

It has been shown that $[^{124}I]$-insulin, injected into the plasma, is concentrated in neuronal endings in the CVO, from where it may be transported deeper into the central nervous tissue (van Houten and Posner, 1983). If labelled insulin is injected into the CSF, uptake by surrounding hypothalamic tissue around the third ventricle can be demonstrated (Baskin *et al.*, 1988). From these studies it has been concluded that insulin has access to the brain across the CVO areas, both from blood, when it enters the neural tissue directly without crossing the blood–brain barrier, or from the CSF into the interstitial tissue of the CVOs (Baskin *et al.*, 1987). A possible physiological role of insulin receptors at the CVO may be to respond promptly to the rapid fluctuations of the plasma insulin level, thus continuously mediating its actions on the central nervous system.

Other Hormones

Specific receptors were also found for angiotensin II in the subfornical organ and organum/vasculosum of the lamina terminalis, and it has been suggested that these CVO receptors may be sensitive to blood-borne angiotensin II, taking part in physiological control of body fluid tonicity and hydration (McKinley *et al.*, 1987). Receptor-mediated transport has also been demonstrated for prolactin in the median eminence (Walsh *et al.*, 1987), which can mediate effects of sudden changes in prolactin plasma levels on the brain. Receptors for vasopressin, presumably of the V_1 type, have also been characterized in the CVO regions, possibly mediating some of the VP effects on the central nervous system (Ermisch *et al.*, 1988). Thus, in conclusion, one may say that, although the blood–brain barrier, from the quantitative point of view, plays a major role in peptide and protein homoeostasis in the central nervous system, the CVO non-barrier regions may be of particular value in mediating rapid effects of peptides in the brain.

Therapeutic Applications

Various strategies have been developed for drug delivery to the central nervous system (see, for review, Greig, 1989) and some of them may be applicable to peptides with more or less success.

Intra-CSF Injections

One group of methods is based on circumvention of the blood–brain barrier (Table 3.12) when the procedure involves an intracerebrospinal fluid administration of the drug, which is subsequently distributed throughout the CSF compartments and, secondarily, within both the brain and spinal cord. Clinically, the intraventricular route is commonly used and it requires the surgical placement of an Ommaya reservoir (Ommaya, 1963).

The reservoir is implanted subcutaneously and attached to a catheter, the tip of which is placed in the lateral ventricle. This route appears to be satisfactory for leptomeningeal diseases, as, for instance, in leukaemic infiltration, but may not be satisfactory for delivery of drugs into the brain parenchymal tissue, owing to high efflux from the ventricular compartment into the superior sagittal sinus, which is faster than the diffusion of drug from CSF into the brain. Owing to the deep convexities of the human brain surface, the distances of most brain regions from ependymal and/or cortical surface of the CSF compartment are too large for rapid diffusional equilibration. On the basis of the value for the diffusion coefficient for a given peptide of 2×10^{-6} cm^2/s with an average molecular weight of 2000–5000, the distance moved by free diffusion during 1 h would be approximately 1.2 mm. However, the estimated distances of brain regions from the site of injection may be within the range 0.5–1.0 cm, and, in the case of CSF-unstable peptides, possible enzymatic degradation has also to be taken into account. Thus, although this way of drug administration may be successful during anticancer treatment (see Greig, 1989), or in the treatment of some neurological disorders such as Alzheimer's disease (Harbaugh *et al.*, 1984), it may not be appropriate for peptide delivery to the brain.

Table 3.12 Possible strategies for peptide delivery to the central nervous system. According to Pardridge (1988)

Group	Strategy
Invasive	Intraventricular infusion Hyperosmotic carotid infusions
Pharmacological	Liposomes Latentation (lipid-soluble prodrugs)
Physiological	Chimeric peptides

Nasal Spray

One variation of the intrathecal approach may be to administer the peptide via a nasal spray, since intranasally administered substances are directly taken up by the brain as a consequence of the continuity of the subarachnoid space of the olfactory lobe and the submucous space of the nose. Recent studies have demonstrated that this route may represent an important additional pathway for the CSF drainage mechanism, allowing big protein molecules, such as ferritin, to pass from CSF into the submucosal nasal compartment (see, for review, McComb, 1983). So far, this way of peptide administration has been extensively used in the treatment of diabetes insipidus, when ADH is usually successfully applied locally in the form of a nasal spray.

Blood–Brain Route

Another group of methods is based on the use of the blood–brain barrier route. These techniques may be used (a) to influence primarily morphofunctional characteristics of the BBB, (b) to alter physicochemical properties of a given drug or peptide and (c) to utilize the known blood–brain barrier carrier, transport or receptor system. The invasive approach involves administration of the peptide in hyperosmotic carotid injections containing osmotically active substances such as mannitol and/or arabinose, which result in shrinkage of the brain endothelial cells and transient opening of the barrier (Neuwelt and Rapoport, 1984). This approach has been reported in chemotherapy of brain tumours but the estimated size of pores generated by hyperosmotic opening cannot offer passage for proteins such as an enzyme decodeaminidase A. An additional difficulty for peptide delivery by this way is their extreme sensitivity to plasma enzymes, even during a single capillary circulation (Zloković *et al.*, 1988a). Also, the toxicity of such a procedure is high and the incidence of seizures may be as great as 20%.

Liposomes

Among the pharmacological strategies, the use of liposomes for peptide delivery across the blood–brain barrier has been shown to be inappropriate, since liposomes, although avidly taken up by the cells of the reticuloendothelial system in the liver and spleen, are not measurably transported across the blood–brain barrier (Patel, 1984).

Latentiation

Another potentially powerful approach is latentiation, which involves conversion of the functional group of the peptide molecule from a water-soluble to a lipid-soluble compound. For instance, diketopiperazines are formed by coupling the terminal carboxy- and amino groups; this results in a large increase in the lipophilicity of the peptides due to the loss of several functional hydrogen bonds of the parent molecule (Pardridge, 1986a). Non-cyclized peptides, such as glycyl-leucine and glycyl-phenylalanine are poorly transported across the barrier (Zloković *et al.*, 1983), while the cyclized dipeptide or diketopiperazine of the oxytocin C-terminal leucyl-glycine (Hoffman *et al.*, 1977) or C-terminal histidyl-proline of TRH (Peterson *et al.*, 1984) were transported readily across the barrier.

Chimeric Peptides

The formation of chimeric peptides (Pardridge, 1985) is an example of a physiologically based strategy which exploits the possibility that some proteins, which exhibit measurable transport across the blood–brain barrier by receptor-mediated transcytosis, may be conjugated to a given peptide, or other protein, that is naturally poorly transported. Newly formed peptide–protein complexes consist of a transportable protein and non-transportable peptide covalently coupled to the protein that should be preferably cleaved from its parent compound once in brain tissue. The chimeric peptide may be then transported using the receptor-mediated transfer of a naturally transported protein such as insulin, transferrin or cationized albumin. For example, the β-endorphin-cationized albumin chimeric complex is rapidly taken up and endocytosed by isolated bovine brain caillaries via a process that is saturated by unlabelled cationized albumin, but not by unconjugated β-endorphin or native albumin (Kumagai *et al.*, 1987; Pardridge *et al.*, 1990).

Established Transporters

Another approach in physiological strategies is the use of a known transporter; this has been exploited with great success in the treatment of Parkinson's disease by delivering the dopamine precursor, L-DOPA, via the L-amino acid carrier. Within the central nervous system this is converted to dopamine, which is necessary for the function of the nigrostriatal pathway. Recently it has been shown that the L-amino acid carrier is able to transport an anticancer agent, melphalan (Figure 3.13), which is structurally related to the amino acid phenylalanine (see, for review,

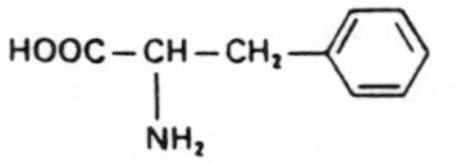

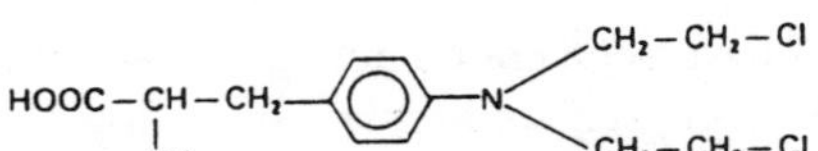

Figure 3.13 Chemical structural relationship between melphalan (anti-cancer agent) and L-phenylalanine enables melphalan to use large neutral amino acid BBB transporter. According to Vistica (1983)

Vistica, 1983). The hypothesis that some small peptides can use the amino acid carrier has been studied during an *in vivo* vascular brain perfusion, but for none of the tested molecules, including leucine-enkephalin (Zloković *et al.*, 1987), DSIP (Zloković *et al.*, 1989b) and VP (arginine) (Zloković *et al.*, 1989a), could a sharing of transporter be demonstrated.

Psychoendocrinology

Several peptides, peptide agonists and peptide antagonists have been used as therapeutic agents in psychoendocrinology to treat depression, mania, schizophrenia, dementia, Alzheimer's disease, amnesia, Korsakoff syndrome, etc.

TRH

Among them, TRH is probably most frequently used to treat patients with depression but its reported efficacy seems to vary (Pranje *et al.*, 1987). In general, oral application of the tripeptide has no value but intravenous administration seems to be more promising. In manic patients, the intravenous administration of TRH has given encouraging results, probably via TRH central cholinomimetic actions (Yarbrough, 1976). Studies on the antidepressant action of β-endorphin revealed more positive than negative results, as well as oral application of MIF-1 (Van der Velde, 1983).

Endorphins

The antipsychotic action of endorphins was tested in a number of clinical trials, but the responses of the patients varied individually from no response to complete remission of psychotic symptoms (Van Ree *et al.*, 1982). It was observed, with further analysis, that there is a particularly sensitive group of schizophrenic patients who, in response to γ-type endorphin treatment, exhibit a variety of motor symptoms, such as retardation and catatonic symptoms, which inhibited the response to peptide treatment. In addition, reduced responsiveness was also observed in patients for the long duration of recent psychotic episodes who had been treated previously with high doses of neuroleptics.

CCK-related Peptides

Extensive clinical trials have been conducted to evaluate the antipsychotic action of CCK-related peptides in schizophrenia, including CCK-33, CCK-8 and ceruletide (Van Ree *et al.*, 1987). In general, an improvement in symptomatology was reported for most studies with an effect that was rather rapid and persisted for several days or weeks, even after a single injection of peptide. However, although this effect was, in some patients, clinically significant, the amelioration was, in general, partial and not always impressive.

Vasopressin

Human studies with VP (arginine), VP (lysine) and their synthetic analogues, DDAVP and DGAVP, have indicated that vasopressin and its analogues may improve memory and learning both in normal adults and in patients with either psychiatric or neurological disorders accompanied with amnesia. Also, vasopressin-related peptides were applied with potentially good results in amnesia of alcoholic and post-traumatic origin, after electroconvulsive therapy, Korsakoff syndrome, Lesch–Nyhan disease, depression and various memory disturbances (de Wied, 1987).

Peptide Challenge Tests

A considerable effort in clinical research has also been focused on the various peptide challenge tests, which are all based on the principle of provoking secretion of the adenohypophyseal hormones by giving, systemically, hypothalamic releasing factors. Among the first studies reported in this field was the finding of a diminished TSH response to TRH in euthyroid depressed patients (Prange *et al.*, 1972). A number of subsequent studies have provided evidence with respect to an altered TSH response to TRH in various affective disorders, but the mechanism underlying these changes is still a matter of controversy, and it is not easy to explain how these results can be related to the conditions of mania and depression (Prange *et al.*, 1987). CRF infusion in patients with depression has shown a reduced response to ACTH, while in manic patients no changes in ACTH or cortisol response to CRF were reported (Gold and Chrousos, 1985). It has also been shown that, in depressed patients, the ACTH response to CRF is strongly influenced by basal cortisol levels. On the other hand, LHRH infusion in depressed patients failed to show any significant changes in LH and FSH responses (Winokur *et al.*, 1982).

In conclusion, we may point out that clinical and fundamental research studies on the possible therapeutic application of peptides in different disorders of the central nervous system have opened a new area in neuropharmacology and neuroendocrinology, encouraging the further development of biological and physicochemical strategies for delivery of peptides and proteins to the brain.

Peptides and Proteins in the CSF

CSF:Plasma Ratio (R_{CSF}) of Proteins

Kabat *et al.* (1942) published the first analysis of the protein composition of the CSF, showing that the concentrations were very much less than in plasma. Although it has been generally accepted that the majority of CSF proteins come from the plasma, it has not yet been established whether the major site of their entry into the central nervous system is located at (a) the non-barrier regions exclusively, (b) at the barrier regions or (c) at both of these sites. Also, with respect to the principal mechanism of transfer, it has been suggested that (a) diffusion, (b) transendothelial non-specific endocytosis or (c) receptor-mediated endocytosis, both at the barrier and non-barrier regions may take place. There are also possible exceptions of some plasma lipoproteins that could not be detected in the CSF and some CSF proteins that owe their origin to brain tissue and are absent from plasma.

For some proteins, such as prealbumin (thyroxine-binding prealbumin, retinol-binding protein, etc.), which comprise 0.5% of the total protein content in serum, but constitute some 6–10% in the CSF, there is evidence for an *in situ* synthesis by the brain and by the choroid plexus, followed by secretion in the CSF. Similar findings were observed for transferrin and ceruloplasmin, which are synthesized by both the brain and choroid plexus epithelium (Dickson *et al.*, 1985; Aldred *et al.*, 1987; Møllgard *et al.*, 1988).

Variations in Concentration

Various protein CSF fractions expressed as a percentage of the total protein content in normal human CSF are given in Table 3.13. The concentration of proteins in the CSF varies along the length of the neuroaxis, with sex, and with the age of the subject. High levels of CSF proteins have been demonstrated in the developing brain in many different species (Dziegielewska and Saunders, 1988a), with the clear peak that may be related, most appropriately, to the phase of brain maturation rather than to the time of birth (Figure 3.14). By immunofluorescence methods, it has been confirmed that proteins in fetal or post-natal CSF are indistinguishable from those in the plasma (Dziegielewska and Saunders, 1988b).

Table 3.13　Concentration of various proteins in normal human serum and cerebrospinal fluid. From Davson *et al.* (1987)

		Total proteins			Globulins				
n	*Puncture*	(mg/100 ml)	*Prealbumin*	*Albumin*	α_1	α_2	β	τ	γ
21	L	40.0	5.31±1.71	60.99±3.76	5.10±0.92	6.13±1.25	8.47±1.36	5.28±1.50	8.80±1.22
80	L	37.0±9.1	4.9±1.10	63.7±4.25	3.4±1.15	4.9±1.00	8.8±1.30	6.1±1.65	8.3±1.50
60	L	33.6±8.75	5.5±1.60	61.6±5.55	3.9±1.30	5.2±1.25	8.8±1.40	6.0±1.70	9.0±2.65
19	L	18.0	4.3±1.5	54.5±4.2	6.1±1.4	8.2±1.8	15.5±1.9		11.3±0.8
33	CM	31.6±5.8	7.2±1.4	56.2±6.0	5.2±1.4	5.5±1.1	15.7±2.6		9.8±1.5
50	CM	20.5±4.12	5.8±1.29	56.04±3.58	4.10±1.44	6.73±1.65	9.69±2.05	5.97±1.44	11.64±1.88
110	CM	29.73±8.06	5.77±1.89	62.81±6.46	43.46±1.26	4.74±1.43	9.35±2.25	6.01±1.91	7.85±2.12
73	CM	25.14±6.41	6.78±2.34	60.73±6.38	3.87±1.26	5.17±1.52	10.06±2.01	5.92±1.72	7.30±1.79

Means ± s.d.

L. lumbar; CM. cisterna magna.

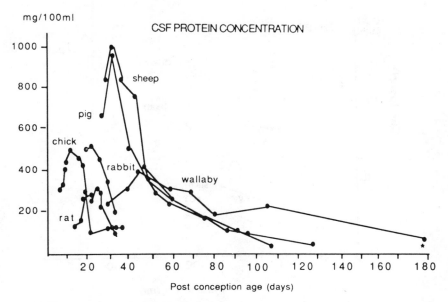

Figure 3.14   Total protein concentration in the cerebrospinal fluid in various species during development. Modified from Dziegliewska and Saunders (1988b)

Peptides

Most peptides of different origin, including gastrointestinal peptides, hypothalamo–hypophysiotropic peptides, adenohypophyseal peptides, neurohypophyseal peptides, etc., have been identified in the CSF by various sensitive and specific radioimunnoassay and HPLC procedures. The relationship between peptide CSF-to-plasma level has often been regarded as a good indicator for blood–CSF barrier permeability to a peptide. Figure 3.15 illustrates the CSF-to-plasma ratios for a number of peptides as determined from ventricular or posterior fossa CSF or from lumbar CSF. Assuming that blood–CSF barrier permeability to peptides is governed only by physicochemical factors, such as molecular weight and lipophilicity, the estimated concentration of peptide in the CSF should be much smaller than that actually measured, and the expected CSF/plasma ratio would be only 1–3% (Pardridge, 1986a). However, as shown in Figure 3.15, for a number of peptides, the basal level is more than 10% of that found in plasma, and a similar ratio was determined for prolactin (Lenhard and Deftos, 1982), thyrocalcitonin (Morimoto *et al.*, 1982) or glucagon (Hoossein and Gurd, 1984). The concentrations of adenohypophyseal peptides in the CSF are particularly high, yielding a CSF/plasma ratio of 10–100% (Table 3.14). The fact that the actual CSF peptide concentration is usually higher than one would expect on the ground that their blood–CSF barrier permeability is regulated by physicochemical factors, may indicate either that (a) peptides are selectively transported into the CSF across the

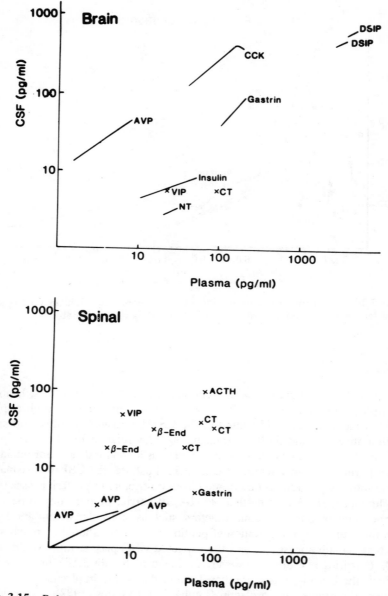

Figure 3.15 Relationship between cerebrospinal fluid and plasma levels for various peptides as determined from the ventricles and posterior fossa (brain) or lumbar (spinal) cerebrospinal fluid. Lines represent a correlation between the cerebrospinal fluid and plasma levels for the peptide, while crosses represent no correlation with the means of cerebrospinal fluid and plasma values. All data are taken from healthy humans or untreated animals. All values are in pg/ml, except for insulin (units/ml). Abbreviated peptide nomenclature as in Table 3.1. From Banks and Kastin (1985a, b)

Table 3.14 Cerebrospinal fluid to blood ratio and concentration of pituitary hormones in the cerebrospinal fluid. Modified from Lenhard and Deftos (1982)

Peptide	Concentration	CSF/blood ratio (%)
ACTH	75 pg/ml	100
CT	250 pg/ml	50
β-E	100 pg/ml	<100
FSH	20 mIU/ml	10
GH	500 pg/ml	16
LH	25 mIU/ml	10
PRL	1000 pg/ml	33
TSH	2.5 mU/ml	10

blood–brain barrier and non-barrier regions or (b) peptides are neurosecreted by the brain into the CSF.

Role of Tanycytes

Peptides may also pass from blood into the CSF of the third ventricle via transcytosis across tanycytes that may combine both mechanisms: transport and neurosecretion. Thus, tanycytes connect the blood and CSF compartments, since they line the ependymal surface of the ventricle and have their processes in the portal spaces of the median eminence. Receptor-mediated endocytosis of peptides in the median eminence similar to that previously shown for apolipoprotein E (Boyles *et al.*, 1985) may be followed by subsequent transfer across the tanycyte cytoplasm and exocytosis at the ependymal end of the tanycyte. Although this mechanism has not been studied so far in detail, with respect to peptide CSF homoeostasis, it may be responsible for the selective enrichment of the CSF compartment by peptides neurosecreted by the brain in the median eminence. By circulating in the CSF, peptides may have access to specific receptors at the intracranial site, and, using this 'short loop', they may serve an important regulatory role, either affecting the target areas of the brain and pituitary gland that are accessible via the CSF, or by a feedback mechanism regulating their own secretion (Ben-Jonathan *et al.*, 1974).

Role of the Choroid Plexus

It has been recently argued that the choroid plexus may represent a potentially important site for selective delivery of water-soluble compounds and ions from blood into the brain (Spector, 1977; Johanson, 1989). Although, from the quantitative viewpoint, a relatively minor role can be attributed to the choroid plexus in comparison with the central nervous capillaries, it has been recently emphasized that certain organic transport systems may be present only at the choroid plexus epithelium but not at the central nervous capillaries, as well as that the transport capacity of some inorganic ion antiport and symport systems in the choroid plexus may exceed the capacity of similar systems described previously for the blood–brain barrier.

Endocytosis

Extensive endocytotic activity of the choroidal epithelial cells has been demonstrated in a number of secretory and reabsorptive studies. For instance, proteins such as microperoxidase (MRP) (Reese *et al.*, 1971), HRP (van Deurs, 1980) and cytochrome C (Milhorat *et al.*, 1973) are endocytosed by the basolateral side of the choroidal epithelium as well as macromolecules such as ferritin (Hurley *et al.*, 1981), which is followed by subsequent sequestration of these markers in their lysosomal apparatus, indicating that lysosomes act as an enzymic barrier or intracellular sink. Vesicular blood-to-CSF transport of MRP and HRP has not been shown in these studies, while larger markers such as diodrast may even be trapped by the basement membrane which will prevent the endocytosis at the basolateral side.

Fetal Pathway

The possibility of the existence of a transcellular pathway in the choroid plexus epithelium in early fetal life, which may be in the form of a tubular system of endoplasmic reticulum cisterns (Møllgard and Saunders, 1977), has been suggested to be responsible for relatively unrestricted transport of protein molecules across the fetal blood–CSF barrier (Møllgard *et al.*, 1988).

R_{CSF} Values

A number of studies have demonstrated that the basal CSF and plasma levels of many peptides correlate with each other (Woods and Porte, 1977; Meisenberg and Simmons, 1983), but because of the complexity of the blood–CNS interfaces involved in the interaction of a blood-borne peptide, this type of study could not provide the proof that a peptide had crossed from blood into the CSF at the BBB, choroid plexus or CVOs. Studies involving incubation of choroid plexus *in vitro* have shown that receptors and/or carriers may be responsible for uptake of many peptides by the epithelial cells. For example, extensive concentration of the tripeptide, Tyr–D–Ala–Gly (TAG) (Huang, 1982), DAME (Huang and Lajtha, 1978), insulin (Baskin *et al.*, 1988), melatonin (Mess and Trentini, 1974) and prolactin (Posner *et al.*, 1983) has been shown in the choroid plexus, which may be consistent with their regulatory roles in maintaining peptide concentrations and distribution in the CSF. However, there is uncertainty as to whether the uptake takes place at the basolateral or the CSF side of the plexus, as well as to what extent peptidergic nerve terminals are involved in the uptake process.

Perfused Choroid Plexus

Peptide interactions at the basolateral side of the choroid plexus epithelium have recently been studied in an *in situ* perfused choroid plexus of the sheep according to the techniques of Segal and Pollay (1977). The paired-tracer indicator dilution method, with D-mannitol as an extracellular space marker, has revealed a significant cellular uptake of enkephalin-leucine and its synthetic analogue, DADLE, which can be strongly self-inhibited, suggesting the presence of a saturable carrier-mediated mechanism for opioid peptides at the blood–CSF barrier (Zloković *et al.*, 1988b). Self-inhibition was more pronounced with the synthetic enkephalin analogue, which may be attributed to its greater resistance to hydrolysis. More detailed analysis has revealed that, besides a saturable component that represents uptake of the intact peptide by the choroid plexus epithelium, there is also a non-saturable mechanism that reflects enzymic degradation of peptide in the blood and/or at the choroid epithelium, with liberation of the N-terminal amino acid residue. The presence of a similar non-saturable mechanism for peptides has been previously shown for TRH (Zloković *et al.*, 1985b). Carrier-mediated uptake of delta sleep-inducing peptide (DSIP) at the basolateral side of perfused sheep choroid plexus, with a K_m of 5 nM and a V_{max} of 272 fmol/min, has been shown by means of steady-state kinetic analysis (Figure 3.16).

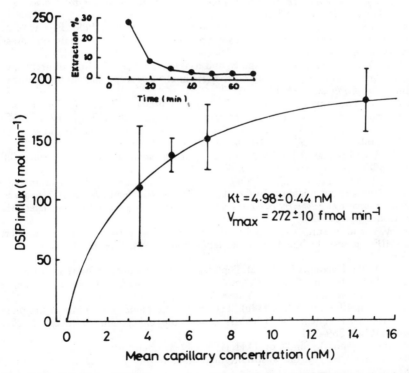

Figure 3.16 Kinetics of blood-to-cerebrospinal fluid flux of DSIP across the choroidal epithelium of the perfused plexuses of the sheep. The inset illustrates the extraction of DSIP during 70 min of perfusion in one experiment. From Zloković *et al.* (1988b)

Kinetic analysis revealed also a saturable vasopressin uptake at the basolateral face of the choroid plexus in the guinea-pig and sheep with a K_m value of about 30 nM (Zloković *et al.*, 1991). It is suggested that a specific VP mechanism in the choroid plexus can detect circulatory hormone primarily by V_1 receptors.

Although this type of study characterizes the first step during an interaction of the blood-borne peptide with the choroid plexus, it cannot provide experimental proof with respect to the actual passage of peptide into the CSF. Theoretically, the peptide may be taken up by binding to the basolateral side of the choroid epithelium, or it may be internalized and then transported transcellularly into the CSF; alternatively, it may be sequestered by the lysosomal apparatus and prevented from access into the CSF.

References

Abbott, J., Butt, A.M. and Zloković, B.V. (1988). Techniques for study of blood–brain barrier in non-mammalian species. In Rakić, Lj., Begley, D.J., Davson, H. and Zloković, B.V. (Eds), *Peptide and Amino Acid Transport Mechanisms in the Central Nervous System.* Macmillan, London, pp. 293–397

Adam, G., Joó, F., Temesvari, P., Dux, E. and Szerdahelyi, P. (1988). Effects of acute hypoxia on the adenylate cyclase activity and albumin transport of brain microvessels. *Neurochem. Int.* (in press)

Akmal, M.D., Goldstein, A., Multani, S. and Massry, S.G. (1984). Role of uremia, brain calcium and parathyroid hormone on changes in electroencephalogram in chronic renal failure. *Am. J. Physiol.*, **246**, F575–F579

Aldred, A.R., Dickson, P.W., Marley, P.D. and Schreiber, G. (1987). Distribution of transferrin synthesis in brain and other tissues in the rat. *J. Biol. Chem.*, **262**, 5293–5297

Banks, W.A. and Kastin, A.J. (1983). CSF–plasma relationships for DSIP and some other neuropeptides. *Pharmacol. Biochem. Behav.*, **19**, 1037–1040

Banks, W.A. and Kastin, A.J. (1985). Aluminium alters blood–brain barrier permeability to non-peptides. *Neuropharmacology*, **24**, 407–412

Banks, W.A. and Kastin, A.J. (1986a). Aging, peptides and the blood–brain barrier: implications and speculations. In Crook, T., Bartus, R., Ferris, S. and Gerhson, S.M. (Eds), *Treatment Development Strategies for Alzheimer's Disease.* Powley Associates, Madison, Conn., pp. 245–265

Banks, W.A. and Kastin, A.J. (1989b). Modulation of the carrier-mediated transport of Tyr–MIF-1 across the blood–brain barrier by essential amino acids. *J. Pharmacol.*, **239**, 668–672

Banks, W.A. and Kastin, A.J. (1988a). Peptides and the blood–brain barrier. In Rakić, Lj., Begley, D.J., Davson, H. and Zloković, B.V. (Eds), *Peptide and Amino Acid Transport Mechanisms in the Central Nervous System.* Macmillan, London, pp. 21–32

Banks, W.A. and Kastin, A.J. (1988b). Twenty-one hormones fail to inhibit the brain to blood transport system for Tyr–MIF-1 and the enkephalins in mice. *J. Pharm. Pharmacol.*, **40**, 289–291

Banks, W.A., Kastin, A.J. and Coy, D.H. (1983). Delta sleep-inducing peptide (DSIP)-like materials absorbed by the gastrointestinal tract of the neonatal rat. *Life Sci.*, **33**, 1587–1897

Banks, W.A., Kastin, A.J., Fishman, A.J., Coy, D.H. and Strauss, S.L. (1986). Carrier mediated transport of enkephalins and N-Tyr–MIF-1 across the blood–brain barrier. *Am. J. Physiol.*, **251** (*Endocrinol. Metab.*, 14), E477–E482

Banks, W.A., Kastin, A.J., Horvath, A. and Michals, E.A. (1987). Carrier-mediated transport of vasopressin across the blood–brain barrier of the mouse. *J. Neurosci. Res.*, **18**, 326–332

Banks, W.A., Kastin, A.J. and Nager, B.J. (1988). Analgesia and the blood–brain barrier transport system for Tyr–MIF-1 enkephalin: evidence for dissociation. *Neuropharmacology*, **27**, 175–179

Banks, W.A., Kastin, A.J. and Siznick, J.K. (1985). Modulation of immunoactive levels of DSIP and blood–brain barrier permeability by lighting and diurnal rhythm. *J. Neurosci. Res.*, **14**, 347–355

Bar, R.S., DeRose, A., Sandra, A., Peacock, M.L. and Owen, W.G. (1983). Insulin binding to microvascular endothelium of intact heart: a kinetic and morphometric analysis. *Am. J. Physiol.*, **244**, E447–E543

Barrera, C.M., Kastin, A.J. and Banks, W.A. (1987). D-[Ala¹]–Peptide T amide is transported from blood to brain by a saturable system. *Brain Res. Bull.*, **19**, 629–633

Barry, D.I., Paulson, O.B. and Hertz, M.M. (1980). The blood–brain barrier: an overview with special reference to insulin effect on glucose transport. *Acta Neurol. Scand.*, **778**, 147–156

Baskin, D.G., Dorsa, D.M., Figlewicz, D.P., Corp, E.S., Wilcox, B.J., Wallum, B.J. and Woods, S.C. (1988). Insulin as a regulatory peptide in the CNS. In Rakić, Lj., Begley, D.J., Davson, H. and Zloković, B.V. (Eds), *Peptide and Amino Acid Transport Mechanisms in the Central Nervous System.* Macmillan, London, pp. 79–90

Baskin, D.G., Figlewicz, D.P., Woods, S.C., Porte, D. and Dorsa, D.M. (1987). Insulin in the brain. *Ann. Rev. Physiol.*, **49**, 335–347

Baskin, D.G., Woods, S.C., West, D.B., van Houten, M., Posner, B.I., Dorsa, D.M. and Porte, D. Jr. (1983). Immunocytochemical detection of insulin in rat hypothalamus and its possible uptake from cerebrospinal fluid. *Endocrinology*, **112**, 1818–1825

Bayliss, W.M. and Starling, E.H. (1902). The mechanism of pancreatic secretion, *J. Physiol.*, **28**, 325–353

Beckwith, B.E., Couk, D.I. and Till, T.S. (1983). Vasopressin analog influences the performance of males on a reaction time task. *Peptides*, **4**, 707–709

Begley, D.J. and Chain, D.G. (1982). Clearance of glutamic acid, glutamine and pyroglutamic acid from the cerebrospinal fluid of the rabbit: a comparison with thyrotropin releasing hormone. *J. Physiol.*, **326**, 22–23

Begley, D.J. and Chain, D.G. (1988). Transport of encephalin from cerebrospinal fluid of the rabbit. In Rakić, Lj., Begley, D.G., Davson, H. and Zloković, B.V. (Eds), *Peptide and Amino Acid Transport Mechanisms in the Central Nervous System.* Macmillan, London, pp. 55–64

Begley, D.J., Michaelson, I.A. and Davson, H. (1980). Clearance of the dipeptide glycyl-L-leucine from rabbit cerebrospinal fluid. *J. Physiol.*, **307**, 83P

Begley, D.J., Squires, L.K., Zloković, B.V. and Mitrović, D.M. (1990). Permeability of blood–brain barrier to the immuno-suppressive cyclic peptide cyclosporin A. *J. Neurochem.*, **55**, 1222–1230

Begley, J.D. and Zloković, B.V. (1986). Neuropeptides and the blood–brain barrier. In Suckling, A.J., Rumsby, M.G. and Bradbury, M.W. (Eds), *Blood–Brain Barrier in Health and Disease.* Verlagsgesellschaft, Weinheim, 98–108

Ben-Jonathan, N., Mical, R.S. and Porter, J.C. (1974). Transport of LRF from CSF to hypophysial portal systemic blood and the release of LH. *Endocrinology*, **95**, 18–25

Bloom, F.E. (1987). Molecular diversity and cellular functions of neuropeptides. In de Kloet, E.R., Wiegant, A.M. and de Wied, D. (Eds), *Neuropeptides and Brain Function. Progress in Brain Research*, Vol. 72, pp. 213–223

Boyles, J.K., Pitas, R.E., Wilson, E., Mahley, R.W. and Taylor, J.M. (1985). Apolipoprotein, E: associated with astrocytic glia of the central nervous system and with non-myelinating glia of the peripheral nervous system. *J. Clin. Invest.*, **76**, 1501

Bradbury, W.B. (1989). Transport across the blood–brain barrier. In Neuwelt, E.A. (Ed.),

Implications of the Blood–Brain Barrier and Its Manipulation. Plenum Medical Book Company, New York, pp. 119–137

Brightman, M.W. and Reese, T.S. (1969). Junctions between intimately opposed cell membranes in the vertebrate brain. *J. Cell Biol.*, **40**, 648–677

Broadwell, R.D., Balin, B.J. and Salcman, M. (1988). Transcytotic pathway for blood-borne protein through the blood–brain barrier. *Proc. Natl Acad. Sci. USA*, **85**, 632–636

Broadwell, R.D., Balin, B.J., Salcman, M. and Kaplan, R.S. (1983). Brain–blood barrier? Yes and no. *Proc. Natl Acad. Sci. USA*, **80**, 7352–7356

Buijs, R.M. and Van Heerikhuize, J.J. (1982). Vasopressin and oxytocin release in the brain—a synaptic event. *Brain Res.*, **252**, 71–76

Burbach, J.P., Kovacs, G.L., De Wied, D., van Nispen, J.W. and Greven, H.M. (1983). A major metabolite of arginine vasopressin in the brain is a highly potent neuropeptide. *Science*, **221**, 1310–1312

Cefalu, W.T. and Pardridge, W.M. (1985). Restrictive transport of a lipid-soluble peptide (cyclosporin) through the blood–brain barrier. *J. Neurochem.*, **45**, 1954–1956

Coghlan, J.P., Congiu, M., Denton, D.A., Fei, D.T. and Park, R.G. (1986). Augmented plasma renin levels in dehydrated sheep with periventricular lesions. *Brain Res.*, **376**, 416–419

Cohen, S.L., Knight, M., Tamminga, C.A. and Chase, T.N. (1983). Tolerance to the antiavoidance properties of cholecystokinin-octapeptide. *Peptides*, **4**, 67–70

Congiu, M., Denton, D.A., Park, R.G., Penschow, J., Simpson, J.B., Tarjan, E., Weisinger, R.S. and Wright, R.D. (1984). The anterior wall of the third cerebral ventricle and homeostatic responses to dehydration. *J. Physiol. (Paris)*, **79**, 421–427

Connelly, J.C., Skidgel, R.A., Schulz, W.W., Johnson, A.R. and Erdos E.G. (1985). Neutral endopeptidase 24.11 in human neutrophils: cleavage of chemotactic peptide. *Proc. Natl Acad. Sci. USA*, **82**, 8737–8741

Cornford, E.M., Braun, L.D., Crane, P.D. and Oldendorf, W.H. (1978). Blood–brain barrier restrictions of peptides and the low uptake of enkephalins. *Endocrinology*, **103**, 1297–1303

Corp, E.S., Woods, S.C., Porte, D., Jr., Dorsa, D.M., Figlewicz, D.P. and Baskin, D.G. (1986). Localization of I-insulin binding sites in the rat hypothalamus by quantitative autoradiography. *Neurosci. Lett.*, **70**, 17–22

Davis, J.L. and Pico, R.M. (1984). Arginine vasotocin delays extinction of a conditioned avoidance behavior in neonatal chicks. *Peptides*, **5**, 1221–1223

Davson, H. (1955). A comparative study of the aqueous humor and cerebrospinal fluid in the rabbit. *J. Physiol.*, **129**, 11–133

Davson, H. and Oldendorf, W.H. (1967). Transport in the central nervous system. *Proc. Roy. Soc. Med.*, **60**, 326–328

Davson, H. and Segal, M.B. (1970). The effects of some inhibitors and accelerators of sodium transport on the turnover of ^{22}Na in the cerebrospinal fluid. *J. Physiol.*, **209**, 131–153

Davson, H., Welch, K. and Segal, M.B. (1987). *Physiology and Pathophysiology of the Cerebrospinal Fluid.* Churchill Livingstone, Edinburgh

Denbow, D.M. and Myers, R.D. (1982). Eating, drinking and temperature responses to intracerebroventricular cholecystokinin in the chick. *Peptides*, **3**, 739–743

Derian, C.K. and Moskowitz, M.A. (1986). Polyphosphoinoside hydrolysis in endothelial cells and carotid artery segments. Bradykinin-2 receptor stimulation is calcium-dependent. *J. Biol. Chem.*, **261**, 3831–3837

de Sousa, E.B. and Kuhar, H.J. (1986). Corticotrophin-releasing factor receptors: autoradiographic identification. In Martin, J.B. and Barchas, J.D. (Eds), *Neuropeptides in Neurologic and Psychiatric Disease.* Raven Press, New York, pp. 179–198

de Wied, D. (1987). The neuropeptide concept. In de Kloet, E.R., Wiegant, N.M. and de Wied, D. (Eds), *Neuropeptides and Brain Function. Progress in Brain Research*, Vol. 72, Elsevier, Amsterdam, pp. 93–108 de Wied, D., Gaffori, O., van Ree, J.M. and de Jong, W. (1984). Central target for the behavioral effects of vasopressin peptides. *Nature*, 308, 276–278

Dickson, P.W., Aldred, A.P., Marley, P.D., Guo-Fen, T., Howlett, G.J. and Schreiber, G. (1985). High prealbumin and transferrin mRNA levels in the choroid plexus of rat brain. *Biochem. Biophys. Res. Commun.*, 127, 890–895

Doczi, T., Joó, F., Szerdahelyi, P. and Bodosi, M. (1988). Regulation of brain water and electrolyte contents: the opposite actions of central vasopressin and atrial natriuretic factor (ANF). *Acta Neurochir.*, 43, (Suppl.), 186–188

Dodd, J. and Kelly, J.S. (1981). The actions of cholecystokinin and related peptides on pyramidal neurones of the mammalian hippocampus. *Brain Res.*, 205, 337–356

Du Vigneaud, V. (1954). Hormones of the posterior pituitary gland: oxytocin and vasopressin. *Harvey Lectures*, 50, 1–26

Dux, E. and Joó, F. (1982). Effects of histamine on brain capillaries: fine structural and immunohistochemical studies after intracarotid infusion. *Exp. Brain Res.*, 47, 252–258

Dziegielewska, K.M. and Saunders, N.R. (1988a). The development of the blood–brain barrier: proteins in fetal and neonatal CSF, their nature and origins. In Meisami, E. and Timiras, P.J. (Eds), *Handbook of Human Growth and Biological Development*. CRC Press, Boca Raton, Florida, pp. 103–118

Dziegielewska, K.M. and Saunders, N.R. (1988b). The origins and functions of proteins in CSF in the developing brain. In Rakić, L., Begley, D.J., Davson, H. and Zloković, B.V. (Eds), *Peptide and Amino Acid Transport Mechanisms in the Central Nervous System*. Macmillan, London, pp. 105–121

Edvinsson, L., Fahrenburg, J., Hanko, J., McCulloch, J., Owman, C. and Uddman, R. (1981). Vasoactive intestinal polypeptide and effects on cerebral blood flow and metabolism. In Cervos-Navarro, J. and Fritschka, E. (Eds), *Cerebral Blood Flow and Metabolism*. Raven Press, New York, pp. 147–155

Ermisch, A. (1987). Blood–brain barrier and peptides. *Wiss. Z. Karl-Marx-Univ. Leipzig, Math.-Naturwiss. R.*, 36, 72–77

Ermisch, A., Landgraf, R., Brust, P., Kretzschmar, R. and Hess, J. (1988). Peptide receptors of the cerebral capillary endothelium and the transport of amino acids across the blood–brain barrier. In Rakić, Lj., Begley, D.J., Davson, H. and Zloković, B.V. (Eds), *Peptide and Amino Acid Transport Mechanisms in the Central Nervous System*. Macmillan, London, pp. 43–55

Ermisch, A., Landgraf, R. and Mobius, P. (1986). Vasopressin and oxytocin in brain areas of rats with high or low behavioral performance. *Brain Res.*, 379, 21–29

Fahzenkrug, J. (1979). Vasoactive intestinal polypeptide: measurement distribution and putative neurotransmitter function. *Digestion*, 19, 149–169

Feldman, S.C. and Kastin, A.J. (1984). Localization of neurones containing immunoreactive delta sleep-inducing peptide in the rat brain: an immunocytochemical study. *Neuroscience*, 11, 303–317

Figlewicz, D.P., Lacour, F., Sipols, A., Porte, Jr., D. and Woods, S.C. (1987). Gastroenteropancreatic (GEP) peptides in the central nervous system. *Ann. Rev. Physiol.*, 49, 383–395

Frank, H.J.L., Jankovic-Vokis, T., Pardridge, W.M. and Morris, W.L. (1985). Enhanced insulin binding to blood–brain barrier *in vivo* and to brain microvessels *in vitro* in newborn rabbits. *Diabetes*, 34, 728–733

Frank, H.J.L., Pardridge, W.M., Morris, W.L., Rosenfeld, R.G. and Choi, T.B. (1986). Binding and internalization of insulin and insulin-like growth factors by isolated brain microvessels. *Diabetes*, 35, 654

Freedman, F. and Johnson, J.A. (1969). Equilibrium and kinetic properties of the Evans blue–albumin system. *Am. J. Physiol.*, 216, 675–681

Gafford, J.T., Skidgel, R.A., Erdos, E.G. and Hersh, L.B. (1983). Human kidney 'enkephalinase', a neutral metalloendopeptidase that cleaves active peptides. *Biochemistry*, 22, 3265–3271

Gaudreau, P., Quirion, R., St. Pierre, S. and Pert, C.B. (1983). Characterization and visualization of cholecystokinin receptors in rat brain using ^{3}H-pentagastrin. *Peptides*, **4**, 755–762

Giles, T.D. and Sander, G.E. (1983). Mechanism of the cardiovascular response to systemic intravenous administration of leucine-enkephalin in the conscious dog. *Peptides*, **4**, 171–175

Gjedde, A. (1988). Exchange diffusion of large neutral amino acids between blood and brain. In Rakić, Lj., Begley, D.J., Davson, H. and Zloković, B.V. (Eds), *Peptide and Amino Acid Transport Mechanisms in the Central Nervous System*. Macmillan, London, pp. 213–223

Gjedde, A. and Bodsch, W. (1987). Facilitated diffusion across the blood–brain barriers interactions between receptors and transporters. *Wiss. Z. Karl-Marx Univ. Leipzig, Math.-Naturwiss. R.*, **36** (1), 67–71

Gold, P.W. and Chrousos, G.P. (1985). Clinical studies with corticotropin releasing factor: implications for diagnosis and pathophysiology of depression, Cushing's disease, and adrenal insufficiency. *Psychoneuroendocrinology*, **10**, 401–419

Gold, P.W., Chrousos, G., Kellner, C., Post, R., Roy, A., Augerinos, P., Schulte, H., Oldfield, E. and Loriaux, D.L. (1984). Psychiatric implications of basic and clinical studies with corticotropin-releasing factor. *Am. J. Psychiat.*, **J41**, 619–623

Goldman, H. and Murphy, S. (1981). An analog of ACTH/MSH ORG-2766, reduces permeability of the blood–brain barrier. *Pharmacol. Biochem. Behav.*, **14**, 845–848

Goldmann, E.E. (1909). Die äussere und innere secretetion des gesunden und kranken organismus im lichte der 'vitalon tarbung'. *Beitz. Klin. Chirurg.*, **64**, 192–265

Goldmann, E.E. (1913). Vitalfarbung am Zentral Nervensystem (Abh. Preuss. Akad. Wiss.). *Phys-Math. Kl.*, **1**, 1–60

Goodman, R.F., Fricker, L.D. and Snyder, S.H. (1983). Enkephalins. In Kreiger, D.T., Browstein, J. and Martin, J.B. (Eds), *Brain Peptides*. Wiley, New York, pp. 828–849

Greig, N.H. (1989). Drug delivery to the brain by blood–brain barrier circumvention and drug modification. In Neuwelt, E.A. (Ed.), *Implications of the Blood–Brain Barrier and Its Manipulation*. Plenum Medical Book Company, New York, pp. 311–312

Griffin, D.E. and Giffels, J. (1982). Study of protein characteristics that influence entry into the cerebrospinal fluid of normal mice and mice with encephalitis. *J. Clin. Invest.*, **70**, 289–293

Gros, C., Giros, B. and Schwartz, J.C. (1985). Identification of aminopeptidase M as an enkephalin-inactivating enzyme in rat cerebral membranes. *Biochemistry*, **24**, 2179–2185

Gross, P.M., Kadekaro, M., Andrews, D.W., Sokoloff, L. and Saavedra, J.M. (1985). Selective metabolic stimulation of the subfornical organ and pituitary neural lobe by peripheral angiotensin II. *Peptides*, **6** (Suppl. 1), 145–152

Guglietta, A., Strunk, C.L., Irons, B.J. and Lazarus, L.H. (1985). Central neuromodulation of gastric acid secretion by bombesin-like peptides. *Peptides*, **6** (Suppl. 3), 75–81

Hanko, J., Hardebo, J.E. and Owman, C. (1981). In Cervos-Navarro, J. and Fritschka, E. (Eds), *Cerebral Microcirculation and Metabolism*. Raven Press, New York, pp. 157–161

Harbaugh, R.E., Roberts, D.W., Coombs, D.W., Saunders, R.L. and Reeder, T.M. (1984). Preliminary report: intracranial cholinergic drug infusion in patients with Alzheimer's disease. *Neurosurgery*, **15**, 514–517

Hassen, A.H., Feuerstein, G. and Faden, A.I. (1983). Differential cardiovascular effects mediated by mu and kappa opiate receptors in hindbrain nuclei. *Peptides*, **4**, 621–625

Heidenreich, K.A., Zahniser, N.R., Berhanu, P., Brandenburg, D. and Olefsky, J.M. (1983). Structural differences between insulin receptors in the brain and peripheral target tissues. *J. Biol. Chem.*, **258**, 8527–8530

Hersch, L.B. (1982). Degradation of enkephalins: the search for an enkephalinase. *Mol. Cell Biochem.*, **47**, 35–43

Hersch, L.B., Aboukhair, N. and Watson, S. (1987). Immunohistochemical localization of aminopeptidase M in rat brain and periphery: relationship of enzyme localization and enkephalin metabolism. *Peptides*, 8, 523–532

Hess, J., Gjedde, A. and Jessen, H. (1987). Vasopressin receptors at the blood–brain barrier in rats. *Wiss. Z. Karl-Marx-Univ. Leipzig, Math.-Naturwiss. R.*, 36, 81–83

Hoehler, F.K. and Sandman, C.A. (1981). Effects of alpha-MSH and beta-endorphin on startle reflex in rat. *Peptides*, 2, Suppl. 1, 137–141

Hoffman, P.L., Szabo, G. and Tabakoff, B. (1988). The effects of vasopressin and related peptides on tolerance to ethanol. In Rakić, Lj., Begley, D.J., Davson, H. and Zloković, B.V. (Eds), *Peptide and Amino Acid Transport Mechanisms in the Central Nervous System*. Macmillan, London, pp. 147–156

Hoffman, P.L., Walter, R. and Bulat, M. (1977). An enzymatically stable peptide with activity in the central nervous system: its penetration through the blood–CSF barrier. *Brain Res.*, 122, 87

Holtman, J.R., Buller, A.L., Hamosh, P. and Gillis, R. (1986). Central respiratory stimulation produced by thyrotropin-releasing hormone in the cat. *Peptides*, 7, 207–212

Hoosein, N.M. and Gurd, R.S. (1984). Identification of glucagon receptors in rat brain. *Proc. Natl Acad. Sci. USA*, 84, 4368–4372

Huang, J.T. (1982). Accumulation of peptides by choroid plexus *in vitro*: Tyr-D-Ala-Gly as a model. *Neurochem. Res.*, 7, 1541–1548

Huang, J.T. and Lajtha, A. (1978). The accumulations of ^{3}H-enkephalinamide (2-D-alanine-5-methioninamide) in rat brain tissues. *Neuropharmacology*, 17, 1075–1079

Huang, M., Hanley, D.A. and Rorstad, O.P. (1983). Parathyroid hormone stimulates adenylate cyclase in rat cerebral microvessels. *Life Sci.*, 32, 1009–1014

Huang, M. and Rorstad, O.P. (1983). Effects of vasoactive intestinal polypeptide, monoamines, prostaglandins and 2-choloroadenosine on adenylate cyclase in rat cerebral microvessels. *J. Neurochem.*, 40, 719–726

Huffman, L.J., Campbell, G.T. and Gilmore, J.P. (1983). Renal function and pituitary hormone release during cerebral osmostimulation and TRH in dogs. *Peptides*, 4, 843–847

Hughes, J., Smith, T.W., Kosterlitz, H.W., Fothergill, L.A., Morgan, B.A. and Morris, H.R. (1975). Identification of two related pentapeptides from the brain with potent opiate agonist activity. *Nature*, 258, 577–579

Hurley, J.V., Anderson, R.McD. and Sexton P.T. (1981). The fate of plasma protein which escapes from blood vessels of the choroid plexus of the rat-An electron microscopic study. *J. Pathol.*, 134, 57–70

Iversen, L.L., Lee, C.M., Gilbert, R.F., Hunt, S. and Emson, P.C. (1980). Regulation of neuropeptide release. *Proc. R. Soc.*, 210, 91–111

Jackson, I.M. and Lechan, R.M. (1983). Thyrotropin releasing hormone. In Kreiger, D.T., Browstein, J. and Martin, J.B. (Eds), *Brain Peptides*. Wiley, New York

Jeffries, W.A., Brandon, M.R., Hunt, S.V., Williams, A.F., Gatter, K.C. and Mason, D.Y. (1984). Transferrin receptor on endothelium of brain capillaries. *Nature*, 312, 162

Johanson, C.E. (1989). Potential for pharmacological manipulation of the blood–cerebrospinal fluid barrier. In Neuwelt, E.A. (Ed.), *Implications of the Blood–Brain Barrier and Its Manipulation*. Plenum Medical Book Company, New York, pp. 223–261

Jones, P.M. and Robinson, I.C.A.F. (1982). Clearance of neurohypophysial peptides from cerebrospinal fluid. *J. Physiol.*, 326, 23P

Joó, F. (1972). Effect of N^6, O^6-dibutyryl cyclic 3′,5′-adenosine monophosphate on the pinocytosis of brain capillaries in mice. *Experientia*, 28, 1470–1471

Joó, F. (1986). New aspects to the function of the cerebral endothelium. *Nature*, 321, 197–198

Joó, F. (1988). Cyclic nucleotide-mediated regulation of albumin transport in brain microvessels. In Rakić, Lj., Begley, D.J., Davson, H. and Zloković, B.V. (Eds), *Peptide and Amino Acid Transport Mechanisms in the Central Nervous System*. Macmillan, London, pp. 119–128

Joó, F., Temesvari, P. and Dux, E. (1983). Regulation of the macromolecular transport in the brain microvessels: the role of cyclic GMP. *Brain Res.*, 278, 165–174

Kabat, E.A., Moore, D.H. and Landow, H. (1942). An electrophoretic study of the protein components in the cerebrospinal fluid and their relationship to serum protein. *J. Clin. Invest.*, **21**, 571–577

Kalin, N.H., Shelton, S.E., Kraemer, G.W. and McKinney, W.T. (1983). Associated endocrine, physiological and behavioral changes in Rhesus monkeys after intravenous corticotropin-releasing factor administration. *Peptides*, **4**, 211–215

Kapadia, S.E. and DeLanerolle, N.C. (1984). Immunohistochemical and electron microscopic demonstration of vascular innervation in the mammalian brainstem. *Brain Res.*, **292**, 33–39

Karnushina, I., Palacios, J.M., Barbin, G., Dux, E., Joó, F. and Schwartz, J.C. (1980). Studies on a capillary-rich fraction isolated from brain: histaminic components and characterization of the histamine receptors linked to adenylate cyclase. *J. Neurochem.*, **34**, 1201–1208

Kastin, A.J. and Dickson, J.C. (1987). Hypophysectomy increases Tyr-MIF-1 like immunoreactivity in rat plasma. *Neuroendocrinology*, **45**, 177–181

Kastin, A.J., Nissan, C. and Coy, D.H. (1981). Permeability of blood–brain barrier to DSIP peptides. *Pharmacol. Biochem. Behav.*, **15**, 955–959

Kastin, A.J., Nissan, C., Schally, A.V. and Coy, D.H. (1976). Blood–brain barrier, half time disappearance, and brain distribution for labeled enkephalin and a potent analog. *Brain Res. Bull.*, **1**, 583–589

Kastin, A.J., Olson, R.D., Schally, A.V. and Coy, D.H. (1979). CNS effects of peripherally administered peptides. *Life Sci.*, **25**, 401–414

Katusic, Z.S., Shepherd, J.T. and Vanhoutte, P.M. (1984). Vasopressin causes endothelium-dependent relaxations of the canine basilar artery. *Circ. Res.*, **55** (5), 575–579

Katusic, Z.S., Shepherd, J.T. and Vanhoutte, P.M. (1986). Oxytocin causes endothelium-dependent relaxations of canine basilar arteries by activating V_1-vasopressinergic receptors. *J. Pharmacol. Exp. Ther.*, **236**, 166–170

Kordon, C., Blauet-Pajot, M.T., Clausen, H., Drouva, S., Enjabert, A. and Epelbaum, Y. (1987). New designs in neuroendocrine systems. In de Kloet, E.R., Wiegant, N.M. and de Wied, D.C. (Eds), *Neuropeptides and Brain Function. Progress in Brain Research*, Vol. 72, Elsevier, Amsterdam, pp. 27–34

Koslo, R.J., Gmerek, D.E. and Porreca, F. (1986). Intrathecal bombesin-induced inhibition of gastrointestinal transit: requirement for an intact pituitary–adrenal axis. *Reg. Peptides*, **14**, 237–242

Kowarski, D., Shuman, H., Somlyo, A.P. and Somlyo, A.V. (1985). Calcium release by noradrenaline from central sarcoplasmic reticulum in rabbit main pulmonary artery smooth muscle. *J. Physiol.*, **366**, 153–175

Kragh-Hansen, U. (1981). Molecular aspects of ligand binding to serum albumin. *Pharmacol. Rev.*, **33**, 17–53

Kretzschmar, R., Landgraf, R., Gjedde, A. and Ermisch, A. (1986). Vasopressin binds to microvessels from rat hippocampus. *Brain Res.*, **380**, 325–330

Kreiger, D.T. (1986). An overview of neuropeptides. In Martin, J.B. and Barchas, J.D. (Eds), *Neuropeptides in Neurologic and Psychiatric Diseases*. Raven Press, New York, pp. 1–32

Kumagai, A.K., Eisenberg, J. and Pardridge, W.M. (1986). Rapid binding and internalization of cationized albumin by isolated brain capillaries. *Clin. Res.*, **34**, 69A

Kumagai, A.K., Eisenberg, J. and Pardridge, W.M. (1987). Absorption-mediated endocytosis and cationized albumin and a beta-endorphin-cationized albumin chimeric peptide by isolated brain capillaries. Model system of blood–brain barrier transport. *J. Biol. Chem.*, **262**, 15214–15219

Lackoff, A. and Jackson, I.M.D. (1981). Calcium dependency of potassium-stimulated thyrotropin-releasing hormone secretion from rat neurohypophysis *in vitro*. *Neurosci. Lett.*, **27**, 17

Landgraf, R., Hess, J. and Ermisch, A. (1978). The influence of vasopressin on the regional uptake of [³H]orotic acid by rat brain. *Acta Biol. Med. Ger.*, **37**, 655–658

Landgraf, R., Hess, J. and Hartmann, E. (1977). Der Einfluss von Ocytocin auf die regionale ³H Orotsaure-Aufnahme durch das Rattengehirn. *Endokrinologie*, **70**, 45–52

Lee, R.J. and Lomax, P. (1983). Thermoregulatory, behavioral and seizure modulatory effects of AVP in the gerbil. *Peptides*, **4**, 801–805

Lenhard, L. and Deftos, L.J. (1982). Adenohypophysial hormones in the CSF. *Neuroendocrinology*, **34**, 303–308

Levin, M.J., Tuil, D., Uzan, G., Dreyfus, J.C. and Kahn, A. (1984). Expression of the transferrin gene during development of nonhepatic tissues: high levels of transferrin mRNA in fetal muscle and adult brain. *Biochem. Biophys. Res. Commun.*, **122**, 212

Levine, R., Frederics, W. and Rapoport, S. (1982). Entry of bilirubin into the brain due to opening of the blood–brain barrier. *Pediatrics*, **69**, 255–259

Levitan, H., Ziylan, Z., Smith, Q. *et al.* (1984). Brain uptake of food dye, erythrosin B, prevented by plasma protein binding. *Brain Res.*, **322**, 131–134

Lipton, J.M. and Glyn, J.R. (1980). Central administration of peptides alters thermoregulation in the rabbit. *Peptides*, **1**, 15–18

McComb, J.G. (1983). Recent research into the nature of cerebrospinal fluid formation and absorption. *J. Neurosurg.*, **59**, 369–383

McKinley, M.J., Allen, A., Clevers, T., Dentin, D.A., Mendlesohn, F.A.O., Oldfield, B.J., Tarjan, E. and Weisirger, R.S. (1987). Angiotensin II receptors in the brain of the sheep. *Wiss. Z. Karl-Marx-Univ. Leipzig Math.-Naturwiss. R.*, **36**, 189–192

Makara, G.B. (1985). Mechanisms by which stressful stimuli activate the pituitary–adrenal system. *Fed. Proc.*, **45**, 149–153

Matsas, R., Stephenson, S.L., Hryszko, J., Kenny, A.J., and Turner, A.J. (1985). The metabolism of neuropeptides: phase separation of synaptic membrane preparations with triton X-114 reveals the presence of aminopeptidase N. *Biochem. J.*, **231**, 445–449

Matsumoto, T., Kanaide, H., Nishimura, J., Shogakiuchi, Kobayshi, S. and Nakamura, M. (1986). Histamine activates H_1-receptors to induce cytosolic free calcium transients in cultured vascular smooth muscle cells from rat aorta. *Biochem. Biophys. Res. Commun.*, **135**, 172–177

Meisenberg, G. and Simmons, W.H. (1983). Peptides and the blood–brain barrier. *Life Sci.*, **32**, 2611–2633

Mess, B. and Trentini, G.P. (1974). ³H-melatonin level in cerebrospinal fluid and choroid plexus following intravenous administration of the labeled compound. *Acta Physiol. Acad. Sci. Hung.*, **45**, 225–231

Milhorat, T.H., Davis, D.A. and Lloyd, B.J. (1973). Two morphologically distinct blood–brain barriers preventing entry of cytochrome c into cerebrospinal fluid. *Science*, **180**, 76–78

Møllgard, K., Balslev, Y. and Saunders, N. (1988). Structural aspects of the blood–brain and blood–CSF barriers with respect to endogenous proteins. In Rakić, Lj., Begley, D.J., Davson, H. and Zloković, B.V. (Eds), *Peptide and Amino Acid Transport Mechanisms in the Central Nervous System.* Macmillan, London, pp. 93–101

Møllgard, K. and Saunders, N.R. (1977). A possible transepithelial pathway via endoplasmic reticulum in foetal sheep choroid plexus. *Proc. Roy. Soc. B*, **199**, 321–326

Møllgard, K. and Saunders, N.R. (1986). The development of the human blood–brain and blood–CSF barriers. *Neuropath. Appl. Neurobiol.*, **12**, 337–358

Moody, T.W., O'Donohue, T.L. and Jacobowitz, D.M. (1981). Biochemical localization and characterization of bombesin-like peptides in discrete regions of rat brain. *Peptides*, **2**, 75–79

Morimoto, S., Nishimura, J., Miyauchi, A., Takai, S.I., Okada, Y., Onishi, T., Fukuo, K., Lee, S. and Kumahara, Y. (1982). Calcitonin in plasma and cerebrospinal fluid from normal subjects and patients with medullary thyroid carinoma: possible restriction of calcitonin by blood–brain barrier. *J. Clin. Endocrinol. Metab.*, **55**, 597–596

Morley, J.E., Levine, A., Oken, M.M., Grace, M. and Kneip, J. (1982). Neuropeptides and thermoregulation: the interactions of bombesin, neurotensin, TRH, somatostatin, naloxone and prostaglandins. *Peptides*, **3**, 1–6

Neuwelt, E.A. and Rapoport, S.I. (1984). Modification of the blood–brain barrier in the chemotherapy of malignant brain tumors. *Fed. Proc.*, **43**, 214–221

Niewoehner, D.E., Levine, A.S. and Morley, J.E. (1983). Central effects of neuropeptides on ventilation in the rat. *Peptides*, **4**, 277–281

North, A.R. (1986). Electrophysiological effects of neuropeptides. In Martin, J.B. and Broebes, J.D. (Eds), *Neuropeptides in Neurologic and Psychiatric Disease*. Raven Press, New York, pp. 71–77

Ohno, K., Pettigrew, K.D. and Rapoport, S.I. (1978). Lower limits of cerebrovascular permeability to non-electrolytes in conscious rat. *Am. J. Physiol.*, **235**, H299–H307

Oldendorf, W.M. (1981). Blood–brain barrier permeability to peptides, pitfalls in measurement. *Peptides*, **2** (Suppl. 2), 109–111

Ommaya, A. (1963). A subcutaneous reservoir and pump for sterile access to ventricular cerebrospinal fluid. *Lancet* ii, 983–984

Pardridge, W.M. (1979). Carrier-mediated transport of thyroid hormones through the rat blood–brain barrier: Primary role of albumin-bound hormone. *Endocrinol.*, **105**, 605–612

Pardridge, W.M. (1981). Transport of protein-bound hormones into tissues *in vivo*. *Endocrin. Rev.*, **2**, 103–123

Pardridge, W.M. (1985). Strategies for drug delivery through the blood–brain barrier. In Borchardt, R.T., Repta, A.J. and Stella, V.J. (Eds), *Directed Drug Delivery: A Multidisciplinary Problem*. Humana Press Inc., Clifton, N.J. p. 83

Pardridge, W.M. (1986a). Receptor-mediated peptide transport through the blood–brain barrier. *Endocr. Rev.*, **7** (3), 31–33

Pardridge, W.M. (1986b). Blood–brain barrier: interface between internal medicine and the brain. *Ann. Intern. Med.*, **105**, 82–95

Pardridge, W.M. (1987). Plasma protein mediated transport of steroid and thyroid hormones. *Am. J. Physiol.*, **252**, E157–E164

Pardridge, W.M. (1988). Recent advances in blood–brain barrier transport. *Ann. Rev. Pharmacol. Toxicol.*, **28**, 25–39

Pardridge, W.M., Eisenberg, J. and Cefalu, W.T. (1985a). Absence of albumin receptor on brain capillaries *in vivo* or *in vitro*. *Am. J. Physiol.*, **249**, E264

Pardridge, W.M., Eisenberg, J. and Yang, J. (1985b). Human blood–brain barrier insulin receptor. *J. Neurochem.*, **44**, 1771

Pardridge, W.M., Eisenberg, J. and Yang, J. (1987). Human blood–brain barrier transferrin receptor. *J. Neurochem.*, **49**, 1394–1401

Pardridge, W.M. and Oldendorf, W.H. (1975). Kinetic analysis of blood–brain barrier transport of amino acids. *Biochim. Biophys. Acta*, **401**, 128–136

Pardridge, W.M., Triguero, D. and Buciak, J.L. (1990). β-Endorphin chimeric peptides: transport through the blood–brain barrier *in vivo* and cleavage of disulfide linkage by brain. *Endocrinology*, **126** (2), 977–984

Patel, H.M. (1984). Liposomes: bags of challenge. *Biochem. Soc. Trans.*, **12**, 333

Peterson, J.S., Kalivas, P.W. and Prasad, C. (1984). Cyclo (His-Pro) (cHP) regulates striatal dopaminergic function. *Soc. Neurosci. Abstr.*, **10**, 1123

Posner, B.I., van Houten, M., Patel, B. and Walsh, R.J. (1983). Characterization of lactogen binding sites in choroid plexus. *Exp. Brain*, **49**, 300–306

Prange, A.J., Gazzbutt, J., Loosen, P.T., Bissette, G. and Nemeroff, C.B. (1987). The role of peptides in affective disorders: a review. *Prog. Brain Res.*, **72**, 235–279

Prange Jr, A.J., Wilson, I.C., Lara, P.P., Alltop, L.B. and Breese, G.R. (1972). Effects of thyroptropin releasing hormone in depression. *Lancet*, **ii**, 999–1002

Rap, Z.M. (1981). Inhibitory effect of antidiuretic hormone on outflow of the cerebrospinal fluid in vasogenic brain edema induced by cold lesion. In Cervos-Navarro, J. and Fritschke, E. (Eds), *Cerebral Microcirculation and Metabolism*. Raven Press, New York, pp. 171–175

Rap, Z.M., Kozniewska, E. and Skolasinska, K. (1980). Effect of vasopressin on cerebral blood flow and cerebrospinal fluid outflow. In Betz, E., Grobe, J. and Hauser, D. (Eds), *Pathophysiology and Pharmacotherapy of Cerebrovascular Disorders*. Verlag G. Witzstrock, Köln, pp. 12–14

Rapoport, S.I., Klee, W.A., Pettigrew, K.D. and Ohno, K. (1980). Entry of opioid peptides into the central nervous system. *Science*, **207**, 84–86

Reese, T.S., Feder, N. and Brightman, M.W. (1971). Electron microscopic study of the blood–brain and blood–cerebrospinal fluid barriers with microperoxidase. *J. Cell. Biol.*, **34**, 207–217

Reese, T.S. and Karnovsky, M.J. (1967). Fine structural localization of a blood–brain barrier to exogenous peroxidase. *J. Cell Biol.*, **34**, 207–217

Reichlin, S. (1983a). Somatostatin. *New Engl. J. Med.*, **309**, 1495–1501

Reichlin, S. (1983b). Somatostatin. *New Engl. J. Med.*, **309**, 1556–1562

Reith, J., Ermisch, A., Diemer, N.H. and Gjedde, A. (1987). Saturable retention of vasopressin by hippocampus vessels *in vivo*, associated with inhibition of blood–brain transfer of large neutral amino acids. *J. Neurochem.*, **49**, 1471–1479

Rivier, C. and Vale, W. (1985). Effects of corticotropin-releasing factor, neurohypophyseal peptides and catecholamines on pituitary function. *Fed. Proc.*, **44**, 189–195

Rogers, R.C. and Hermann, G.E. (1985). Dorsal medullary oxytocin, vasopressin, oxytocin antagonist, and TRH effects on gastric acid secretion and heart rate. *Peptides*, **6**, 1143–1148

Sandman, C.A., Beckwith, B.E. and Kastin, A.J. (1980). Are learning and attention related to the sequence of amino acids in ACTH/MSH peptides? *Peptides*, **1**, 277–280

Sarna, G.S., Bradbury, M.W.B. and Cavanagh, J. (1978). Permeability of the blood–brain barrier after porto-caval anastomosis in the rat. *Brain Res.*, **138**, 550–554

Schaffer, M.M. and Moody, T.W. (1986). Autoradiographic visualization of CNS receptors for vasoactive intestinal peptide. *Peptides*, **7**, 283–286

Schivers, B.D., Harlan, R.E., Romano, J.G., Howills, R.D. and Phaff, G.W. (1986). Cellular localization of pre-enkephalin in RNA in rat brain: gene expression in the caudate putamen and cerebral cortex. *Proc. Natl Acad. Sci. USA*, **83**, 6221–6225

Schutz, W., Steuer, G. and Tuisl, E. (1982). Functional identification of adenylate cyclase-coupled adenosine receptors in rat brain microvessels. *Eur. Pharmacol.*, **85**, 177–184

Schwartz, J.C. (1983). Metabolism of enkephalins and the inactivating peptide concept. *Trends Neursci.*, **6**, 5–8

Schwartz, J.C., Malfroy, B. and De La Baume, S. (1981). Biological inactivation of enkephalins and the role of enkephalin dipeptidyl-carboxypeptidase ('Enkephalinase') as neuropeptidase. *Life Sci.*, **29**, 1715–1740

Segal, M.B. and Pollay, M. (1977). The secretion of cerebrospinal fluid. *Exp. Eye Res.*, **25** (Suppl.), 205–228

Segal, M.B. and Zloković, B.V. (1990). *The Blood–Brain Barrier, Amino Acids and Peptides*, Kluwer, Dordrecht, Boston, London

Siggins, G.R. and Groul, D.L. (1986). Synaptic mechanisms in the vertebrate central nervous system. In Bloom, F.E. (Ed.), *Handbook of Physiology*. Volume on *Intrinsic Regulatory Systems of the Brain*. American Physiological Society, Bethesda, Maryland, pp. 1–114

Simantov, R. and Snyder, S.H. (1976). Morphine-like peptides in mammalian brain: isolation, structure, elucidation, and interactions with opiate receptors. *Proc. Natl Acad. Sci. USA*, **73** (7), 2515–2519

Smith, Q.R., Momma, S., Aoyagi, M. and Rapoport, S.I. (1987). Kinetics of neutral amino acid transport across the blood–brain barrier. *J. Neurochem.*, **49**, 1651–1658

Smith, Q.R., Takasato, Y. and Rapoport, S. (1984). Kinetic analysis of L-leucine transport across the blood–brain barrier. *Brain Res.*, **311**, 167–170

Spector, R. (1977). Vitamin homeostasis in the central nervous system. *New Engl. J. Med.*, **296**, 1393–1398

Spector, R. (1982). Nucleoside transport in choroid plexus: Mechanism and specificity. *Arch. Biochem. Biophys.*, **216**, 693–703

Speth, R.C. and Harik, S.I. (1985). Angiotensin II receptor binding sites in brain microvessels. *Proc. Natl Acad. Sci. USA*, **82**, 6340–6343

Strikant, C.B. and Patel, Y.C. (1981). Somatostatin receptors: identification and characterization in rat brain membranes. *Proc. Natl Acad. Sci. USA*, **78**, 3930–3934

Stephenson, S.L. and Kenny, A.J. (1987). The hydrolysis of alpha-human atrial natriuretic peptide by pig kidney microvillar membranes is initiated by endopeptidase 24.11. *Biochem. J.*, **243**, 183–187

Stewart, P.A. and Wiley, M.J. (1981). Developing nervous tissue induces formation of blood–brain barrier characteristics in invading endothelial cells: a study using quail-chick transplantation chimeras. *Dev. Biol.*, **84**, 183–192

Stickrod, G., Kimble, D.P. and Smotherman, W.P. (1982). Met-enkephalin effects on associations formed *in utero*. *Peptides*, **3**, 881–883

Susic, V. and Masirevic, G. (1988). In Rakić, Lj., Begley, D.J., Davson, H. and Zlokovic, B.V. (Eds), *Peptide and Amino Acid Transport Mechanisms in the Central Nervous System*. Macmillan, London, pp. 141–147

Susic, V., Masirevic, G. and Totic, S. (1987). The effects of delta sleep inducing peptides (DSIP) on wakefulness and sleep patterns in the cat. *Brain Res.*, **414**, 262–270

Tache, Y., Vale, W., Rivier, J. and Brown, M. (1981). Brain regulation of gastric acid secretion in rats by neurogastrointestinal peptides. *Peptides*, **2** (Suppl. 2), 51–55

Takasato, J., Momma, S. and Smith, Q.R. (1985). Kinetic analysis of cerebrovascular isoleucine transport from saline and plasma. *J. Neurochem.*, **45**, 1013–1020

Takasato, Y., Rapoport, S.I. and Smith, Q.R. (1984). An *in situ* brain perfusion technique to study cerebrovascular transport in the rat. *Am. J. Physiol.*, **247**, H484–H493

Tenner, T.E.J., Yang, C.M., Chang, J.K., Schimizu, M. and Pang, P.K.T. (1980). Pharmacological comparison of bPTH-(1-34) and other hypotensive peptides in the dog. *Peptides*, **1**, 285–288

Triguero, D.J., Buciak, J.B., Yang, J. and Pardridge, W.M. (1989). Blood–brain barrier transport of cationized immunoglobulin G: enhanced delivery compared to native protein. *Proc. Natl Acad. Sci. USA*, **86**, 4761–4765

Uddman, R., Edvinsson, L., Owman, C. and Sundler, F. (1981). Perivascular substance P: occurrence and distribution in mammalian pial vessels. *J. Cereb. Blood Flow Metab.*, **1**, 227–232

Uddman, R., Edvinsson, L., Owman, C. and Sundler, F. (1983). Nerve fibres containing gastrin-releasing peptide around pial vessels. *J. Cereb. Blood Flow Metab.*, **3**, 386–390

Urban, I.J.A. (1981). Brain vasopressin: from electrophysiological effects to neurophysiological function. In de Kloet, E.R., Wiegant, V.M. and de Wied, D. (Eds), *Neuropeptides and Brain Function. Progress in Brain Research*, Vol. 72, pp. 163–172

Van der Velde, C.D. (1983). Rapid clinical effectiveness of MIF-1 in the treatment of major depressive illness. *Peptides*, **4**, 297–300

van Deurs, B. (1977). Vesicular transport of horseradish peroxidase from brain to blood in segments of the cerebral microvasculature in adult mice. *Brain Res.*, **124**, 1–8

van Deurs, B. (1980). Structural aspects of brain barriers, with special reference to the permeability of the cerebral endothelium and choroidal epithelium. *Intern. Rev. Cytol.*, **63**, 117–191

van Deurs, B., von Bülow, F. and Møller, M. (1981). Vesicular transport of cationized ferritin by the epithelium of the rat choroid plexus. *J. Cell Biol.*, **89**, 131–139

Van Dijk, A., Richards, J.G., Trzeeiak, A., Gillessen, D. and Mohler, H. (1984). Cholecystokinin receptors: biochemical demonstration and autoradiographical localization in rat brain and pancreas using ^{3}H-cholecystokinin as radioligand. *J. Neurosci.*, **4**, 1021–1033

van Houten, M. and Posner, B.I. (1983). Circumventricular organs: receptors and mediators of direct peptide hormone action on brain. In Szabo, A. (Ed.), *Advances in Metabolic Disorders*, Vol. 10. Academic Press, New York, pp. 269–289

Van Ree, J.M., Caffe, A.M. and Wolterink, G. (1982). Non-opiate beta-endorphin fragments and dopamine. III. γ-Type endorphins and various neuroleptics counteract the hypoactivity elicited by injection of apomorphine into the nucleus accumbens. *Neuropharmacology*, **21**, 1111–1117

Van Ree, J.M., Verhoven, Z.K. and de Wied, D. (1987). Animal and clinical research on neuropeptides and schizophrenia. *Prog. Brain Res.*, **72**, 249–267

Varagic, V.M., Stojanovic, V. and Dzoljic, E. (1988). The effect of enkephalins and enkephalinase inhibitors on the central cholinergic mechanisms participating in the peripheral adrenergic activation. In Rakić, Lj., Begley, D.J., Davson, H. and Zloković, B.V. (Eds), *Peptide and Amino Acid Transport Mechanisms in the Central Nervous System.* Macmillan, London, pp. 157–166

Vistica, D.T. (1983). Cellular pharmacokinetics of the phenylalanine mustards. *Pharmac. Ther.*, **22**, 379–406

Walsh, R.J., Slaby, F. and Posner, B.I. (1987). Prolactin transport from blood to cerebrospinal fluid: a receptor mediated process. *Wiss. Z. Karl-Marx-Univ. Leipzig Math.-Naturwiss. R.*, **36** (1), 119–120

Wenger, T. (1987). The role of organum vasculosum of the lamina terminals in the regulation of pituitary gonadotrophic hormone secretion. *Wiss. Z. Karl-Marx-Univ. Leipzig Math.-Naturwiss. R.*, **36** (1), 52–55

Westergaard, E. and Brightman, M.W. (1973). Transport of proteins across normal cerebral arterioles. *J. Comp. Neurol.*, **152**, 17–44

Wilson, K.M. and Fregley, M.J. (1985). Factors affecting angiotensin II-induced hyperthermia in rats. *Peptides*, **6**, 695–701

Winokur, A., Amsterdam, J., Caroff, S., Snyder, P.J. and Brunswich, D. (1982). Variability of hormonal responses to a series of neuroendocrine challenges in depressed patients. *Am. J. Psychiatr.*, **139**, 39–44

Wolf, B.A., Turk, J., Sherman, W.R. and McDaniel, M.L. (1986). Intracellular Ca^{2+} mobilization by arachidonic acid. *J. Biol. Chem.*, **261**, 3501–3511

Woods, S.C. and Porte, D. Jr. (1977). Relationship between plasma and cerebrospinal fluid insulin levels of dogs. *Am. J. Physiol.*, **233**, E331–E334

Yarbrough, G.G. (1976). TRH potentiates excitatory actions of acetylcholine in cerebral cortical neurons. *Nature*, **263**, 523–524

Zadina, J.E., Banks, W.A. and Kastin, J.E. (1986). Central nervous system effects of peptides 1980–1985. *Peptides*, **7**, 497–537

Zerbe, R.L., Kirtland, S., Faden, A.I. and Feuerstein, G. (1983). Central cardiovascular effects of mammalian neurohypophysical peptides in conscious rats. *Peptides*, **4**, 627–630

Zloković, B.V. (1990). *In vivo* approaches for studying peptide interactions at the blood–brain barrier. *J. Control. Rel.*, **13**, 185–202

Zloković, B.V., Begley, D.J. and Chain, D.G. (1983). Blood–brain barrier permeability to di-peptides and their constituent amino acids. *Brain Res.*, **271**, 66–71

Zloković, B.V., Begley, D.J. and Chain-Eliash, D.G. (1985a). Blood–brain barrier permeability to leucine-enkephalin, D-alanine^2 D-leucine^5-enkephalin and their N-terminal amino acid (tyrosine). *Brain Res.*, **336** 125–132

Zloković, B.V., Hyman, S., McComb, J.G., Tang, G., Davson, H. and Lipovać, M.N. (1990a). Kinetics of arginine-vasopressin uptake at the blood–brain barrier. *Biochim. Biophys. Acta*, **1025**, 191–198

Zloković, B.V., Lipovac, N.M., Begley, D.J., Davson, H. and Rakić, Lj. (1987). Transport of leucine-enkephalin across the blood–brain barrier in the perfused guinea pig brain. *J. Neurochem.*, **49**, 310–315

Zloković, B.V., Lipovac, M.N., Begley, D.J., Davson, H. and Rakić, Lj. (1988a). Slow penetration of thyrotropin releasing hormone across the blood–brain barrier of *in situ* perfused guinea-pig brain. *J. Neurochem.*, **51**, 252–257

Zloković, B.V., McComb, J.G., Perlmutter, L. and Davson, H. (1991). *Neuroactive Peptides and Amino Acids at the Blood–Brain Barrier: Possible Implications to Drug Abuse.* NIDA Research Monographs, Washington, D.C. (in press)

Zloković, B.V., Mackić, J.B., Duricić, B. and Davson, H. (1989a). Kinetic analysis of leucine-enkephalin cellular uptake by the blood–brain barrier of an *in situ* perfused guinea-pig brain. *J. Neurochem.*, **53**, 1333–1340

Zloković, B.V., Segal, M.B., Begley, D.J., Davson, D.J. and Rakić, Lj. (1985b). Permeability of the blood—cerebrospinal fluid and blood–brain barriers to thyrotropin releasing hormone. *Brain Res.*, **358**, 191–199

Zloković, B.V., Segal, M.B., Davson, H. and Jankov, R.M. (1988b). Passage of delta sleep-inducing peptide (DSIP) across the blood–cerebrospinal fluid barrier. *Peptides*, **9**, 533–538

Zloković, B.V., Skundrić, D., Segal, M.B., Lipovac, M.N., Mackić, J.B. and Davson, H. (1990b). A saturable mechanism for transport of immunoglobulin G across the blood–brain barrier of the guinea-pig. *Exp. Neurol.*, **107**, 263–270

Zloković, B.V., Susić, V.T., Davson, H., Begley, D.J., Jankov, R.M., Mitrović, D.M. and Lipovac, M.N. (1989b). Saturable mechanisms for delta-sleep inducing peptide (DSIP) at the blood–brain barrier of the vascularly perfused guinea-pig brain. *Peptides*, **10**, 249–254

Note

[1] It has recently been shown that V_1-receptors on the brain capillary may play a significant role in the uptake of blood-borne vasopressin, and this provides some experimental evidence for the above-mentioned hypothesis (Zloković *et al.*, 1990a).

Chapter 4

Transport of Some Precursors of Nucleotides and Some Vitamins

Nucleotide Precursors

The transport of nucleotide precursors, such as the purine and pyrimidine bases and their sugar derivatives, the nucleosides, within the central nervous system is of some interest, since nucleic acid synthesis, although limited in extent within the central nervous system, certainly takes place; and at least some precursors must be derived from the blood (Spector and Eells, 1984). The matter is of clinical interest because the Lesch–Nyhan syndrome, involving neurological and behavioural disturbances, is associated with a deficiency of the enzyme that converts the purine hypoxanthine to nucleoside, namely hypoxanthine-guanine phosphoribosyl transferase.

Neuromodulation

Of special importance to the neurophysiologist is the demonstration that adenosine, although probably not acting as a 'classical transmitter', has a role as a *neuromodulator*—i.e. it belongs to a class of substances that appear to have properties that allow them to regulate neuronal function both at a local level, after release from excitable membranes, and at distant synapses after transport along axons. More specifically it may be said that the neuromodulators relate postsynaptic sensitivity to presynaptic sensitivity, and vice versa, at a single synapse. Thus, adenosine depresses the evoked release of transmitters, cholinergic and adrenergic, peripherally and centrally, acting, therefore, as a feedback regulator of transmitter release (Stone, 1981).

The pharmacological basis for the tranquilizer effect of the benzodiazepines, such as diazepam, probably depends on their inhibition of the transport of adenosine into the cells of the central nervous system, thereby prolonging, or 'potentiating', their action as inhibitory neuromodulators (Paterson *et al.*, 1981; Hammond and Clanachan, 1985).

Cellular Permeability

A high permeability of erythrocytes to both adenine and hypoxanthine and their ribosides was demonstrated by Whittam (1960); thus, within 5 min there was complete equilibration between cells and medium. Cass and Paterson (1973) emphasized the carrier type of transport shown by nucleosides; different purine-based nucleosides competed with each other, as demonstrated by trans-acceleration. Furthermore, pyrimidine-based nucleosides competed; substitutions in the sugar portion of the molecule, however, seriously inhibited transport. [Note 1]

BUI Studies

In their single-pass studies on the rat Cornford and Oldendorf (1975) found negligible passage of pyrimidines, such as cytosine and orotic acid, across the blood–brain barrier; but, as we have repeatedly emphasized, this by no means excludes the possibility of a slow and measurable transport across the blood–brain barrier, which would be revealed by studies involving longer time intervals. The purine bases adenine and inosine did give measurable BUIs of 7.7 and 5.4, respectively; the nucleosides, i.e. purine–sugar complexes, also gave measurable BUIs, that for adenosine being 8.8 and for guanosine 6.2. Penetration exhibited carrier-type kinetics with mutual inhibition between purine and nucleoside, while nucleotides failed to compete, and had no measurable extraction when studied alone. The K_m for adenosine was 0.018 mM and that for adenine 0.027 mM. These compare with plasma concentrations of 0.1 μM and less than 0.2 μM in plasma of the rabbit (Eells and Spector, 1983).

Isolated Brain Capillaries

Wu and Phillis (1982) measured uptake of labelled adenosine by isolated brain capillaries, and their results generally confirmed those of Cornford and Oldendorf in deriving a K_m of 4.7 μM and a V_{max} of 21.7 pmol (mg protein)$^{-1}$ (10 min)$^{-1}$. The system is thus one of high affinity but low capacity. After 10 min of incubation the capillaries had largely metabolized the absorbed adenosine, so that only some 36% of the radioactivity belonged to adenosine, the remainder being mostly in adenine nucleotides. Uptake was inhibited by guanosine, 5′-deoxy-adenosine, inosine and uridine in this order.

Hypoxanthine

This is the principal purine in plasma and CSF; the so-called salvage enzyme, hypoxanthine-guanine phosphororibosyl transferase (HGPRTase) has its highest concentration in the brain, and is responsible for the conversion of hypoxanthine to purine nucleotides, and, as indicated, a deficiency of the enzyme leads to the Lesch-Nyhan syndrome. Spector (1988) showed that the *in vitro* isolated choroid plexus accumulated the purine to give T/M ratios of 22.1 ± 1.4; these were reduced by the presence of adenine, xanthine, uracil and inosine. A large proportion of the accumulated hypoxanthine was released intact from the isolated plexus, showing that accumulation was not due to a metabolic trapping process.

Thymidine

This nucleoside constituent of DNA has been studied in some detail, especially because of its ability to antagonize the anti-DNA activity of methotrexate, an anti-tumour agent employed clinically (Ensminger and Frei, 1977). The transport of nucleosides in animal cells, and of their related synthetic analogues, has been reviewed in detail by Paterson *et al.* (1981). So far as thymidine is concerned, transport by animal cells, such as erythrocytes, is carrier-mediated but non-concentrative, in the sense that gradients of concentration between inside and outside medium are not established by the transport process *per se.* Thus, the accumulation of label, when the labelled nucleoside is placed in the outside medium, may be due primarily to the phosphorylation of the nucleoside within the cell, which has now become 'trapped' because of the relative impermeability of the phosphorylated compound (Plunkett and Cohen, 1977).

Dual System

According to Ungemach and Hegner (1978), however, when the isolated rat hepatocyte was studied, a system that lacks thymidine phosphorylation, there is, indeed, a concentrative process of high-affinity (K_m, 5.4 μM) together with one of low affinity with K_m 480 μM, both acting in tandem. Thus, in phosphorylating cells only the high-affinity system could be detected, while in the absence of phosphorylation thymidine uptake occurred in a manner corresponding to the low-affinity system.

This point has been further emphasized by Wohlhueter *et al.* (1979), whose studies on kinase-deficient cells, i.e. those incapable of phosphorylating nucleosides, have emphasized the rapidity with which thymidine equilibrates with cells by a carrier-mediated process. Thus, at a concentration of 80 μM, i.e. below the K_m for the transport process, 50% equilibration was achieved within about 20 s. They concluded: '. . . it has become clear that the extensive literature on the kinetic characteristics of thymidine uptake in mammalian cells does not pertain to thymidine transport, and that the assessment of transport *per se* demands rapid

Table 4.1 Hypothetical routes of entry of some metabolites according to Spector (1986)

Micronutrients	*Blood–CSF barrier*	*Blood–brain barrier*
Ascorbic acid	Predominant	Minor
Folates	Predominant	Minor
Pantothenic acid	Some	Some
Riboflavin	Some	Unknown
Thiamin	Some	Some
Pyridoxine	Some	Unknown
Inositol	Some	Unknown
Thymidine	Predominant	Minor
Deoxycytidine	Predominant	Minor
Uridine	Some	Some

sampling techniques and the use of non-metabolizable substrates'. Bearing in mind this warning, we may describe experiments on the blood–brain and blood–CSF barriers to thymidine, a subject of some academic interest, since this nucleoside has been included with a number of metabolites, including vitamins, in a category that describes their transport from blood to brain as taking place primarily through the choroid plexuses and subsequent diffusion from the CSF to the adjacent brain tissue. Thus, in these cases the Stern–Gautier hypothesis has been resuscitated (Spector, 1977, 1986). Table 4.1 lists the compounds that have been examined in some detail by Spector and his colleagues with this hypothesis in mind.

Plasma–CSF Transport

The Steady-state Levels
It will be seen from Table 4.2, from Eells and Spector (1983), that the concentrations of thymidine in plasma and CSF are equal at 0.6 μM. This would suggest a relatively high permeability of the blood–CSF barrier.

Intravenous Infusions
Ensminger and Frei (1977) raised the normal plasma concentration in humans of 0.19 μM to one of 1.5 μM by continuous intravenous infusion, and found that, by 2 h, equilibration between CSF and plasma had occurred. When Zaharko *et al.* (1979) raised the plasma concentration to millimolar, instead of micromolar, levels, they found less complete equilibration, so that after 2 h of infusion the value of R_{CSF} was only 0.29, compared with the pyrimidine base's value of 1.03. This might suggest a self-inhibited type of carrier transport across the blood–CSF (and probably blood–brain) barrier, but more elaborate measurements on experimental animals would be required to substantiate the process quantitatively.

Rabbit
Intravenous infusions of [^{3}H]-thymidine in the rabbit showed some penetration into CSF and brain, leading to a value of R_{CSF} after 2.5 h of 0.42 under 'carrier-free' conditions when the plasma level was only 0.31 nM. When this level

Table 4.2 Deoxynucleoside concentrations in adult rabbit CSF and plasma, determined by HPLC. From Eells and Spector (1983)

	Concentration (μM)	
Deoxynucleoside	*Plasma*	*CSF*
Thymidine	0.6 ± 0.0 (5)	0.6 ± 0.1 (4)
Deoxycytidine	1.4 ± 0.2 (5)	1.0 ± 0.1 (4)
Deoxyuridine	—	1.1 ± 0.1 (4)
Deoxyadenosine	<0.1 (5)	<0.1 (4)
Deoxyguanosine	<0.1 (5)	<0.1 (4)

Values are means ± s.e.m., with the numbers of determinations in parentheses.

was raised to 33.3 μM, the value of R_{CSF} at the end of this period of infusion was 0.49, i.e. not much, if at all, altered. With a plasma level of 0.79 mM the value of R_{CSF} was 0.44. Thus, unlabelled thymidine seemed to have little effect on transport from blood to CSF in spite of its very large effect on *in vitro* accumulation in the choroid plexus.

Substrate-facilitated Transport
Transport of a labelled solute from blood to CSF may be accelerated by including unlabelled solute in the CSF; Davson *et al.* (1982) increased rate of penetration of labelled selenomethionine from blood into the fluid perfusing the rabbit's ventricles by raising the concentration of unlabelled selenomethionine in the perfusion fluid. The phenomenon may be described as a reduction of the affinity of the carrier at the CSF side of the barrier, favouring release of the labelled material. Spector and Berlinger (1982) described a similar acceleration of transport of [³H]-thymidine into the rabbit's CSF when unlabelled thymidine was injected into the ventricles.

Intraventricular Injections

Spector (1980b) found that thymidine was rapidly removed from CSF after intraventricular injection, a process that was partially inhibited by including unlabelled thymidine in the injection. This, as Davson *et al.* (1987) pointed out, suggested that thymidine was being removed from the CSF by an active carrier-mediated process similar to that which removes iodide, thiocyanate, prostaglandins, etc. Thus, if the high *in vitro* accumulation of thymidine has significance so far as blood–CSF transport is concerned, it is a sign of active removal of the nucleoside from the CSF rather than being a sign of transport from blood to brain.

Accumulation by Isolated Choroid Plexus

Spector (1980a, 1986) considered that, because the apparent blood–brain barrier to thymidine was high, i.e. that rate of transport was slow, the main route of entry to the brain tissue was via the choroid plexuses and CSF, i.e. he revived the Stern–Gautier doctrine for nutrition of the brain. The evidence in favour of this view seems largely to rest on the apparent accumulation of [³H]-thymidine by the isolated *in vitro* choroid plexus, T/M ratios as high as 60 being obtained at an external concentration of 3 nM; accumulation was suppressed at high concentrations, e.g. 10 μM (Figure 4.1). The process was inhibited by DNP, indicating the involvement of metabolic energy, but this might have been due to inhibition of a phosphorylating trapping mechanism. Brain slices also accumulated the nucleoside but T/M ratios of only 1.5 were obtained (Spector, 1980b).

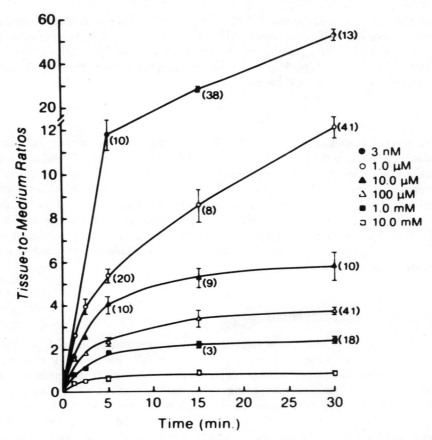

Figure 4.1 Tissue-to-medium ratios (T/M) for choroid plexuses as a function of the medium concentration of [^{3}H]-thymidine and time. Choroid plexuses were incubated for various times at 37 °C in a metabolic shaker under 95% O_2, 5% CO_2 in artificial CSF containing 3 nM [^{3}H]-thymidine and various concentrations of unlabelled thymidine. All values are means ± s.e. All means are derived from six values except where indicated in parentheses. From Spector (1980a)

Nucleoside Analogues

These compounds have been developed primarily as anti-tumour agents, and their chemical basis is the similarity with the natural nucleosides that permits them to share the common transporter molecule in the cell membrane which facilitates transport. Commonly employed is nitrobenzyl thioinosine (NBTI or NBMPR). These are potent inhibitors of the erythrocyte nucleoside transporter, an inhibition that is not determined by the phosphorylation trapping mechanism, since it occurs when this has been abolished by appropriate measures, such as ATP depletion. Of interest is the fact that NBMPR differs from many nucleoside transporter inhibitors which, when added to the outside medium of the cell, accelerate outward transport by the well-established counterflow acceleration. Instead, they block efflux, for example, of uridine from erythrocytes instantaneously (Cass and Paterson, 1972; Cabantchik and Ginsburg, 1977). This is considered to be because NBMPR binds to a site different from the permeant-transporter site, and exerts its influence at a distance, without penetrating the cell. Spector (1982) showed that NBTI (NBMPR), added to the medium in which isolated choroid plexus was immersed, promoted the accumulation of labelled material, as illustrated in Figure 4.2. Spector ascribed the effect to a specific-inhibition of efflux, which might follow from the special action of this inhibitor which apparently does not penetrate the cell.

Accurate Quantitative Studies

The experiments described so far may be described as semiquantitative, largely designed to show that thymidine is transported into the brain tissue by a primary process of accumulation in the choroid plexuses and subsequent transfer to the CSF, from which it diffuses to the adjacent nervous tissue. As a means of transport this is, of course, extremely inefficient, in view of the enormous difference of capillary area of the brain tissue, being some 5000 times that of the choroid plexuses, yet the volumes of fluid that must be supplied by each capillary system, namely CSF and brain extracellular fluid, are not greatly different. Clearly, more precise kinetic studies, under strictly controlled conditions, are necessary. Thus, the escape of thymidine, when injected into the ventricles, can be studied under

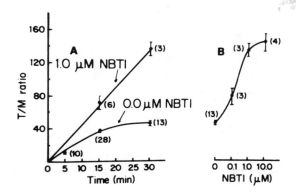

Figure 4.2   Uptake of [^{3}H]-thymidine as a function of time and NBTI concentration. Choroid plexuses were incubated for various times in artificial CSF containing 3 nM [^{3}H]-thymidine at 37 °C under 95% O_2:5% CO_2 with various concentrations of NBTI in the medium in a metabolic shaker. At the end of the incubations, the T/M ratios with and without 1.0 μM NBTI in the medium are shown as a function of time. In B, the T/M ratios determined at 30 min are shown as a function of the NBTI concentration in the medium. All values are means ± s.e., with the number or experiments given in parentheses. From Spector (1982)

controlled conditions by the technique of ventriculocisternal perfusion, while transport across the blood–brain and blood–CSF barriers can be measured with little danger of metabolic removal of the ³H-label, by measuring uptake into the perfused guinea-pig head by the technique of Zloković *et al.* (1986). It is therefore worth describing some recent studies on transport of [³H]-thymidine.

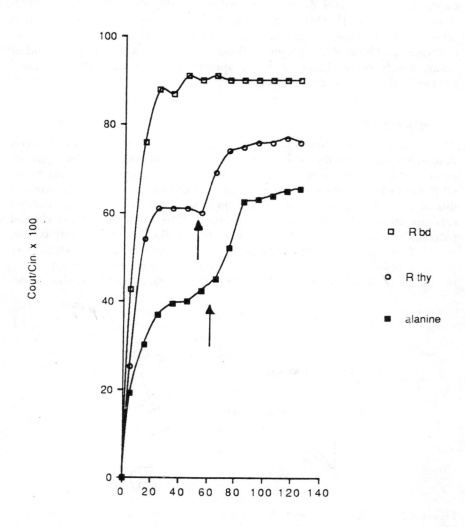

Time (minutes)

Figure 4.3   The ventriculocisternal perfusion of [³H]-thymidine (open circles), alanine (filled squares) and blue dextran (open squares) in the rabbit. From Williams and Davson (unpublished)

Ventriculocisternal Perfusion

With this technique, an artificial CSF containing the substrate of interest, in this case [^{3}H]-thymidine, is perfused through cannulae inserted into the lateral ventricles of the rabbit and removed from a cannula inserted into the cisterna magna. Incorporated in the artificial CSF is a 'marker' that has such a high molecular weight (blue dextran, MW 6×10^6) that any change in its concentration can be attributed to dilution by newly formed CSF, so that changes in concentration of [^{3}H]-thymidine, and other comparable solutes, can be attributed to this cause and allowed for, thus permitting a measurement of the transport of [^{3}H]-thymidine out of the CSF-system. Figure 4.3 shows a typical experiment when [^{3}H]-thymidine and blue dextran were perfused through the rabbit's ventricles for 2 h. At the point marked by an arrow, the perfusion fluid was changed to one of exactly the same composition except that 100 μM unlabelled thymidine was included. The upward rise of the curve shows that absorption from the system was inhibited—self-inhibition of a carrier-mediated process. On the same graph has been included a study of an amino acid, alanine, taken from an earlier study (Davson *et al.*, 1982). Clearly the two metabolites, thymidine and alanine, behave similarly; both are being absorbed from the ventricular system, probably primarily through the choroid plexuses, owing to their proximity to the perfusion fluid, but also by the brain tissue.

Clearances

From the measurement of the steady-state distribution of blue dextran between inflowing and outflowing fluids, R_D, and the corresponding values of the inflowing and outflowing concentrations of the solute being considered, i.e. C_{in} and C_{out}, a clearance, defined as the volume of perfusion fluid carrying out the lost solute at its mean concentration in unit time, can be estimated, given the rate of perfusion (about 60 μl/min). Some clearances for amino acids together with that of thymidine are given in Table 4.3. It is possible to divide this material, lost from the

Table 4.3 Ventriculocisternal perfusion of [^{3}H]-thymidine and some tritiated amino acids in the rabbit. From Williams and Davson (unpublished)

Metabolite	*n*	R_{CSF}	Clearance (μl/min)	R_{br}
Thymidine	5	48.8	39.2	11.2
Alanine	3	49.2 ± 4.1	33.5 ± 3.5	12.6 ± 2.9
Cycloleucine	5	53.6 ± 2.6	30.0 ± 3.0	17.4 ± 1.0
Glycine	6	28.3 ± 3.4	60.4 ± 5.0	48.9 ± 4.1

R_{CSF} is the value of the ratio

$$\frac{\text{Concentration in perfusion fluid at end of perfusion}}{\text{Initial concentration of perfusion fluid}} \times 100.$$

$$R_{br} = \frac{\text{Concentration in brain}}{\text{Mean concentration in perfusion fluid}} \times 100.$$

ventricles, into material that has remained in the brain tissue and that which has been lost to the blood by measuring the amount of [³H]-thymidine in the brain tissue at the end of a period of ventriculocisternal perfusion. Table 4.4 compares the mean results on five 2 h perfusions of [³H]-thymidine with those on some amino acids described earlier by Davson *et al.* (1982).

The two tables indicate the strong similarity between the treatments of nucleoside and amino acid; thus, the clearance of [³H]-thymidine can be matched with that of alanine and cycloleucine, while uptake by brain, indicated by R_{br} is also comparable. The analysis of the clearances in Table 4.4 emphasizes the relatively small percentage of the perfused thymidine and alanine that is retained by the brain, some four to five times the amount given up by the perfusing fluid being returned to the blood. Thus, viewed as a means of supplying the brain tissue with thymidine or an amino acid such as alanine, a blood–CSF route, relying on transport through the circulating CSF, would be highly inefficient.

Simultaneous Measurement of Blood–CSF and Blood–Brain Barriers
Clearly, the obvious way to determine the contributions of the blood, across the blood–brain barrier, and of the CSF across the interfaces between it and the brain tissue, is to measure precisely the passage from blood to CSF and brain tissue in the same experiment. When such experiments have been carried out earlier (e.g. Davson, 1955, on sodium and the thioureas, Kleeman *et al.*, 1962, on urea, and Oldendorf and Davson, 1967, on sucrose), it has become clear that both barriers are qualitatively similar, but that *quantitatively* the transport across the blood–brain barrier is more efficient, so that the CSF tends to act as a 'sink' to the brain rather than a source, as suggested by the Stern–Gautier hypothesis.

Perfused Guinea-pig Head
The preparation has been described in Chapter 1 and many of the valuable results of its applications to the transport of neuropeptides have been described in Chapter 3; in no case, however, has simultaneous measurement into CSF and brain tissue been carried out. In some preliminary experiments in which the brain was perfused for 15 min (the maximal viable period of the preparation is some 30

Table 4.4 Analysis of clearance of [³H]-thymidine and some tritiated amino acids from the ventricles of the rabbit. From Williams and Davson (unpublished)

Metabolite	n	Lost (1)	Brain (2)	Blood (1) − (2)
[³H]-Thymidine	5	43.6	7.4	36.3
Alanine	3	42.8 ± 4	8.7 ± 2	34.1 ± 2
Cycloleucine	4	38.4 ± 2	10.7 ± 2	27.7 ± 4
Glycine	6	62.4 ± 5	27.0 ± 2	35.4 ± 5

Column (1) indicates the percentage of the perfused metabolite lost from the perfusion period during 2 h. Column (2) indicates the percentage remaining in the brain at the end of the perfusion period. The difference between the two values indicates the percentage of the perfused material that has escaped into the blood, via choroid plexuses and brain capillaries.

min), the following values were obtained for R_{CSF} and R_{br}, indicating the ratio of concentrations of [³H]-thymidine, or its phosphorylated products, in CSF and brain tissue, on the one hand, and in the circulating perfusion fluid, consisting of a suspension of sheep erythrocytes in Ringer's solution:

$$R_{br} \qquad\qquad R_{CSF}$$
$$0.051 \pm 0.009 \qquad 0.050 \pm 0.009$$

The limits are s.e.m. and the number of experiments was 9.

Possible Sink Action of CSF

These values of R_{br} and R_{CSF} are consistent with a tendency of [³H]-thymidine to pass from brain extracellular fluid into CSF; thus, if the [³H]-thymidine in brain were distributed throughout the total brain water, there would be a gradient favouring transport from extracellular fluid to CSF. If a considerable part of the ³H-labelled material were trapped intracellularly in the form of nucleotides, then, of course, the situation might be reversed. Thus, without accurate estimates of the concentrations of free [³H]-thymidine in the two compartments, it would be unwise to conjecture as to the role of the CSF as either a source or a sink so far as the brain tissue is concerned.

Possible Supply of Brain by CSF

Nevertheless it is possible to estimate the potentialities of the CSF as a supplier of brain. Thus, the rate of flow of CSF in the guinea-pig is some 3.5 µl/min (Davson *et al.*, 1987). If the newly secreted CSF contained [³H]-thymidine, during intravascular perfusion of the brain, at the same concentration as that in the plasma, from the known weight of the brain (on average in our experiments 3.7 ± 0.1 g) it is possible to estimate the maximum value of R_{br} at the end of 15 minutes of perfusion, this maximum being given by the assumption that the circulating CSF has given up all its [³H]-thymidine to the brain on its passage through the ventricles. The estimated value of R_{br} on this basis is 0.0013, compared with the mean of 0.05. Thus, only if the choroid plexuses were secreting a CSF at a concentration some 38 times that in the plasma, and if the CSF relinquished all the secreted [³H]-thymidine to the brain would it be possible to obtain the measured R_{br}. That all the secreted [³H]-thymidine is *not* relinquished to the brain is clear from the measured value of R_{CSF}.

Deoxycytidine

Spector and Huntoon (1983) showed that isolated choroid plexus accumulated deoxycytidine. As with thymidine, large T/M ratios could only be obtained in the presence of 1 µM NBTI; the effect of NBTI could be mimicked by 1 µM unlabelled deoxycytidine, which would be consistent with a competitive inhibition of the passive step in the transport process. When accumulation was from a medium containing a very low concentration, i.e. less than 1 µM, it apparently depended on a phosphorylation trapping mechanism; at higher concentrations, however, phosphorylation was unimportant. NBTI reduced phosphorylation, in the same way as the higher concentration of deoxycytidine; this suggests an action on the phosphorylation process, but the effect could be interpreted on the basis of a limited ability of the cell to phosphorylate, so that the greater the accumulation of deoxycytidine the smaller the *percentage* phosphorylation, which is what was found. Moreover, this is consistent with the statement of Paterson *et al.* (1981) that NBMPR and congeners do not interfere with nucleoside phosphorylation.

CSF Penetration

Intravenous perfusion of [^{3}H]-deoxycytidine led to penetration into the CSF and brain, so that after 2.2 h, under carrier-free conditions, the value of R_{CSF} was 0.38 and of R_{br} 0.30. BUI studies, however, indicated an actually smaller uptake than that of sucrose. As with thymidine, intraventricularly injected deoxycytidine was eliminated rapidly, a process that was reduced by unlabelled solute.

Nucleoside Transporter

Strong evidence favouring the function of the blood–brain barrier in controlling penetration from blood to brain through the action of a carrier-mediated process, is provided by the study of Kalaria and Harik (1986), who used [^{3}H]-nitrobenzylthioinosine (NBTI or NBTMBR) as a probe that bound reversibly and with high affinity to specific sites in the brain and choroid plexus, acting as a powerful inhibitor of nucleoside transport. Photoactivation caused the inhibitor to form a covalent link at the binding site and enabled the isolation of a protein of 60 kD. Specific binding of [^{3}H]-NBMPR was very high in isolated cerebral microvessels and in choroid plexus and was comparable with that of erythrocyte membranes (Table 4.5).

Table 4.5 Specific binding of [^{3}H]-NBMPR, a nucleoside probe, to cerebral microvessels, cerebral cortex and choroid plexus for the pig and rat. From Kalaria and Harik (1986)

Species, tissue	n	B_{max} (fmol/mg of protein)	K_D (nM)
Rat			
Cerebral cortex	3	90 ± 11	0.06 ± 0.03
Microvessels	5	323 ± 32	0.14 ± 0.04
Erythrocyte 'ghosts'	4	525 ± 60	0.16 ± 0.04
Pig			
Cerebral cortex	6	79 ± 7	0.43 ± 0.07
Microvessels	7	376 ± 37	0.63 ± 0.08
Choroid plexus	4	381 ± 47	0.48 ± 0.14

Data are mean $\pm$ s.e.m. values for the number (*n*) of preparations. [^{3}H]-NBMPR concentrations ranged between 0.01 and 5 nM.

Barrier Co-operation

Thus, these studies on ventriculocisternal perfusion and specific binding to receptors support the view, developed throughout this book, that the two barriers co-operate in controlling exchanges between blood and brain; the high concentration of nucleoside receptors in both choroid plexus and brain microvessels would indicate that the choroidal epithelium and brain capillary endothelium control transport by a facilitated or carrier-mediated process. The great bulk of brain capillaries compared with choroid plexus capillaries (5000:1) would indicate that, if either of the processes were 'predominant', that across the blood–brain barrier would be, and the CSF would rather act as a sink for the brain than as a source.

Vitamins

The number of vitamins is large, and there is little point in describing the experimental studies on their penetration of the blood–brain barrier in detail; the interested reader may be referred to Spector's reviews (1977, 1986; Spector and Eells, 1984) and to Davson et al. (1987). Here we shall consider, very arbitrarily, the behaviour of ascorbic acid (vitamin C), thiamine (vitamin B_1), pantothenic acid and biotin.

The homoeostatic mechanisms controlling the levels of certain vitamins in the CSF have been summarized by Spector (1977). In Table 4.6 the concentrations of some vitamins in plasma, CSF, choroid plexus and brain, gathered from several sources, are presented. It will be seen that the value of R_{CSF} for most is greater than unity, suggesting an active accumulation within the CSF.

Ascorbic Acid or Vitamin C

Ascorbic acid is accumulated in CSF in concentrations greater than those in plasma, a situation similar to that observed with the aqueous humour of the eye, although in some species, such as the rabbit, values of R_{CSF} are greater than 20 (Kinsey, 1947). Figure 4.4 shows the concentration in human CSF when the plasma levels were varied. At low plasma concentrations the value of R_{CSF} is about

Table 4.6 Concentrations of some vitamins in plasma, CSF, choroid plexus and brain tissue. From Spector (1977)

Vitamin	Plasma (μM)	CSF (μM)	R_{CSF}	Choroid plexus (μM)	Brain (μM)
Ascorbic acid	57	232	4.1	1085	1867
Inositol	89	472	5.3	3428	11275
Folates	0.014	0.068	4.9	7.7	0.6
Thiamine	0.41	0.36	0.9	15.3	10.3
Vitamin B_6	0.30	0.39	1.3	14.9	9.6

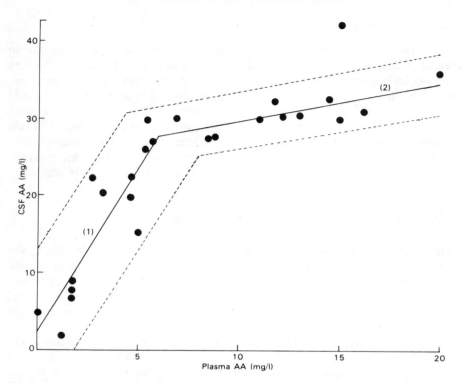

Figure 4.4   CSF ascorbic acid (AA) as a function of plasma ascorbic acid in 25 human subjects being treated for epilepsy. Dashed lines are 95% confidence limits. From Ridge and Fairhurst (1976)

4, but at plasma concentrations above 4 mg/l the CSF level does not rise in the same proportion, to give values of R_{CSF} of about 1.5, suggesting that the accumulation process is saturable, just as with the aqueous humour. It will be noted that the concentration of ascorbic acid in brain is high; this is unlikely to be due to local synthesis of the vitamin, since it is observed in man, who is incapable of synthesis of the vitamin.

Transport from Blood

Hammerström (1966) measured the penetration of ^{14}C-labelled ascorbic acid from blood into brain and choroid plexuses of mice by radioautography. As early as 2 min after intravenous injection there was a remarkably high concentration in the choroid plexuses, and with the passage of time the tissue adjacent to the ventricles showed higher and higher concentrations. According to Hammerström, the blood–brain barrier to ascorbic acid was very high, so that penetration from blood to brain was taking place secondarily to a primary transport across the choroid plexuses. This thesis was developed by Spector (1977) on the basis of experiments on the accumulation of ascorbic acid by isolated choroid plexuses. Thus, T/M ratios as high as 10 were obtained with the *in vitro* preparation, and, in view of the high values of R_{CSF}, this is consistent with an active accumulation of ascorbic acid in the newly secreted CSF.

Intraventricular Injections

Spector (1981) injected $[^{14}C]$-ascorbic acid and known slow penetrators of the blood–brain barrier, such as mannitol, into the left lateral ventricles of rabbits. After 2 or 4 h the brain was removed and a portion of midbrain was cut into successive sections so that the concentration profile from the CSF in the aqueduct could be measured. The profiles indicated that ascorbic acid was being accumulated in brain tissue, by contrast with mannitol. Thus, a plausible case could be made out for the proposed primary route of entry, namely the freshly secreted CSF.

Participation by Brain Capillaries

In view of the strong similarity between the blood–CSF and blood–brain barriers revealed by the work summarized in Chapter 1, the possibility that transport across the brain capillaries contributes to the measured uptake from blood to brain must be considered. Thus, the power of the brain capillary to actively transport ascorbic acid from blood to extracellular fluid, and, again, the power of brain cells to accumulate the vitamin from the extracellular fluid, must be explored. That the brain tissue can accumulate ascorbic acid has already been shown by Spector's intraventricular injections, mentioned above. Further studies involving continuous perfusion of the ventricles by the technique of ventriculocisternal perfusion, and analysis of the concentration profiles in the brain, should shed more light on this process. Thus, the cells could be accumulating the vitamin, while losses to the brain capillaries would be kept low if these vessels were capable of actively transporting ascorbic acid from the lumen to the extracellular fluid, i.e. behaving similarly to the choroidal epithelium. The strongest evidence favouring Spector's hypothesis is Hammerström's observation of an apparent spread of ascorbic acid from choroid plexuses to brain tissue. These organs undoubtedly accumulate the vitamin, so that autoradiographically some spill-over from their roots could be expected, and this might obscure a more steady transport across the capillaries of the brain tissue.

Thiamine (Vitamin B₁)

This is not synthesized by brain, so the thiamine normally present in the tissue, where it acts as a coenzyme, must be derived from blood. As with other vitamins, there is a clear homoeostasis that permits reasonably constant levels in brain in the face of large variations in plasma level; a saturable accumulation by brain cells, as described by Sharma and Quastel (1965), using brain slices, contributes to this, while a saturable process of penetration into CSF and brain from plasma is a dominant factor.

Uptake from Blood

Spector (1976) showed that uptake into brain and choroid plexus was by a carrier-mediated process; Greenwood *et al.* (1982) found that influx into rat brain was rapid, so that a steady-state distribution between blood and brain was reached in some 15 min. The value of C_{br}/C_{pl} of 0.14 under these conditions suggests a largely extracellular uptake. In a more quantitative study on rats, using Gjedde's (1980) analysis, Reggiani *et al.* (1984) confirmed that influx varied with the concentration of the vitamin, and deduced a value of 2.3 μM for K_m, 9.3 nmol h^{-1} for V_{max}, and 0.09 h^{-1} for K_D. The rates of influx at physiological levels of the vitamin in the plasma were in the region of 0.44 and 0.65 nmol g^{-1} h^{-1}, depending on the brain region: these rates were very much greater than those for the monophosphate. In general, the system was described as a high-affinity low-capacity system, and the authors agreed with Greenwood *et al.* that there was little margin of spare transport capacity, thus emphasizing the vulnerability of brain to thiamine deficiency.

In vitro *Accumulation*

When labelled thiamine is added to the medium of an *in vitro* incubated choroid plexus, a substantial amount is converted to phosphates; if this phosphorylation is prevented by preincubation with pyrithiamine, an inhibitor of thiamine phosphokinase, an active accumulation of thiamine can be demonstrated, giving T/M ratios of about 8. This was suppressed by high concentrations (0.16 μM to 30 mM) of unlabelled thiamine; by the metabolic inhibitor, DNP, and also by the mono- and pyrophosphates of thiamine (Spector, 1976, 1982). The K_m for the saturable component of accumulation was 1.56 mM. Release of thiamine from the choroid plexuses could also be inhibited by high concentrations of the unlabelled material. As indicated above, *in vitro* brain slices accumulate thiamine, with a half-saturation of approximately 0.3 μM, which is similar to the normal concentration in rabbit plasma.

Thiamine Deficiency

This, and chronic alcoholism, give rise to a characteristic encephalopathy—the Wernicke syndrome—with ophthalmoplegia, cerebellar ataxia and mental changes. According to Harper (1979), enlarged ventricles and haemorrhages in the periaqueductal region of the brain stem, extending to the substantia nigra, are a feature. In a study of B vitamins in malnutrition and alcoholism, Dastur *et al.* (1976) found that decreases in plasma thiamine (and vitamin B$_6$) were accompanied by considerable decreases in CSF concentration.

Blood–Brain Barrier Breakdown

Phillips and Cragg (1984) found an increase in the permeability–area product, *PS*, for penetration of [^{14}C]-sucrose into the brain of thiamine-deficient rats, which could be prevented by feeding thiamine.

Relation to Nerve Conduction

Von Muralt (1947) stimulated the nerves of frogs and found a release of thiamine into the bathing solution. During degeneration, the thiamine content of nerves decreased; and Von Muralt considered that thiamine was essential for 'maintenance of the internal equilibrium of the nerve'. This release was confirmed by Cooper *et al.* (1963), working on the spinal cord; they showed that the tissue would take up ^{32}S-labelled thiamine. More modern studies (e.g. Doerge *et al.*, 1982) have implicated the vitamin in perhaps modifying acetylcholine receptors at synapses, besides influencing the permeability changes that take place during transmission.

Pantothenic Acid

This vitamin is not synthesized by mammals and so must enter the brain from the blood; coenzyme-A is synthesized from pantothenic acid, the rate-controlling step being its phosphorylation by ATP. Interest in the blood–brain relations has been aroused by the fact that the brain is highly resistant to coenzyme-A deficiency. Spector and Boose (1984) showed that the choroid plexuses accumulated pantothenic acid to give T/M ratios of about 8, using carrier-free material; this was suppressed by about 100 μM unlabelled solute. Brain slices accumulated the vitamin but to a much smaller extent. After intravenous infusion into rabbits for 3 h the concentration in the CSF was found to be about equal to that in plasma, more than 90% of the ^{3}H being associated with pantothenic acid; penetration was suppressed by 70% by inclusion of unlabelled vitamin in the infusion fluid. When the vitamin was injected intraventricularly together with mannitol, the clearance of the vitamin was much more rapid, suggesting choroid plexus uptake; probenecid inhibited the clearance, indicating a clearance pathway common to organic acids such as HIAA, *p*-aminohippurate and prostaglandins.

Perfused Rat Brain

Using the technique of Takasato *et al.* (1984) for perfusing the rat's brain, Spector *et al.* (1986) showed that transport across the blood–brain barrier was carrier-mediated, with a K_m of 19 μM and a V_{max} of 0.21 nmol g^{-1} min^{-1}; probenecid inhibited penetration. The K_m is actually some ten times the concentration of that in the plasma, and the authors concluded that transport of pantothenic acid across the blood–brain barrier did not play an important role in regulating the synthesis of CoA in the brain.

Biotin

This vitamin, after being covalently incorporated into various enzymes, is involved in carboxylation reactions in brain and other tissues. Spector and Mock (1987) have shown that it crosses the blood–brain barrier in the perfused rat brain by a carrier-mediated process, with a K_m of about 100 μM; probenecid and nonanoic acids inhibited transport, whereas the methylated ester of biotin did not, indicating the importance of the free acid for transport on the carrier. The value of PS, i.e. the transfer constant, was $1 \times 10^{-4}\,s^{-1}$ or 0.006 min^{-1}, a rate of transport corresponding approximately to that of ^{24}Na across the blood–brain barrier (Davson, 1955) and some 25 times that measured for mannitol, across the guinea-pig blood–brain barrier, namely 2.4×10^{-4} min^{-1}.

References

Cabantchik, Z.I. and Ginsburg, H. (1977). Transport of uridine in human red blood cells. Demonstration of a simple carrier mechanism. *J. Gen. Physiol.*, **69**, 75–96

Cass, C.E. and Paterson, A.R.P. (1972). Mediated transport of nucleosides in human erythrocytes. Accelerative exchange diffusion of uridine and thymidine and specificity toward pyrimidine nucleosides as permeants. *J. Biol. Chem.*, **247**, 3314–3320

Cass, C.E. and Paterson, A.R.P. (1973). Mediated transport of nucleosides by human erythrocytes. Specificity toward purine nucleosides as permeants. *Biochim. Biophys. Acta*, **291**, 734–736

Cooper, J.R., Roth, R.H. and Kini, M.M. (1963). Biochemical and physiological function of thiamine in nervous tissue. *Nature*, **199**, 609–610

Cornford, E.M. and Oldendorf, W.H. (1975). Independent blood–brain barrier transport systems for nucleic acid precursors. *Biochim. Biophys. Acta*, **394**, 211–219

Dastur, D.K. *et al.* (1976). The B-vitamins in malnutrition with alcoholism. *Br. J. Nutr.*, **36**, 143–159

Davson, H. (1955). A comparative study of the aqueous humour and cerebrospinal fluid in the rabbit. *J. Physiol.*, **129**, 111–133

Davson, H., Hollingsworth, J.G., Carey, M.B. and Fenstermacher, J.D. (1982). Ventriculo-cisternal perfusion of twelve amino acids in the rabbit. *J. Neurobiol.*, **13**, 293–318

Davson, H., Welch, K. and Segal, M.B. (1987). *Physiology and Pathophysiology of the Cerebrospinal Fluid*. Churchill Livingstone, London

Doerge, D.R., McNamee, M.G. and Ingraham, L.L. (1982). Some neurochemical properties of thiamin. *Ann. N.Y. Acad. Sci.*, **378**, 422–434

Eells, J. and Spector, R. (1983). Determination of ribonucleosides, deoxyribonucleosides and purine and pyrimidine bases in adult rabbit cerebrospinal fluid and plasma. *Neurochem. Res.*, **8**, 1307–1320

Ensminger, W.D. and Frei, E. (1977). The prevention of methotrexate toxicity by thymidine infusion in humans. *Cancer Res.*, **37**, 1857–1863

Gjedde, A. (1980). Rapid steady-state analysis of blood–brain glucose transfer in the rat. *Acta Physiol. Scand.*, **108**, 331–339

Greenwood, J., Love, E.R. and Pratt, O.E. (1982) Kinetics of thiamine transport across the blood–brain barrier. *J. Physiol.*, **327**, 95–103

Hammerström, L. (1966). Autoradiographic studies on the distribution of C^{14}-labelled ascorbic acid and dehydroascorbic acid. *Acta Physiol. Scand.*, **70** (Suppl. 289)

Hammond, J.R. and Clanachan, A.S. (1985). Species differences in the binding of ^{3}H-nitrobenzylthioinosine to the nucleoside transport system in mammalial central nervous system membranes: evidence for interconvertible conformations of the binding site/transporter complex. *J. Neurochem.*, **45**, 527–533

Harper, C. (1979). Wernicke's encephalopathy: a more common disease than realised. *J. Neurol. Neurosurg. Psychiat.*, **42**, 226–231

Kalaria, R.N. and Harik, S.I. (1986). Nucleoside transporter of cerebral microvessels and choroid plexus. *J. Neurochem.*, **47**, 1849–1856

Kinsey, V.E. (1947). Transfer of ascorbic acid and related compounds across the blood–acqueous barrier. *Am. J. Ophthalmol.*, **30**, 1262–1266

Kleeman, C.R., Davson, H. and Levin, E. (1962). Urea transport in the central nervous system. *Am. J. Physiol.*, **203**, 739–747

Oldendorf, W.H. and Davson, H. (1967). Brain extracellular space and the sink action of the cerebrospinal fluid. *Arch. Neurol.*, **17**, 196–205

Paterson, A.R.P., Kolassa, N. and Cass, C.E. (1981). Transport of nucleoside drugs in animal cells. *Pharmacol. Ther.*, **12**, 515–536

Phillips, S.C. and Cragg, B.G. (1984). Blood–brain barrier dysfunction in thiamine-deficient rats. *Acta Neuropathol.*, **62**, 235–241

Plunkett, W. and Cohen, S.S. (1977). Penetration of mouse fibroblasts by 2′-deoxyadenosine 5′-phosphate and incorporation of the nucleotide into DNA. *C. Cell Physiol.*, **91**, 261–270

Reggiani, C., Patrini, C. and Rindi, G. (1984). Nervous tissue thiamine metabolism *in vivo*. I. Transport of thiamine and thiamine monophosphate from plasma to different brain regions of the rat. *Brain Res.*, **293**, 319–327

Ridge, B.D. and Fairhurst, E. (1976). Ascorbic acid concentrations in human plasma and cerebrospinal fluid. *Proc. Nutr. Soc.*, **35**, 57–58A

Sharma, A.K. and Quastel, J.H. (1965). Transport and metabolism of thiamine in rat brain cortex *in vitro. Biochem. J.*, **94**, 790–800

Spector, R. (1976). Thiamine transport in the central nervous system. *Am. J. Physiol.*, **230**, 1101–1107

Spector, R. (1977). Vitamin homeostasis in the central nervous system. *New Engl. J. Med.*, **296**, 1393–1398

Spector, R. (1980a). Thymidine accumulation by choroid plexus *in vitro. Arch. Biochem. Biophys.*, **205**, 85–93

Spector, R. (1980b). Thymidine transport in the central nervous system. *J. Neurochem.*, **35**, 1092–1098

Spector, R. (1981). Penetration of ascorbic acid from cerebrospinal fluid into brain. *Exp. Neurol.*, **72**, 645–653

Spector, R. (1982). Nucleoside transport in choroid plexus: mechanism and specificity. *Arch. Biochem. Biophys.*, **216**, 693–703

Spector, R. (1986). Nucleoside and vitamin homeostasis in the mammalian central nervous system. *Ann. N.Y. Acad. Sci.*, **481**, 221–230

Spector, R. (1988). Hypoxanthine transport and metabolism in the central nervous system. *J. Neurochem.*, **50**, 969–978

Spector, R. and Berlinger, W.G. (1982). Localization and mechanism of thymidine transport in the central nervous system. *J. Neurochem.*, **39**, 837–841

Spector, R. and Boose, B. (1984). Accumulation of pantothenic acid by the isolated choroid plexus and brain slices *in vitro. J. Neurochem.*, **43**, 472–478

Spector, R. and Eells, J. (1984). Nucleoside and vitamin transport into the central nervous system. *Fed. Proc.*, **43**, 196–200

Spector, R. and Huntoon, S. (1983). Deoxycytidine transport and mechanism in choroid plexus. *J. Neurochem.*, **40**, 1474–1480

Spector, R. and Mock, D. (1987). Biotin transport through the blood–brain barrier. *J. Neurochem.*, **48**, 400–404

Spector, R., Sivesind, C. and Kinzelaw, D. (1986). Pantothenic acid transport through the blood–brain barrier. *J. Neurochem.*, **47**, 966–971

Stone, T.W. (1981). Physiological roles for adenosine and adenosine 5′-triphosphate in the nervous system. *Neuroscience*, **6**, 523–555

Takasato, Y., Rapoport, S.I. and Smith, Q.R. (1984). An *in situ* brain perfusion technique to study cerebrovascular transport in the rat. *Am. J. Physiol.*, **247**, H484–H493

Ungemach, F.R. and Hegner, D. (1978). Uptake thymidine into isolated rat hepatocytes. *Hoppe-Seyler's Z. Physiol. Chem.*, **359**, 845–856

Von Muralt, A. (1947). Thiamine and peripheral neurophysiology. *Vitamins & Hormones*, **5**, 93–118

Whittam, R. (1960). The high permeability of human red cells to adenine and hypoxanthine and their ribosides. *J. Physiol.*, **154**, 614–623

Wohlhueter, R.M., Marg, R. and Plagemann, G.W. (1979). Thymidine transport and specificity of the transport system. *Biochim. Biophys. Acta*, **553**, 262–283

Wu, P.H. and Phillis, J.W. (1982). Uptake of adenosine by isolated rat brain capillaries. *J. Neurochem.*, **38**, 687–690

Young, J.D. (1978). Nucleoside transport in sheep erythrocytes: genetically controlled transport variation and its influence on erythrocyte ATP concentrations. *J. Physiol.*, **277**, 325–378

Zaharko, D.S., Boltern, B.J., Chiuten, D. and Wiernik, P.H. (1979). Pharmacokinetic studies during phase 1 trials of high-dose thymidine infusions. *Cancer Res.*, **39**, 4777–4781

Zloković, B.V., Begley, D.J., Djuricić, B.M. and Mitrović, D.M. (1986). Measurement of solute transport across the blood–brain barrier in the perfused guinea pig brain. *J. Neurochem.*, **46**, 1444–1459

Note

[1] Young (1978) has shown that there are two varieties of sheep with greatly differing powers of transporting nucleoside, such as inosine, across their erythrocyte membranes, a difference that is genetically controlled. Thus, some 5% of the sheep studied by Young had a rapid transporting system for inosine, with a K_m of 0.26 mM and a V_{max} of 2.5 mmol per litre of cell per hour. The remaining 95% of animals had no carrier-mediated system, and exhibited a very slow uptake from the medium. As sheep cells are utilized during guinea-pig head perfusions, it is worth bearing in mind the varying possibilities of uptake by the cells during any perfusion.

Chapter 5

Experimental Models in the Study of the Pathology of the Blood–Brain Barrier

Introduction

Transport across the blood–brain barrier has a protective and regulatory role, and in this chapter we shall consider some behavioural dysfunctions that may be related to a disturbance of the barrier. The prerequisite for studies on barrier dysfunction is the establishment of suitable experimental animal models. Many, but far from all, models in experimental medicine are homologous, i.e. there is a correspondence in the aetiology of the disease and the model. Other models, on the other hand, may be described as only isomorphic, so that, despite a parallelism between the model and the human condition, the cause of the condition in the model may be quite different from that in man. Finally, the model may have no resemblance to the disease but simply be a non-homologous or non-isomorphic representation that has value in either reflecting some aspects of the disease or for studying the therapy used for treating the disease.

Researchers in the field of neuropsychiatric disorders are not as fortunate as those working in areas of medical science, where the defining characteristics of the disorder are easily quantified, such as arterial blood pressure, vital capacity, and so on. Corresponding situations in the monkey are easily transposed to the human subject. With psychiatric disorders, however, the establishment of analogies is far more difficult.

The neurobiological basis of psychiatric disorders in humans has greatly expanded over the last two decades, and a major part of this expansion has been due to a great increase in our understanding, at the cellular level, of the mechanisms and the sites of action of drugs used to treat mental illness. This heavy investment in pharmacological research has been based on the assumption that knowledge of where, and how, the therapeutically active drugs act in the central nervous system might give us significant clues to the pathology of the underlying neuropsychiatric disorders (Seeman, 1980).

In this chapter we shall describe some experimental models that contribute to the understanding of the role of blood–brain barrier permeability in pathological conditions. Those that we shall deal with are: experimental psychosis; acute experimental allergic encephalomyelitis; and brain lesions. At the same time we shall describe certain recent clinical observations on the state of the blood–brain barrier in humans after brain lesions.

Perfused Guinea-pig Brain

The technique has been described in Chapter 1, and some applications in Chapter 3. To recapitulate, the guinea-pig brain is perfused with blood and the state of the blood–brain barrier is determined by measurement of uptake of an inert polar molecule, such as mannitol, a molecule that, in the normal animal, penetrates the brain from blood very slowly, but, after various insults, penetrates more rapidly. The permeability of the barrier is given quantitative expression by a unidirectional transfer constant, K_{in}. This may be translated into a permeability constant, with dimensions of cm/s, if the area of capillaries exposed to unit volume of brain is known. In these studies there is also measured a 'rapidly equilibrating space', i.e. a fraction of the brain that comes into very rapid equilibration with the blood, and probably represents tissue on the blood side of the blood–brain barrier, or else regions of the brain where a limited rapid escape occurs, such as the paraventricular organs.

Amphetamine Experimental Psychosis

Amphetamine has a powerful stimulant action in the central nervous system, related to its ability to increase the release, and block the re-uptake of central catecholamine neurotransmitters (Davson *et al.*, 1987). Stimulation of central adrenergic and dopamine receptors has been shown to elevate cerebral metabolism and consequently to increase cerebral blood flow (McCulloch and Harper, 1977). Extensive clinical data indicate that prolonged amphetamine abuse may lead to a reversible behavioural syndrome closely resembling paranoid schizophrenia (Snyder, 1976). In several animal species, behavioural responses to amphetamine consisting of increased locomotor activity, stereotypy, hypervigilance and social withdrawal following systemic administration occur (Anqrist and Gerson, 1970). Many laboratories have investigated neurochemical and neurophysiological correlates of chronic and acute amphetamine administration in animals in order to attempt to elucidate the basis for stimulation-induced psychosis in humans.

Blood–Brain Barrier and Psychosis

Dida *et al.* (1982) demonstrated that chronic amphetamine treatment produced characteristic changes in animal behaviour and selective changes in serum protein fractions similar to those in patients with schizophrenia. So far as the blood–brain barrier is concerned, an early study of McCulloch and Harper (1977) suggested that amphetamine induced a breakdown of the barrier to Evans Blue, due to the beta-adrenergic action of the drug, since the beta-antagonist, propranolol, greatly reduced the effect. On the other hand, Domer *et al.* (1980) have suggested that an alpha-adrenergically induced vascular hypertension that would 'open' the barrier to large molecules such as RISA, is the cause of amphetamine-induced changes. A number of studies, however, have shown that hypertension cannot account for the observed opening of the barrier. Thus, the mean rise in arterial pressure in amphetamine-treated guinea-pigs was only 20 mmHg, and it has been shown that a rise of 21 mmHg, as in the study of McCulloch and Harper (1977), due to a p_{CO_2} of 45 mmHg, was inadequate to open the barrier. This has been confirmed in the isolated perfused rat brain preparation of Takasato *et al.* (1984) and the perfused guinea-pig brain of Zloković *et al.* (1986b), where thresholds for mechanical opening of the barrier were between 160 and 190 mmHg and between 160 and 200 mmHg, respectively. These findings have led to the conclusion that, in amphetamine-induced experimental psychosis, there must be some other influence on the blood–brain barrier, involving perhaps its metabolic activity (Joó, 1986), that is responsible for allowing penetration of blood-borne substrates into the central nervous system.

Experimental Study

We may now briefly describe an experimental study on the guinea-pig in which changes in barrier function were measured quantitatively, using mannitol and a polyethylene glycol (PEG) of MW 4000 daltons as test molecules for normality, or otherwise, of the blood–brain barrier. Amphetamine psychosis was induced by chronic treatment with 5 mg amphetamine daily intraperitoneally, divided into two doses at 7 a.m. and 7 p.m. for 14 and 20 days prior to measurement of the barrier to the two solutes by the technique described by Zloković *et al.* (1986b), the unidirectional transfer constant, K_{in}, and V_i, the initial volume of distribution being deduced from plots of C_{br}/C_{pl} against time, as indicated earlier. As explained in Chapter 1, K_{in} computed in this manner has the dimension time^{-1}; it may be converted into a permeability coefficient, with dimensions cm/s, by multiplying by the volume/area quotient, V/S. Thus, if we accept a value of 100 cm^2 area of capillary per unit volume of brain, the value of K_{in} must be multiplied by 1/100 to convert the transfer coefficient to a permeability coefficient.

Mannitol and PEG

Figure 5.1 shows penetration of the two solutes; that of mannitol is significant in controls, whereas that of the larger PEG is not significant. In amphetamine-treated animals the penetration of mannitol increases a little but that of PEG increases by much more. The very large difference in control rates of penetration of mannitol and PEG is best attributed to the presence of water-filled pores that are too small to allow PEG to pass through at a significant rate, but large enough to allow some penetration of the smaller mannitol. The change caused by amphetamine could be attributed to an expansion of the pores that would permit some or all of them to allow the larger PEG molecule through. Since, on this assumption, the smaller mannitol can pass through the normal-sized pores, we need not expect a large increase in penetration, expressed as a percentage change, as with the large PEG molecule. Estimated values of K_{in} and V_i for different brain regions are shown in Table 5.1. It will be seen that extension of the amphetamine treatment

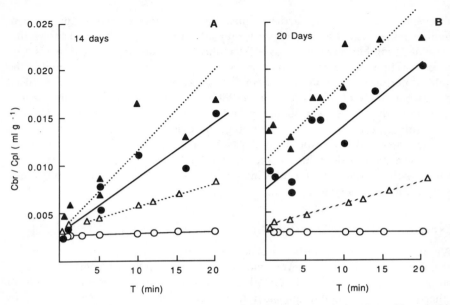

Figure 5.1 Amphetamine-induced increase of the unidirectional transport of inert polar molecules across the BBB of vascularly perfused caudate nucleus of the guinea-pig. Each point represents a single experiment of simultaneously perfused D-[^{14}C]-mannitol (Δ, control; $\blacktriangle$, amphetamine) and [^{3}H]-PEG ($\bigcirc$, control; $\bullet$, amphetamine). Guinea-pigs were i.p. treated with D-amphetamine sulphate as explained (A) for 14 days ($n = 7$) and (B) for 20 days ($n = 10$). [^{3}H]- and [^{14}C]-radioactivity (dpm g^{-1} brain/dpm ml^{-1} plasma perfusate) is plotted against the perfusion time, T. K_{in} values (10^{-3} ml min^{-1} g^{-1}) were computed from graphic multiple-time brain uptake analysis and expressed as mean $\pm$ s.e., for mannitol and PEG, respectively, in amphetamine-treated animals for 14 days (0.64 ± 0.18; 0.57 ± 0.16) and for 20 days (0.61 ± 0.20; 0.62 ± 0.20). Linear correlation coefficient determined for either molecule in amphetamine-treated animals ranged between 0.87 and 0.92 ($P < 0.01$), and K_{in} values for mannitol and PEG were significantly higher in comparison to corresponding control values, by analysis of variance ($P < 0.001$)

from 14 to 20 days increased the transfer constant (Table 5.1; Figure 5.1). The permeability changes are reversible, since, in animals treated for 20 days, 7–28 days after cessation of treatment permeability had returned to normal (Table 5.2; Figure 5.2).

Permeability Ratios

In control animals the ratio of permeabilities to mannitol and PEG is, as we have seen, very high, about 50. This shows a marked drop to 1–1.2 after 14 days' treatment. After cessation of treatment the ratio returns to its normal value (Figure 5.3). If both solutes were diffusing through large pores in the abnormal state, we would expect the ratio of permeabilities to be in the ratio of the square roots of their molecular weights (Davson and Danielli, 1942), i.e. 4.65. The fact that the ratio is about unity suggests that the rate of transit across the blood–brain barrier

Table 5.1 Graphically determined unidirectional transfer constant, K_{in}, and initial volume of distribution, V_i, for D-[^{14}C]-mannitol and [^{3}H]-PEG simultaneously perfused in the guinea-pig brain after amphetamine treatment

Treatment	Brain region	n	K_{in} (10^{-3} ml min^{-1} g^{-1})		V_i (ml 100 g^{-1})		P_1	P_2
			D-[^{14}C]-Mannitol	[^{3}H]-PEG	D-[^{14}C]-Mannitol	[^{3}H]-PEG		
Placebo (i.p. saline) control group	Parietal cortex	8	0.22 ± 0.22	0.004 ± 0.0005	0.35 ± 0.07	0.29 ± 0.04		
	Hippocampus	8	0.24 ± 0.02	0.005 ± 0.0005	0.34 ± 0.06	0.30 ± 0.03		
	Caudate nucleus	8	0.22 ± 0.02	0.004 ± 0.0005	0.35 ± 0.08	0.29 ± 0.03		
I.p. D-amphetamine sulphate (5 mg/kg daily) 14 days	Parietal cortex	7	0.75 ± 0.06	0.59 ± 0.04	0.52 ± 0.08	0.40 ± 0.03	0.001	0.001
	Hippocampus	7	0.65 ± 0.05	0.61 ± 0.05	0.42 ± 0.09	0.41 ± 0.04	0.001	0.001
	Caudate nucleus	7	0.69 ± 0.06	0.57 ± 0.06	0.34 ± 0.07	0.27 ± 0.03	0.001	0.001
I.p. D-amphetamine sulphate (5 mg/kg daily) 20 days	Parietal cortex	10	0.53 ± 0.09	0.89 ± 0.07	0.81 ± 0.09	0.32 ± 0.02	0.001	0.001
	Hippocampus	10	0.49 ± 0.15	0.17 ± 0.09	0.78 ± 0.08	0.33 ± 0.03	0.001	0.001
	Caudate nucleus	10	0.81 ± 0.10	0.64 ± 0.08	0.05 ± 0.11	0.76 ± 0.06	0.001	0.001

Values are mean ± s.e., n is number of animals. Vascular permeability, P, was estimated on the basis of the capillary surface area of 100 cm^2 g^{-1} brain tissue. P_1, P_2 are significance of K_{in} values for D-[^{14}C]-mannitol and [^{3}H]-PEG in amphetamine-treated animals compared with control values.

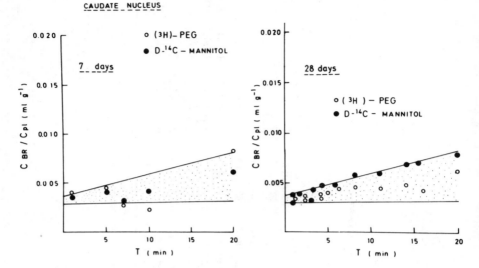

Figure 5.2 Effect of withdrawal of amphetamine treatment (i.p. 5 mg/kg daily divided in two doses at 7 a.m. and 7 p.m. for 20 days) after 7 days ($n = 5$) and 28 days ($n = 12$) on kinetics of entry of D-$[^{14}C]$-mannitol and $[^3H]$-PEG perfused simultaneously in the caudate nucleus. Shadowed area represents interval between regression lines of D-$[^{14}C]$-mannitol and $[^3H]$-PEG in control non-treated animals ($n = 8$). $[^3H]$- vs. $[^{14}C]$-radioactivity, dpm g^{-1} brain/dpm ml^{-1} plasma perfusate is plotted against the perfusion time, T. Each point represents a single experiment

in this abnormal condition is governed by a bulk flow of fluid, which would carry large and small molecules at about the same rate provided that the pores were large. If the bulk flow involved a pinocytotic mechanism, governed by adenylate cyclase activity (Joó, 1986, 1988), then the action of amphetamine might be explained by beta-adrenergic enhancement of adenylate cyclase activity.

Transport of Neuropeptides

The transport of some neuropeptides across the guinea-pig blood–brain barrier has been examined in normal animals recently by Zloković and his collaborators. Thus, for leucine-enkephalin and arginine vasopressin, a carrier-mediated transport has been demonstrated at both blood–brain and blood–CSF barriers (Zloković *et al.*, 1987), while for thyroid releasing hormone (TRH) a non-saturable transport has been demonstrated for penetration of the blood–brain barrier, accompanied by a significant N-terminal hydrolysis (Zloković *et al.*, 1988). In amphetamine-treated animals a 6–10-fold increase in the value of V_i has been found in parietal cortex, hippocampus and caudate nucleus, although permeability constants were unaltered (Figure 5.4; Table 5.3). In the case of arginine vasopressin (AVP) there was also a large—12-fold—increase in V_i, while K_{in}

Table 5.2 Effect of the withdrawal of amphetamine treatment on K_{in} and V_i values for D-[14C]-mannitol and [3H]-PEG simultaneously perfused in the brain of the guinea-pig previously treated with amphetamine (5 mg kg daily) for 20 days

Time after withdrawal of amphetamine treatment	n	Brain region	K_{in} (10^{-3} ml min^{-1} g^{-1})		V_i (ml/100 g)		P_1	P_2
			D-[14C]-Mannitol	[3H]-PEG	D-[14C]-Mannitol	[3H]-PEG		
7 days	5	Parietal cortex	0.13 ± 0.02	0.003 ± 0.0003	0.66 ± 0.05	0.23 ± 0.03	0.05	n.s.
	5	Hippocampus	0.15 ± 0.01	0.002 ± 0.0002	0.53 ± 0.05	0.45 ± 0.05	n.s.	n.s.
	5	Caudate nucleus	0.14 ± 0.01	0.005 ± 0.0002	0.53 ± 0.07	0.46 ± 0.05	0.5	n.s.
28 days	12	Parietal cortex	0.23 ± 0.02	0.004 ± 0.0005	0.36 ± 0.03	0.29 ± 0.03	n.s.	n.s.
	12	Hippocampus	0.21 ± 0.03	0.004 ± 0.0004	0.38 ± 0.04	0.31 ± 0.04	n.s.	n.s.
	12	Caudate nucleus	0.22 ± 0.02	0.005 ± 0.0004	0.34 ± 0.07	0.30 ± 0.04	n.s.	n.s.

Values are mean ± s.e., n is number of animals, P_1 and P_2 are significance of K_{in} values for D-[14C]-mannitol and [3H]-PEG after the withdrawal of amphetamine treatment compared with control values taken from Table 5.1.

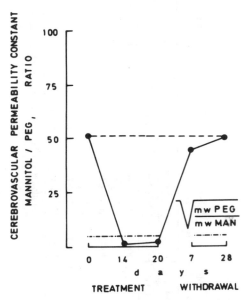

PARIETAL CORTEX

Figure 5.3 Cerebrovascular permeability constant, P, mannitol/PEG ratio for vascularly perfused guinea-pig forebrain during the course of chronic amphetamine intoxication after 14 and 20 days of treatment with D-amphetamine sulphate (i.p. 5 mg/kg daily), and 7 and 28 days after cessation of 20 days' chronic treatment with amphetamine. P value was estimated on the assumption of the surface area of 100 cm² g⁻¹ brain tissue from means of 5–12 animals. Interrupted line represents $P_{mannitol}/P_{PEG}$ ratio obtained in control, non-treated animals; dashed line represents mannitol/PEG ratio of reciprocal values of the square root of molecular weight. Olive oil/water partition coefficient $P–C$ ratio of mannitol/PEG is 1:30

showed an increase in the caudate nucleus and hippocampus (Figure 5.5; Table 5.3). On the other hand, no such changes could be shown for TRH (Table 5.3). The initial volume of distribution, V_i, for TRH has markedly decreased by a factor of 4–5, while there was a tendency for K_{in} to increase in the parietal cortex and hippocampus. However, in the presence of bacitracin (an aminopeptidase and amidase inhibitor) and unlabelled TRH, a reverse effect was obtained, namely a 2–5-fold increase in V_i and a similar decrease in K_{in}.

The Nature of V_i

The interpretation of these studies on neuropeptides is not easy and must await clarification of the nature of the parameter V_i, i.e. a fraction of the brain water that comes into rapid equilibrium with the blood, and thus is a compartment that may be considered to be in parallel with the blood–brain barrier, i.e. a fraction of the extracellular fluid not insulated from the blood by the barrier, as with paraventricular organs, astrocytes and possibly peptidergic nerve terminals, or perhaps the

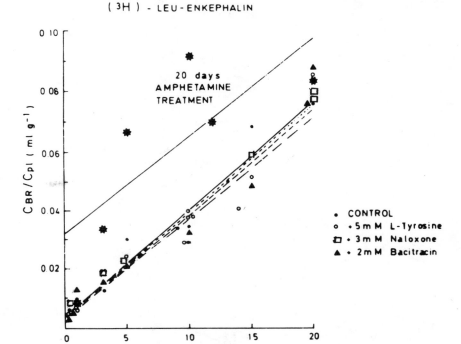

Figure 5.4   Effect of amphetamine (i.p. 5 mg/kg daily for 20 days) on kinetics of entry of [³H]-Leu-enkephalin (✱) in hippocampus of the perfused guinea-pig brain. Control values of the unidirectional [³H]-Leu-enkephalin transfer, as well as the effects of L-tyrosine (5 mM), naloxone (3 mM) and bacitracin (2 mM) on [³H]-Leu-enkephalin transfer are taken from Zloković *et al.* (1987)

cytoplasm of the capillary endothelial cells, if these had an asymmetry so that their luminal sides were more permeable than their abluminal sides. Until the nature of this compartment is elucidated, it would be unwise to speculate as to the mechanism by which amphetamine changes its magnitude. The effects on permeability are also not easy to interpret. Thus, the studies on inert polar molecules such as mannitol and PEG have indicated that amphetamine causes a breakdown of the blood–brain barrier, leading to a rise in K_{in}, and it is not easy to see why the neuropeptides should not share in this pathway. Amphetamine caused on average a 3–4-fold increase in K_{in} for mannitol (Table 5.1), yet with leucine-enkephalin there has been virtually no change (Table 5.3).

Possible Human Studies on Neuropeptides

By means of specific and highly sensitive radioimmunoassay (RIA) studies, concentrations of different peptides may be determined in the CSF and plasma of

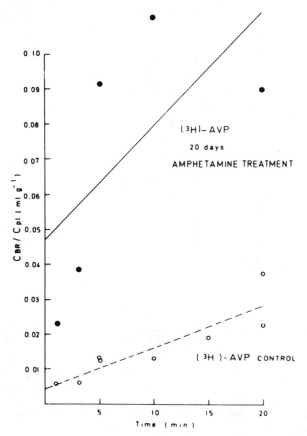

Figure 5.5 Effect of amphetamine (i.p. 5 mg/kg daily for 20 days) on kinetics of entry of [^{3}H]-AVP in the caudate nucleus in the perfused guinea-pig brain, control line represents control caudal uptake of [^{3}H]-AVP. [^{3}H]-radioactivity, dpm g^{-1} brain/dpm ml^{-1} plasma perfusate, is plotted against the perfusion time, T

patients with various neurological and psychiatric disorders. Although the available information with respect to CSF concentrations of neuropeptides in patients with extrapyramidal disorders is limited, such measurements might well contribute to a better understanding of interactions between peptidergic and classical neuro-transmitters in these disorders, as well as having some diagnostic and prognostic value. It has been suggested that the CSF concentrations of peptides, classical neurotransmitters and their metabolites may reflect corresponding changes within the brain in some extrapyramidal diseases (Gerstenbrand and Poewe, 1986).

For example, the enkephalin-methionine level in the CSF of patients with Parkinson's disease may be either normal or increased in comparison with a control group, according to the phase and duration of the disease (Sheehy *et al.*, 1981). Contradictory results have been reported with respect to the concentration

Table 5.3 Blood–CNS barrier permeability to [³H]-Leu-enkephalin, [³H]-AVP and [³H]-TRH in various regions of perfused guinea-pig forebrain in amphetamine-treated animals (i.p. 5 mg/kg daily for 20 days)

Structure	$P_{amphetamine}/P_{control}$	$V_{i,amphetamine}/V_{i,control}$
	[³H]-Leu-enkephalin	
Parietal cortex	1.1	6.2
Caudate nucleus	1.0	10.6
Hippocampus	0.98	7.7
	[³H]-AVP	
Parietal cortex	1.8	7.0
Caudate nucleus	2.7	11.6
Hippocampus	2.6	7.4
	[³H]-TRH	
Parietal cortex	1.2	0.16
Caudate nucleus	1.0	0.20
Hippocampus	1.5	0.25
2 mM Bacitracin + 1 mM TRH		
Parietal cortex	0.53	1.6
Caudate nucleus	0.20	5.0
Hippocampus	0.22	2.4

Cerebrovascular permeability, P, is determined from the multiple-time brain uptake series ($n = 5$–6 in amphetamine-treated animals, $n = 5$–8 in control) on the assumption of capillary surface area of 100 cm²/g brain.

of substance P in the CSF of patients with Parkinson's disease; and elevation of this peptide in the CSF may best be explained in terms of compensatory hyperactivity of an excitatory striatonigral substance P pathway in response to the nigral dopaminergic hypoactivity (Gerstendbrand and Poewe, 1986). In this connection, we may mention that the peptide concentrations in the CSF of patients with various affective disorders have been reviewed by Provje *et al.* (1987). In depression, the CSF concentrations of CRF, TRH and substance P may be elevated, while concentrations of beta-endorphin, BBS, DSIP, calcitonin and CCK are unchanged in unipolar depression. The CSF concentrations of SRIF, VP (arginine) and CCK are reduced in unipolar depression, and that of VIP in endogenous depression. In mania, the levels of SRIF, CCK, bombesin and VIP in the CSF have been found normal, while that of arginine vasopressin was increased in some manic patients and the calcitonin levels could be reduced.

Transport of Putative Amino Acid Transmitters

The transport of [³H]-gamma-aminobutyric acid (GABA) and [³H]-glutamic acid has been examined in the perfused guinea-pig brain. As transmitters we may expect their transport from blood to nervous tissue to be strongly restrained, and this is true although there is no absolute impermeability of the blood–brain barrier to these amino acids (Zloković *et al.*, unpublished). In amphetamine-treated guinea-pigs the changes from normal were similar to those found for peptidergic transmitters, leucine-enkephalin and arginine vasopressin—namely for both amino acids there was a marked 3–8-fold increase in the initial volume of distribution, V_i, and a more moderate but significant increase in K_{in} (Table 5.4). Once again the interpretation of the change in V_i depends on our view of the meaning, in anatomical terms, of this volume.

Summary

To summarize recent work on the amphetamine-induced syndrome in guinea-pigs, we have to emphasize that a great deal of work must be carried out on the model before a relation between barrier breakdown and the psychotic syndrome can be interpreted in terms of altered neurotransmitter relations between blood and the cortical neurons involved in the disturbance. As a model that is reproducible in the laboratory, the amphetamine-psychotic guinea-pig represents a valuable contribution to the investigation of psychiatric disturbances, and it is to be hoped that the model will be employed in future studies. We must emphasize, however, that an amphetamine-induced breakdown of the blood–brain barrier is not a new discovery: Domer *et al.* (1980) showed that the increased blood pressure caused by amphetamine in rats was accompanied by an increased permeability of the blood–brain barrier to labelled protein, the increased uptake running parallel with the rise in arterial pressure. The changes in the barrier of the amphetamine-psychotic guinea-pig described here, however, cannot be attributed to a raised arterial pressure, since the changes were not large enough, so we must envisage two, probably closely connected, effects. One is an opening of the barrier due to a raised arterial blood pressure, probably with a metabolic origin, mediated through a catecholaminergic effect on beta-receptors on the capillary membrane, since propranolol markedly reduced the uptake of labelled protein in amphetamine-

Table 5.4 Graphically estimated unidirectional transfer constant, K_{in}, for simultaneously perfused D-[^{3}H]-mannitol and [^{14}C]-PEG in the caudate nucleus in the guinea-pig following ipsilateral or contralateral cortical lesion[a]

Day after lesion	K_{in} (ml min^{-1} g^{-1} × 10^3)			
	Ipsilateral cortical lesion		*Contralateral cortical lesion*	
	[^{14}C]-PEG	D-[^{3}H]-Mannitol	[^{14}C]-PEG	D-[^{3}H]-Mannitol
2	0.23 ± 0.04	0.82 ± 0.08	0.38 ± 0.15	1.22 ± 0.25
	(A) 0.89 ± 0.03	1.30 ± 0.05	1.32 ± 0.68	2.00 ± 0.41
7	0.24 ± 0.02	1.06 ± 0.02	1.56 ± 0.40	3.16 ± 0.66
	(A) 0.93 ± 0.16	1.80 ± 0.32	2.02 ± 0.46	4.36 ± 0.25
28	1.18 ± 0.21		1.34 ± 0.28	
	(A) 1.30 ± 0.29	1.99 ± 0.42	0.68 ± 0.02	2.72 ± 0.15
32		2.56 ± 0.31		2.46 ± 0.12
		(A) 3.14 ± 0.10		4.58 ± 1.25

[a] Effect of amphetamine (A) on K_{in} values has been studied in a separate series of experiments. Values are means ± s.e.; number of animals, 4–6.

treated rats (Carlsson and Johansson, 1978). The other effect of amphetamine, described in the psychotic guinea-pig, is independent of raised arterial pressure and is revealed as a breakdown of the barrier of a more complex kind; whether amphetamine, under these chronic conditions, can induce a carrier mechanism that permits transport across the capillary endothelium of neuropeptides that would otherwise have been excluded from the central nervous system remains as an interesting possibility.

Experimental Allergic Encephalomyelitis

In experimental neurology, allergic encephalomyelitis (EAE) has been studied frequently as an analogue of the human disease, multiple sclerosis (MS) (Lassman and Vass, 1986). A number of EAE models have been described in various animals with a certain degree of similarity with respect to the clinical signs of MS. However, there are marked differences in histology between animal models of EAE and that of MS, so that sometimes a comparison between the two conditions is difficult.

Guinea-pig Model

Colover (1980, 1984) has developed a model in the guinea-pig, induced by homologous myelin basic protein (MBP) after pretreatment with foreign protein and muramyl dipeptide (MDP), which bears a remarkable histological resemblance to human MS (Colover, 1988). In the work to be described below, the transport of immunoglobin (IgG) into the brain of the perfused guinea-pig has been measured in EAE animals and compared with that of D-mannitol.

Technique of EAE Development

In outbred adult Hartly guinea-pigs EAE was induced by homologous MBP after pretreatment with ovalbumin (OA) and MDP, according to the method of Colover, using the following scheme: (a) on day 1, animals were injected s.c. with a water-in-oil emulsion of 15 μg of MDP, 200 μg of OA and Freund incomplete adjuvant (FIA); (b) on day 28, they were injected i.p. with 10 mg of OA in saline under a Piriton cover; and (c) on day 35 the survivors were injected with 50 μg of MBP and 0.1 ml of Freund complete adjuvant (FCA). Following MBP injections, animals were observed daily for clinical score and sacrificed up to 45 days. Brain and spinal cord, contralateral to the vascular perfusion side, were fixed in formol saline, and paraffin embedded sections were stained with hematoxylin and eosin for routine histology and gallocyanin–Darrow red stain for myelin. Brains were perfused with $[^{125}I]$-IgG for 10 min followed by sampling and preparation for scintillation counting. In a further series of experiments brains were perfused with D-$[^3H]$-mannitol from 1 to 20 min, followed by multiple sampling and preparation for scintillation counting. In a further series of experiments brains were perfused with unlabelled homologous immunoglobulin G for 10 min, followed by preparation for immunocytochemistry. Immunoglobulin G was labelled with ^{125}I by the micro-chloramine-T method (Hunter and Greenwood, 1962) modified by adding a 10-fold excess of chloramine-T as well as phosphate-buffered saline (PBS) of pH 7.4. Unbound iodide was removed by gel filtration on Sephadex G-25 and homogeneity was verified by thin-layer chromatography. The specific activity was 2–3 μCi/nmol. That enables the use of highly radioactive perfusion fluids at low concentrations of immunoglobulins.

Brains from non-perfused EAE animals and EAE animals perfused with 4 mg/ml unlabelled immunoglobulin G or only with a perfusion medium as well as brains from non-treated animals vascularly perfused were prepared for immuno-histochemistry. The avidin–biotin–peroxidase method on 4- to 5-μm paraffin sections, briefly summarized, involves incubations with (a) anti-guinea-pig IgG (raised in goat), (b) biotinylated anti-goat IgG, (c) avidin–peroxidase, and (d) diamino benzidine (specific substrate for peroxidase reaction). Preparations were lightly stained with haematoxylin–eosin.

Samples of CSF (50–100 μl) and plasma from anaesthetized EAE and normal guinea-pigs were taken from cisterna magna and jugular vein, respectively, before the vascular perfusion was started. Immunoglobulin G was determined by means of the enzyme-linked immunosorbent assay (ELISA) method, while albumins were measured by means of rocket immunoelectrophoresis.

Clinical Signs

A specimen of 45 randomly chosen sensitized animals showed that 64% had developed a varying degree of clinical signs, ranging from adynamia and weight loss, hind-limb paresis, hind-limb paralysis and overflow incontinentia to peracute course (moribund).

CSF Concentrations

Figure 5.6 illustrates the CSF/serum quotient for albumin and IgG in normal animals as well as in animals with EAE, 21–32 days and 38–45 days, with moderate clinical signs. There is an increase in both quotients (A), the changes being more pronounced for albumin than for IgG, also reflected when the CSF/serum Ig quotient is compared with the CSF/serum albumin quotient (B).

Brain Uptake

When brains of EAE animals were vascularly perfused with $[^{125}I]$-IgG, it was possible to demonstrate an increase in regional brain uptake $C_{br}/C_{pl}(T) - V_i$, in comparison with non-treated animals, after 7 and 20 days of EAE, while in later stages (30–40 days) a tendency towards normalization appeared (Figure 5.7). Experiments with perfusion of EAE animal brain (7 days) with D-$[^3H]$-mannitol demonstrated a moderate increase in the unidirectional transfer constant in the

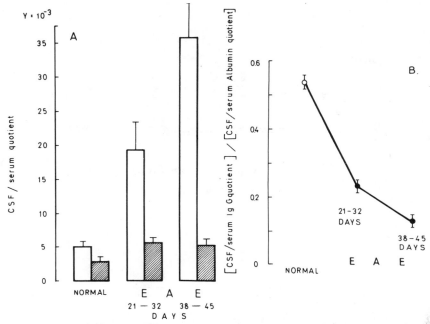

Figure 5.6 (A) CSF/serum quotient for albumin (open bars) and immunoglobulin G (hatched bars) during acute experimental allergic encephalomyelitis (EAE). Values are means ± s.e. from five to six experiments. (B) The same results presented as the ratio of the immunoglobulin G quotient over the albumin quotient

parietal cortex (K_{in} = 0.0003 ml min^{-1} g^{-1}), a marked increase in the hippocampus (K_{in} = 0.0006 ml min^{-1} g^{-1}) and no significant changes in the caudate nucleus (K_{in} = 0.00025 ml min^{-1} g^{-1}) in comparison with non-treated animals (K_{in} = 0.0002 3 ml min^{-1} g^{-1}).

Immunohistochemistry

Immunohistochemistry has confirmed kinetic studies with [^{125}I]-IgG. Figure 5.8 illustrates normal non-treated brain (A) and a brain of an EAE animal vascularly perfused with artificial blood containing 4 mg/ml IgG (B). It is apparent that both the microvessel endothelial cells and the surrounding perivascular areas show an intensive positive avidin–biotin–peroxidase reaction (B), which is not the case in controls.

In general, the results on this relatively new model of multiple sclerosis indicate some breakdown of the blood–brain barrier to the inert polar molecule, D-mannitol. Changes in the concentrations of albumin and IgG in relation to those in plasma, the so-called 'quotients' of Felgenhauer (1974, 1980), could also be interpreted on the same basis; thus, when at the same stage of EAE (7 days) the kinetics of mannitol entry are compared with IgG brain uptake, some pronounced

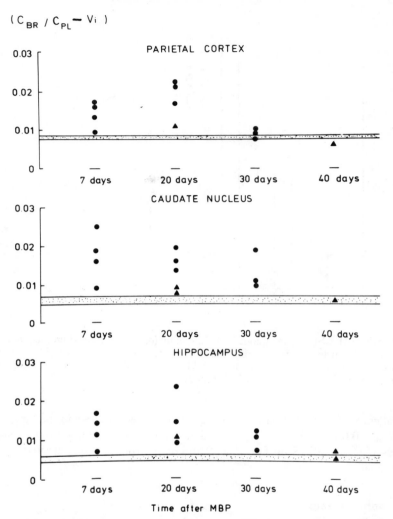

$(C_{BR} / C_{PL} - V_i)$

Figure 5.7 Regional brain uptake of homologous $[^{125}I]$-labelled IgG during 10 min of vascular brain perfusion in the guinea pig with acute allergic encephalomyelitis. Uptake (●) expressed as the C_{br}/C_{pl} ratio corrected for the initial volume of distribution. V_i, is plotted against the time after MBP injection. The shaded area represents the brain uptake (mean ± s.e.) of immunoglobulins in normal animals, obtained by non-linear regression fit. Each point represents a single experiment: (▲) after treatment with MBP_{68-84}

change in permeability to blood-borne IgG also occurs. The increased blood–brain barrier permeability to mannitol described here is in agreement with the results of Daniel *et al.* (1983) on an EAE model in the rat. However, it seems that during the early stages of EAE the enhancement of IgG transport at the blood–brain barrier is independent of the more non-specific multifocal lesions revealed by brain mannitol uptake.

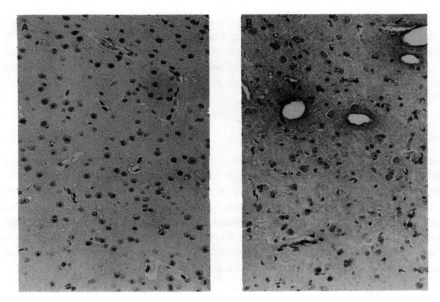

Figure 5.8 Avidin–biotin–peroxidase reaction in a non-treated, control brain (A) and in the brain of an EAE animal vascularly perfused with homologous bloodborne IgG (B). 300×; reduced 30% for reproduction

Cortical Lesions

It is beyond the scope of this chapter to consider in any detailed fashion the changes in the blood–brain barrier resulting from cerebral lesions, either experimental or pathological; the subject has been treated in depth in several publications. It will be recalled from our brief review in Chapter 1 that the consequence of a breakdown of the blood–brain barrier will necessarily be the development of oedema, not necessarily because plasma proteins have escaped into the extracellular space but because the control of the fluid balance of nervous tissue relies on the controlled exchanges of Na^+ and other ions across the capillary endothelium, a control that does not pertain in tissues with highly permeable capillaries, such as muscle and skin. In this section we shall merely consider a guinea-pig model in which the distant effects of cortical lesions are studied, especially with respect to the effects of amphetamine.

In general, various strategies seem to be employed in restoring brain function after lesions (for a review, see, for example, Rozenzweig and Porter, 1984). There is an increasing number of model systems in which correlates between neuronal plasticity and behavioural recovery have been identified (Rakić, 1988). Moreover, many of the neuronal processes involved in recovery of behavioural function after brain damage are likely to be the same as those involved in reorganization processes. Some earlier neurophysiological studies (Rakić, 1984) have suggested an important role of the specific sensorimotor cortical regions for the integrative function of the corpus striatum. Thus, lesions in this area are accompanied by asymmetrical biochemical changes in the striatum as well as in other distant brain regions (Boyeson and Feeney, 1985; Pekovic *et al.*, 1988; Rusić *et al.*, 1988) which may be related to the behavioural deficit after the injury (Pearlson and Robinson, 1981).

Amphetamine

Feeney *et al.* (1982) demonstrated that a single injection of amphetamine, given early following cortical damage, accelerates the recovery of locomotor ability; the drug also produces a reversible increase in permeability of the blood–brain barrier, as described earlier. In the light of these findings it is interesting to see whether right- or left-sensorimotor cortical regions may influence the permeability of the blood–brain barrier in more distant brain regions, and to establish possible interactions between sensorimotor cortical lesions and the effects of amphetamine treatment on blood–brain barrier function.

The Experimental Approach

Sensorimotor cortex of guinea-pigs was unilaterally removed by suction to the depth of the white matter (4 mm lateral from the midline, 2 mm anterior to and 3 mm posterior to the bregma). The effects of these lesions were compared with similar ones made in the occipital lobe or associative cortex. Measurements of the blood–brain barrier to the inert polar molecules mannitol and polyethylene glycol (PEG) were made at different times after the lesions, ranging from 2 to 22 days. The results were compared with measurements on animals with similar lesions but treated with amphetamine (5 mg/kg) daily as before.

Changes in Blood–Brain Barrier Permeability: Caudate Nucleus

Table 5.4 represents values for the unidirectional transfer constant, K_{in}, for PEG and mannitol in the vascularly perfused caudate nucleus with either ipsilateral or contralateral sensorimotor lesions, as well as the effect of amphetamine treatment. For both molecules a significant increase appeared as early as 2 days following the lesion. The changes were more pronounced after a contralateral lesion. The increase in permeability was potentiated by amphetamine after both ipsilateral and contralateral lesions. From 7 to 32 days after the lesions a further increase in the blood–brain barrier permeability to both molecules was found, the changes again being greater after contralateral lesion and potentiated by amphetamine treatment. Similar changes were found in hippocampus and parietal cortex.

The Permeability Ratio

Figure 5.9 illustrates the ratio of cerebrovascular permeability constants for mannitol and PEG in the caudate nucleus, in animals with either ipsilateral or

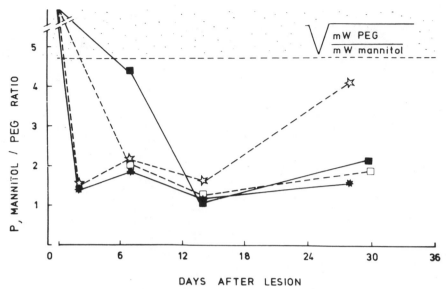

Figure 5.9   Cerebrovascular permeability constant, *P*, and mannitol/PEG ratio estimated during vascular perfusion of the caudate nucleus in guinea-pigs with ipsilateral (■—■) and contralateral (□—□) sensory-motor lesion. Effect of amphetamine transport on *P* and the mannitol/PEG ratio in guinea pigs with ipsilateral (★—★) and contralateral (☆—☆) lesions was estimated from a separate series of experiments. Upper and lower lines of the shaded area represent the *P* and mannitol/PEG ratio obtained in non-treated animals and the mannitol/PEG ratio of the reciprocal values of molecular weights for mannitol and PEG, respectively. The olive oil/water partition coefficient, *P–C*, for mannitol–PEG is 1 : 30

contralateral sensorimotor lesions, as well as the effect of amphetamine treatment. It is apparent that immediately after the lesion (2 days) the normal permeability ratio is altered, and 7 days after the ipsilateral lesion, the P_{man}/P_{PEG} ratio approaches the reciprocal value of the square roots of the molecular weight for two molecules. This is not the case after a contralateral lesion, as well as after amphetamine treatment with either lesion, since the values tend to approach unity. Similar findings were also obtained after ipsilateral lesions. At 30 days following the lesions the permeability ratio remains slightly above unity, while the contralateral lesion and amphetamine treatment at this period produced a ratio close to the reciprocal value of the square roots of the molecular weights for the two molecules.

Hippocampus
Figure 5.10 shows the cerebrovascular permeability constant *P* in the hippocampus for both molecules in animals with ipsilateral (A) and contralateral (B) lesions, as well as the effect of amphetamine treatment. A higher absolute permeability for mannitol than for PEG has been observed as well as potentiation by amphetamine treatment. The absolute increase in permeability for both molecules peaked at 14

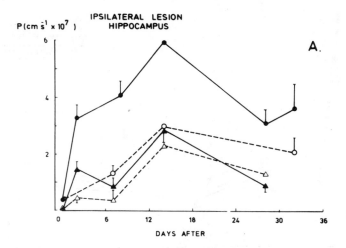

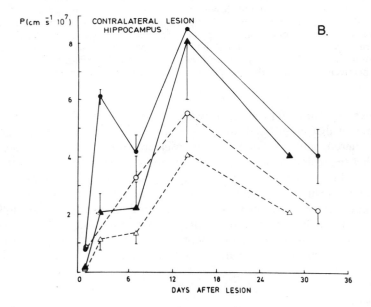

Figure 5.10 Cerebrovascular permeability constant, *P*, for simultaneously perfused D-[³H]-mannitol (○—○) and [¹⁴C]-PEG (△—△) in the hippocampus of the guinea-pigs with ipsilateral (A) and contralateral (B) sensory-motor lesions measured at different times (days) after the lesion. Effect of amphetamine treatment on the *P* values for D-[³H]-mannitol (●—●) and [¹⁴C]-PEG (▲—▲) was estimated in a separate series of experiments. Each point represents the mean ± s.e. of four to six animals

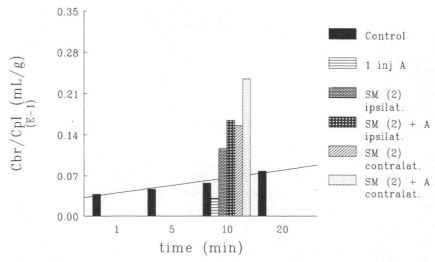

Figure 5.11 Effects of a single injection of amphetamine (A) on the unidirectional transfer of inert polar molecule [³H]-D-mannitol across the blood–CNS barrier in the guinea-pig. SM—sensory-motor cortex

days after the lesion and was more pronounced on the contralateral side. Similar findings were obtained for the parietal cortex and caudate nucleus. In control animals with occipital or associative cortex lesions, no alteration in blood–brain barrier permeability was observed 2 days after lesion.

It is worth stressing that in lesioned animals the changes in barrier permeability appeared, not only after repeated doses of amphetamine but also after single injections of the drug (Figure 5.11).

Summary

To summarize the results of these experiments on the effects of sensorimotor cortex on more distant regions of the brain, it has been demonstrated that there has been an opening of the barrier to inert polar molecules, D-mannitol and PEG, in the parietal cortex, caudate nucleus and hippocampus only following either ipsilateral and/or contralateral sensorimotor cortical lesions (Table 5.5; Figures 5.9, 5.10). In all the distant regions studied at different times after the sensori-motor lesion, the blood–brain barrier permeability to mannitol and PEG was significantly higher on the contralateral side. Also, in all regions studied up to 7 days after the ipsilateral lesion, the P_{man}/P_{PEG} ratios (Figure 5.9) approached the reciprocal value of the square roots of their molecular weight. This may indicate that penetration from the blood to the brain is governed by simple diffusion

Table 5.5 Blood–CNS barrier permeability to $[^3H]$-GABA and $[^3H]$-glutamic acid in various regions of perfused guinea-pig brain in amphetamine-treated animals (i.p. 1 mg/kg or 5 mg/kg daily for 20 days)

| Structure | $P_{amphetamine}/P_{control}$ | | $V_{i, amphetamine}/V_{i, control}$ | |
	$[^3H]$-GABA	$[^3H]$-glutamic acid	$[^3H]$-GABA	$[^3H]$-glutamic acid
Parietal cortex	2.24	0.6	4.5	6.2
Caudate nucleus	0.42	1.0	7.6	3.3
Hippocampus	1.2		2.9	

Cerebrovascular permeability, P, is determined from the multiple-time brain uptake series ($n = 5$–8 in amphetamine-treated and control animals for $[^3H]$-GABA; $n = 5$–6 in amphetamine-treated and control animals for $[^3H]$-glutamic acid) on the assumption of capillary surface area of 100 cm^2/g brain.

through large pores (Davson and Danielli, 1942; Davson *et al.*, 1987), most likely owing to an opening of the tight junctions at the blood–brain barrier. However, in the same period after a contralateral lesion, the P_{man}/P_{PEG} ratio approached unity, indicating transfer independent of the molecular size, which may suggest bulk flow across enlarged tight junctions at the blood–brain barrier and/or an increased non-specific transendothelial vesicular transfer, both processes being governed by the level of intracellular mediators in the endothelial cells (Joó, 1988; Crone, 1986).

It has been shown previously that amphetamine treatment induces reversible breakdown of the blood–brain barrier, most likely by opening channels that permit a flow of fluid, carrying substances at a rate irrespective of their molecular size and lipophilicity (Rakić *et al.*, 1989). The most pronounced effect of amphetamine in this study was after an ipsilateral lesion, since the P_{man}/P_{PEG} ratio was lowered from about 5 towards unity, indicating a change of transfer mechanism for both molecules in the presence of amphetamine.

Human Clinical Studies

As Bakay *et al.* (1986) have pointed out, the evaluation of blood–brain barrier permeability contributes to the prognostic guidance to the severity and likely recovery from brain damage. Thus, it is well known that the clinical assessment of the extent of damage to the central nervous system and the potential for recovery is difficult; extremely variable outcomes can occur in patients with apparently identical lesions.

Brain Oedema

The existence of this condition in brain trauma is too well-known to require emphasis, although its significance with respect to healing is not clear; thus, any flow of fluid through the tissue, or exchanges between extracellular fluid and blood compartments, might contribute to remove cellular debris, etc. We may describe, here, some studies in which the flows of fluid, protein and electrolytes were assessed, using the simple method described in detail by Arežina *et al.* (1990).

Filtration

The volume of filtration was defined by the following equation:

$$F = \frac{HA \times 100}{HV} - 100$$

where F is the volume of fluid filtration and HA and HV are the arterial and venous haematocrit ratios. A positive value of F indicates a flow of filtrate from blood to brain and vice versa. The directional flow and volume of protein filtration, FP, are given by:

$$FP = PV - \frac{100 \times PA}{100 \pm F}$$

where PV and PA are the amounts of protein, in grams, per 100 ml of venous and arterial blood, respectively.

Barrier Measurement

This was assessed by uptake into the cerebrospinal fluid after intravenous injection of ^{32}P-labelled phosphate. It was found that radioactivity reached a maximum at 1–2 h after administration. In normal humans the CSF radioactivity is some 2–3% of that in blood. In patients with treated craniocerebral traumas, on the 3rd day after the injury the CSF radioactivity reached some 8–9% of that in blood, indicating a breakdown in blood–brain permeability. On the 5th day the values were below normal, namely 1.3%, and on the 7th day they increased to 7–8% and finally decreased successively until they returned to normal about the 25th day.

Patient Categories

The patients were grouped in three categories—light, mid-severe and severe. Light cases comprised brain concussions, with no bone injuries. Mid-severe ones included brain contusions, most frequently associated with bone injuries, haematomas, subarachnoid haemorrhagia, and the signs of brain stem injuries and impairment of autonomic functions. Severe injuries meant numerous grave intracranial bleeding, brain and metabolic dysfunctions, and the most serious cases were those with intensified above-mentioned syndromes and permanent deep coma.

Fluid Movements

It was found that, in light and mid-severe cases immediately after the accident, there was entry of fluid from blood to brain tissue (-3.03 ml/100 ml blood); on the 7th day the flow was in the opposite direction (0.21 ml/100 ml blood); after 8–15 days the direction of flow was once again from blood to brain (−1.84 ml/100 ml blood); after the 20th day the direction was from brain to blood (+3.51 ml/100 ml blood). In patients with severe brain trauma, immediately after the injury the flow was directed from blood to brain tissue (−2.23 ml/100 ml blood); on about the 7th day the flow reversed (+0.11 ml/100 ml blood); on the 15th day flow was again directed into the brain tissue (−2.02 ml/100 ml blood), and finally on about the 30th day the direction reversed (+0.65 ml/100 ml blood). Thus, in patients with severe but not fatal brain injuries the phasic character of the flow of fluid was maintained. In those cases that had a lethal outcome the phasic character was either missing or existed for only their first week.

Electrolyte Movements

Essentially similar fluctuations can be observed in transport of electrolytes. Thus, immediately after light and mid-severe injuries there was an influx of sodium from blood to brain, as would be expected from the fluid flow; after 7 days the direction reversed; about the 15th day there was influx of sodium, once again, and finally on the 25th day, after clinical recovery of the patients, there was a further efflux of sodium into the blood. Movements of potassium in cases with the same injuries, followed the same pattern as those of sodium, showing similar phasic variations. With calcium there was an efflux from blood to brain (−0.18 mg/100 ml blood); on the 7th day the direction was reversed (+0.09 mg/100 ml blood); on the 15th day calcium again entered the brain tissue (−0.21 mg/100 ml blood). During the period of the patient's clinical recovery, calcium passed from brain tissue into blood (+0.27 mg/100 ml blood).

In general, it seems that the phasic changes in fluid and ion movements during the course of recovery from non-fatal brain injuries run parallel. In cases with a lethal outcome, the direction of sodium and calcium transport was constant and from blood to brain (influx), while that of potassium was from brain to blood (efflux), i.e. there is some disruption in the normal regulation of ion transport, a disruption that must be taken account of in deciding on therapy. A steady influx of extracellular ions, such as sodium, would be expected of a moribund tissue, while a loss of potassium would also be expected as a result of leakage of the ion from the brain cells. The phasic changes in flux of water and ions observed in non-fatal cases are of obvious interest and merit much further study.

Protein Changes

Without going into detail, we may emphasize that, during light brain injuries, there is influx of albumin and alpha-, beta- and gamma-globulins, an influx that contributes to the development of oedema, although, as pointed out in Chapter 1, oedema may occur in brain tissue entirely as a result of disturbed blood–brain permeability to ions. During the patient's recovery, this influx of proteins is reversible. With severe injuries of lethal outcome, the position is obscured by the effects of tissue necrosis leading to large effluxes of the globulins from brain into the blood.

Biological Markers

During recent years the use of specific markers as indices to brain damage has been increasing. Former investigations have been mostly orientated towards glycolytic and mitochondrial enzymes (Bakay *et al.*, 1986). In the studies presented here the enzymes creatine kinase and gamma-glutamyltransferase have been employed, their concentrations being measured in CSF and serum. Creatine kinase (CK) catalyses the reaction between creatine phosphate and ADP. It is a dimeric enzyme (brain type, −CK−BB), a cathodal isozyme (the skeletal muscle, CK−MM) and a hybrid isoenzyme (the cardiac muscle and glial cell type, CK−MB). These enzymes are not totally specific to the assigned tissues, but relatively they are highly specific either to brain or to myocardium or glial cells, because of the relative abundance of these isoenzymes in the respective organs in comparison with other tissues. Gamma-glutamyltransferase is a marker for epithelial cell membrane, and also for the brain capillary endothelial cell membrane (Pardridge, 1988).

Creatine Kinase
Bakay *et al.* (1986) have reviewed the potential usefulness of CK as a marker in

Table 5.6 CK in serum (μ/l-Worthington)

	Total CK	CK-MM	CK-MB	CK-BB
Control (normal)	5.3–30.5	5–30	0.3–2.11	0–1.8
Acute head injury (contusion)[a]	28–78	26–70	1–5	1–3
Acute head injury (concussion)[a]	25–40	25–37	1–2	0–2

[a] Male subjects, 21–40 years of age, first day after injury.

Table 5.7 Follow-up of CK activity in CSF (μ/l-Worthington) after close head injury (contusion)[a]

	Total CK	CK-MM	CK-MB	CK-BB
Control (normal)	0–4	0	0	0–4
1st day	36–44	4–6	2–4	30–34
7th day	15–30	2–4	2–5	11–20
1 month	10–22	1–2	1–4	2–18
3 months	8–18	6–1	1–3	7–14
1 year	5–10	0	0–2	5–8

[a] Male subjects 21–40 years of age.

analysis of trauma of the central nervous system. Our own results indicate that CK activity increases in the serum (Table 5.6), especially after contusional brain injuries; they are also extremely pronounced in the CSF, beginning from the first day of the injury (Table 5.7). When the CSF changes are followed over a period of up to one year, it is found that increased values, especially of CK–BB, persist for quite a long time. Of especial interest is the correlation between the neurophysiological and clinical parameters (Table 5.8), which indicates that increased values of creatine kinase, especially of CK–MB and CK–BB, are associated with patients exhibiting poor neurophysiological recovery.

Gamma-Glutamyltransferase (GTT)
Immediately after brain injury the activity of this enzyme in CSF, wich is normally insignificant, increases some 15-fold, returning, after the normalization of the clinical picture, to normal some 3 weeks after the injury (Table 5.9). The increase in activity of this enzyme in the CSF presumably reflects uptake from the damaged brain tissue, notably of cell membranes which could include those of the capillary endothelium that regulates the blood–brain barrier.

Table 5.8   Late (1 year) CK activity in CSF following close head injury (contusion)[a]

	Total CK	CK–MM	CK–MB	CK–BB
Control (normal)	0–4	0	0	0–4
Patients with favourable neuropsychological recovery	1–5	0	0	1–5
Patients with poor neuro-psychological recovery	10–16	0	2–6	8–10

[a] Male subjects 21–40 years of age.

Table 5.9   Gamma-glutamyltranspeptidase activity

Control	0.005 ± 0.001 mmol/l
Concussion, 4 days after acute head injury	0.015 ± 0.005 mmol/l
Contusion, days after head injury	
1 day	0.08 ± 0.015 mmol/l
10 days	0.01 ± 0.005 mmol/l
20 days	0.005 ± 0.012 mmol/l
Before lethal end	

References

Allen, I.V. (1986). The relationship of immunological and histological abnormalities in multiple sclerosis. In Hommes, O.R. (Ed.), *Multiple Sclerosis Research in Europe*. MTP Press, Lancaster, pp. 163–167

Anqrist, B.M. and Gerson, S. (1970). The phenomenology of experimentally induced amphetamine psychosis—preliminary observations. *Biol. Psychiat.*, **2**, 95–107

Arežina, P., Atanasova, E., Djordjević, Ž., Lević, Z., Mileusnić, R., Pavlović, V., Ocić, G., Rakić, Lj. and Sekulović, N. (1990). Biological Markers in evaluation of patient outcome after brain injury. *Bull. Sci.* (in press)

Bakay, R.A.E., Sweeney, K.M. and Wood, J.H. (1986). Pathophysiology of cerebrospinal fluid in head injury. Part 2—Biochemical markers for central nervous system trauma. *Neurosurgery*, **18**, No. 3, 376–382

Boyeson, M.G. and Feeney, D.M. (1985). Striate dopamine after cortical injury. *Exp. Neurol.*, **89**, 479–483

Carlsson, C. and Johansson, B.B. (1978). Blood–brain barrier disfunction after amphetamine-administration in rats. *Acta Neuropathol.*, **41**, 125–129

Colover, J. (1980). A new pattern of spinal-cord demyelination in guinea pigs with acute experimental allergic encephalomyelitis mimicking multiple sclerosis. *Br. J. Exp. Pathol.*, **61**, 390–400

Colover, J. (1984). Acute demyelination in EAE after pretreatment with foreign protein and muramyl dipeptide (MDP). In Liss, A.R. (Ed.), *Experimental Allergic Encephalomyelitis: A Useful Model for Multiple Sclerosis.* pp. 37–42

Colover, J. (1988). Myelin debris in demyelinating process: A disease activity marker. In Confavreux, C., Aimard, G. and Dević, M. (Eds), *Trends in European Multiple Sclerosis Research.* Elsevier, London, pp. 229–234

Crone, C. (1986). Modulation of solute permeability in microvascular endothelium. *Fed. Proc.*, **45**, 77–83

Daniel, P.M., Lam, D.K. and Pratt, O.E. (1981). Changes in the effectiveness of the blood–brain and blood–spinal cord barriers in experimental allergic encephalomyelitis. *J. Neurol. Sci.*, **52**, 211–219

Daniel, P.M., Lam, D.K. and Pratt, O.E. (1983). Relation between the increase in the diffusional permeability allergic encephalomyelitis in the Lewis rat. *J. Neurol. Sci.*, **60**, 367–376

Davson, H. and Danielli, J.F. (1942). *The Permeability of Natural Membranes.* Cambridge University Press, Cambridge

Davson, H., Welch, K. and Segal, M.B. (1987). *Physiology and Pathophysiology of Cerebro-spinal Fluid.* Churchill Livingstone, Edinburgh, pp. 458–530

Dida, B., Rosić, N. and Rakić, Lj. (1982). The effects of long-term amphetamine administration on serum-proteins in rat. *IRCS Med. Sci. Biochem.*, **10**, 291–292

Domer, F.R., Sankar, R., Cole, S. and Wellmeyer, D. (1980). Dose dependent amphetamine-induced changes in permeability of blood–brain barrier of normotensive and spontaneously hypertensive rats. *Exp. Neurol.*, **70**, 576–585

Feeney, D.M., Gonzales, A. and Law, W. (1982). Amphetamine, holoperidine and experience interact to affect rate of recovery after motor cortex injury. *Science*, **271**, 855–857

Felgenhauer, K. (1974). Protein size and cerebrospinal fluid. *Klin. Wschr.*, **52**, 1158–1164

Felgenhauer, K. (1980). Protein filtration and secretion at human body fluid barriers. *Pflüg. Arch.*, **384**, 9–17

Gerstenbrand, F. and Poewe, W. (1986). Dopamine–peptidergic interactions in extrapyramidal disorders: a review of the clinical evidence. In Yahr, M.D. and Bergman, K.J. (Eds), *Advances in Neurology*, Vol. 45. Raven Press, New York, pp. 67–73

Hunter, W.M. and Greenwood, F.C. (1962). Preparation of iodine 131 labelled human growth hormone of high specific activity. *Nature*, **194**, 495–498

Joó, F. (1986). New aspects to the function of the cerebral endothelium. *Nature*, **321**, 197–198

Joó, F. (1988). Cyclic nucleotide mediated regulation of albumin transport in brain microvessels. In Rakić, Lj., Begley, D.J., Davson, H. and Zloković, B.V. (Eds), *Peptide and Amino Acid Transport Mechanism in the Central Nervous System.* Macmillan, London, pp. 119–129

Kornetsky, C. (1977). Animal models: promises and problems. In Hanin, I. and Usdin, E. (Eds), *Animal Models in Psychiatry and Neurology*. Pergamon Press, Oxford, pp. 1–9

Lampert, P.W. (1978). Autoimmune and virus-induced demyelinating diseases. *Am. J. Pathol.*, **91**, 176–197

Lassman, H. and Vass, K. (1986). The spectrum of experimental allergic encephalomyelitis. In Hommes, O.R. (Ed.), *Multiple Sclerosis Research in Europe*. MTP Press, Lancaster, pp. 109–115

McCulloch, J. and Harper, M.A. (1977). Cerebral circulatory and metabolism changes following amphetamine administration. *Brain Res.*, **121**, 196–199

Matthyse, A. and Hober, S. (1975). Animal models of schizophrenia. In Ongle, D.J. and Shein, H.M. (Eds), *Model Systems in Biological Psychiatry*. MIT Press, Cambridge, Mass., pp. 4–18

Orlowski, M., Sessa, G. and Green, J.P. (1974). γ-Glutamyl transpeptidase in brain capillaries: possible site of a blood–brain barrier for amino acids. *Science*, **184**, 66

Pardridge, W.M. (1988). Recent advances in blood–brain barrier transport. *Ann. Rev. Pharmacol. Toxicol.*, **28**, 25–39

Pardridge, W.M. and Mieius, L.J. (1981). Enkephalins and the blood–brain barrier: studies of binding and degradation in isolated brain microvessels. *Endocrinology*, **109**, 1138–1145

Pearlson, G.D. and Robinson, R.G. (1981). Suction lesions of the cerebral cortex in the rat induce asymmetrical behavioral and catecholaminergic responses. *Brain Res.*, **218**, 233–242

Peković, S., Rusić, M., Veskov, R. and Rakić, Lj. (1988). Suction ablation of the sensory-motor cortex induce assymmetrical changes in Ca^{2+} uptake in rat brain region synaptosomes. *Adv. Biosci.*, **70**, 133–136

Provje, A.J., Gazzbutt, J., Loosen, P.T., Bissette, G. and Nemeroj, K. (1987). The role of peptides in affective disorders: a review. *Prog. Brain Res.*, **72**, 235–279

Rakić, Lj. (1984). *Systems regulating behaviour*. Mir, Moscow

Rakić, Lj. (1988). Experimental models of restoration of functions of the brain lesions. In Cohadon, F. and Loboantunes, J. (Eds), Fidia Research Series, Vol. 13. Liviana Press, Padova

Rakić, Lj., Zloković, B.V., Davson, H., Begley, D.J., Lipovac, M.N. and Mitrović, D.M. (1989). Chronic amphetamine intoxication and the blood–brain barrier permeability to inert polar molecules in the vascularly perfused guinea-pig brain. *J. Neurol. Sci.*, **91**, 41–50

Reiber, H. (1986). Evaluation of blood-cerebrospinal fluid barrier dysfunction in neurological diseases. In Suckling, A.J., Rumsby, M.G. and Bradbury, M.W.B. (Eds). Ellis Horwood, Chichester, pp. 132–147

Rozenzweig, M.R. and Porter, L.W. (1984). Brain function: neural adaptation and recovery from brain injury. *Ann Rev. Psychol.*, **35**, 2377–2388

Rusić, M., Peković, S., Veskov, R. and Rakić, Lj. (1988). The effects of cortical injury on Na^+,K^+-ATPase activity. *Adv. Biosci.*, **70**, 173–176

Seeman, P. (1980). Brain dopamine receptors. *Pharmacol. Rev.*, **32** (3), 229–313

Sheehy, M., Schachter, M., Mardsen, C.D. and Parkers, J.D. (1981). Enkephalins in motor disorders. In Rose, F.C. and Capildeo, R. (Eds), *Research Progress in Parkinson's Disease*. Pitman Medical, London, p. 165

Snyder, S.H. (1976). The dopamine hypothesis of schizophrenia: focus on the dopamine receptors. *Am. J. Psychiat.*, **133**, 197–204

Takasato, Y., Rapoport, S.I. and Smith, Q.R. (1984). An *in situ* brain perfusion technique to study cerebrovascular transport in rat. *Am. J. Physiol.*, **274**, H484–H493

Zloković, B.V., Begley, D.J., Djuričić, B.M. and Mitrović, D.M. (1986a). Measurement of solute transport across the blood–brain barrier in the perfused guinea-pig brain: method and application to *N*-methyl-α-aminoisobutyric acid. *J. Neurochem.*, **46**, 1444–1451

Zloković, B.V., Begley, D.J., Segal, M.B., Davson, H., Rakić, Lj., Lipovac, M.N., Mitrović, D.M. and Jankov, R.M. (1988). Neuropeptide transport mechanisms in the central nervous system. In Rakić, Lj., Begley, D.J., Davson, H. and Zloković, B.V. (Eds), *Peptide and Amino Acid Transport Mechanisms in the Central Nervous System.* Macmillan, London, pp. 3–21

Zloković, B.V., Lipovac, M.N., Begley, D.J., Davson, H. and Rakić, Lj. (1987). Transport of leucine-enkephalin across the blood–brain barrier in the perfused guinea-pig brain. *J. Neurochem.*, **49**, 310–315

Zloković, B.V., Lipovac, M.N., Begley, D.J., Davson, H. and Rakić, Lj. (1988). Slow penetration of thyrotropin-releasing hormone across the blood–brain barrier of *in situ* perfused guinea-pig brain. *J. Neurochem.* (in press)

Zloković, B.V., Segal, M.B. and Begley, D.J. (1986b). Permeability of the isolated choroid plexus of the sheep to thyrotropin-releasing hormone. In Yudilevich, D.L. and Mann, G.E. (Eds), *Carrier-mediated Transport of Solutes from Blood to Tissue.* Longman, London, pp. 307–312

Zloković, B.V., Segal, M.B., Begley, D.J., Davson, H. and Rakić, Lj. (1985). Permeability of the blood–cerebrospinal fluid and blood–brain barrier to thyrotropin releasing hormone. *Brain Res.*, **358**, 191–199

Zloković, B.V., Segal, M.B., Davson, H. and Mitrović, D.M. (1988). Unidirectional uptake of enkephalins at the blood–tissue interface of blood–cerebrospinal fluid barrier: a saturable mechanism. *Regul. Peptides*, **20**, 33–45

Subject Index

---

b.b.b. = blood–brain barrier.
BUI = brain uptake index.
CVO = circumventricular organs.

EAE = experimental allergic encephalomyelitis
v.c. = ventriculocisternal.